STANDARDIZED APPROACH

Utilizing a standard-format we streamline design, fabrication, and installation for cost-competitive CLT structures.

SPEED AND CAPACITY

As the world's largest CLT manufacturer, our high-speed manufacturing and extensive production capacity can provide American-made CLT as an affordable option for buildings of all sizes and occupancies.

ROBUST LOGISTICS

Having served industrial markets for over a decade, we're highly experienced in the scaled delivery of CLT. You can feel confident about investing in Sterling CLT solutions for your buildings.

Now is the time for timber — and we can help

Contact us at **SterlingStructural.com**

STERLING®
Structural

SAVE THE DATE
FOR THE 8TH ANNUAL

INTERNATIONAL

MassTimber℠
CONFERENCE

March 26–28, 2024
Portland, Oregon USA
Oregon Convention Center

MassTimberConference.com

Produced by Forest Business Network
Editing by Self-Publishing Services LLC
Formatting & Layout by Made Graphic Design
Cover Photo Credit: PDX Next

ISBN: 978-1-7337546-6-8

AUTHORS

Dave Atkins, Treesource
Roy Anderson, *Vice President*, The Beck Group
Emily Dawson, AIA, LEED AP
Peter Moonen, *National Sustainability Manager*, Canadian Wood Council
Lech Muszynski, *Professor,* Department of Wood Science and Engineering, Oregon State University

CONTRIBUTORS

Bryan Beck, *President*, The Beck Group
Craig Rawlings, *President & CEO,* Forest Business Network

The work upon which this document is based was funded in part through a cooperative agreement with the US Forest Service, Wood Innovations Grants. The US Forest Service is an equal opportunity provider, employer, and lender.

DISCLAIMERS

Where applicable in this report, column and row data may not sum to totals and subtotals due to rounding. This variation may also appear in the corresponding analysis where it references data in a table, chart, or other graphic.

Every effort was made to present accurate information from the best sources available, but the authors make no warranty about the completeness, reliability, or accuracy of this information. Any action taken based on information in this report is strictly at your own risk; the authors and contributors will not be liable for any losses or damages in connection with the use of this report.

ON THE COVER

When ZGF Architects presented the Port of Portland with a proposal to build a 9-acre wooden roof over PDX's new main terminal, port leaders responded with a question: can we source all this wood in a way that is better for the land and for our local communities?

Together, the team came up with goals: source all the wood from sustainably managed forests in Oregon and Washington. With equity in mind, source from small landowners, community forests, and tribal lands across the region. And, just like farm-to-table cuisine, trace as much of the wood as possible from forest to frame.

It took two years and many, many phone calls to build a network of foresters, mill owners, brokers, truckers, and construction firms that could join in the Port of Portland's quest to supply forest-to-frame timber.

The result? 100 percent of the wood in PDX's new ceiling lattice (pictured on cover) was sustainably harvested from within 300 miles of the airport and can be traced back to 11 landowners in Oregon and Washington, including the Yakama Nation, Skokomish Indian Tribe.

SPONSOR SPOTLIGHT:
*A special thanks goes to 2023 report sponsors Built by Nature and Weyerhaeuser —
without whose support the report would not be possible.*

BUILT BY NATURE

Accelerating the timber building transformation

Built by Nature is a network and grant-making fund with a vision of a built environment that works in unison with nature.

Built by Nature is a connector, bringing together a pan-European and U.K. movement of industry frontrunners – innovative practitioners representing architects, developers, asset owners, investors, insurers and cities – with the credibility and determination to challenge convention through a common purpose, shared knowledge and the empowerment to act.

Built by Nature is an enabler, funding solutions and investing in research fundamental to supporting the timber transformation through policy and legislation, while realizing the commercial opportunity to drive demand so that urbanization and reforestation can sustainably coexist.

Built by Nature is an amplifier, telling inspiring stories of groundbreaking nature-based projects and presenting wood and biobased materials as viable solutions toward decarbonization of our built environment.

Find out more about Built by Nature, our network and funding opportunities, and become part of our timber building transformation.

builtbn.org

Follow us: in ⊡

TABLE OF CONTENTS

TABLE OF CONTENTS

BUILT BY NATURE:

FUNDING SOLUTIONS, ENABLING THE TIMBER BUILDING TRANSFORMATION

Built by Nature was formed in late 2021 with the recognition that the global climate crisis urgently requires transformative solutions to decarbonize our built environment. As a not-for-profit network and grant-making fund dedicated to accelerating the adoption of mass timber and bio-based materials, our vision is one of a built environment that works in unison with nature.

Across Europe and in the United Kingdom, we convene like-minded industry leaders through our 1,000-plus network of architects, developers, asset owners, investors, insurers, and cities. We work closely with 25 leading organizations to shape the activities of our network, and with their commitment to effective coalitions and knowledge sharing, we can inspire innovation and change.

Enabling transformation also means funding solutions. The Built by Nature Fund awards grants of up to €250,000 toward projects that increase the uptake of sustainable timber and help overcome the most

LEFT: To overcome barriers and accelerate mass timber adoption in Italy and the European Union, Built by Nature funded the Perception of Timber at MIND project: an industry consortium convening a series of workshops and creating a physical and digital prototype at the Milano Innovation District.

RIGHT: The Mass is More installation in Barcelona served as a high-profile public centerpiece to highlight the October 2022 launch of Mass Madera, the Spanish mass timber network established with funding from Built by Nature. *PHOTO: Adria Goula*

challenging barriers to improving the construction industry's climate impact.

To date, the Built by Nature Fund has awarded over a dozen grants in several European countries and the UK. These include projects to address the perceptual barriers to mass timber adoption; promote bio-based building through new financing and valuation models; establish a mass timber network in Spain; and create design principles and methodologies to facilitate construction of mass timber residential buildings in the UK.

Follow us online and visit builtbn.org for details on our funded projects and to sign up for regular updates. Help Built by Nature accelerate the timber building transformation.

PUBLISHER'S MESSAGE

Welcome to the *2023 International Mass Timber Report*, the industry's comprehensive guide to all things mass timber. In recognition of the expertise involved in creating the report and the International Mass Timber Conference, Trifecta Collective has acquired them both. Craig Rawlings, Arnie Didier, and Tom Waddell will continue their leadership roles, and we anticipate strong support from Trifecta to help us continue to grow and improve the report and the conference.

As part of our continuing commitment to providing the latest news on the mass timber industry, the foremost perspective on the biggest issues facing it, and background information on all things mass timber, this year's report includes new and returning material. As we did in 2022, we are featuring 2 stories up front tackling what we think are the most important issues facing the industry today.

One of the first questions almost everyone asks when considering mass timber is "How much does it cost?" Emily Dawson, architect and designer of the first Cross-Laminated Timber building in Oregon, tackled that issue. Her essay, "Putting Numbers to 'It Depends,'" looks at cost trends emerging from a decade of mass timber projects in the US.

Peter Moonen, national sustainability manager for the Canadian Wood Council, took on issues related to the construction labor force in "Mass Timber's Mainstream Future—Training, Knowledge, and Skills Development." He also considers how the industry can address the crucial labor shortages.

In addition, Lech Muszynski, professor of wood science and engineering at Oregon State University, takes a quick look at the use of small-diameter timber in the production of mass timber products.

Recognizing that mass timber's ability to retain carbon is a key asset, we covered the issue extensively in past reports. This year, we tasked forest ecologist Dave Atkins with creating a new chapter focused on carbon and mass timber by compiling all of the previous stories and reviewing the current state of affairs. His chapter 9, "Carbon Considerations and Mass Timber," joins the original chapters 1-8 that provide the total story of mass timber from the forests to the finished buildings.

Roy Anderson of the Beck Group has updated "The Mass Timber Performance Index," which he introduced in 2022 to provide the latest information on mass timber capacity, production, and cost from around the world. This vital information will help you understand where the industry is today and where it is going. We have augmented the 2022 Index with information on cost factors influencing both lumber and mass timber.

We have incorporated a variety of case studies on new technologies and new projects of interest from around the world (see the Case Study Index on page 224). Most of these case studies were submitted to us by mass timber businesses through our portal at masstimberreport.com. We are always interested in new developments, designs, projects, and ideas. Please reach out if you have something you think would make great content for the 2024 report.

As always, thanks to our advertisers, sponsors, and contributors for helping us make this report available to you. We encourage our readers who need mass timber-related products or services to check out our advertisers.

Finally, a downloadable PDF copy of this report is available free to all registered attendees of the International Mass Timber Conference. Purchase a printed copy by searching 2023 Mass Timber Report on Amazon.

Best,

David Parcell
Publisher

ARNIE DIDIER, CRAIG RAWLINGS, AND TOM WADDELL

WEYERHAEUSER

For more than a century, Weyerhaeuser has been growing trees and making forest products that improve lives in fundamental ways. We manage millions of acres of forests on a continuous and sustainable cycle. We are responsible stewards of our land for multiple uses, including recreation, conservation, economic development, and renewable energy. And the products we make are used to build homes of all kinds.

Southern Forestlands

The benefits of wood construction are many. Not only does it decrease the global dependence on emissions-intensive, nonrenewable materials, but it is key to resolving our world's housing crisis.

At Weyerhaeuser, we believe we can significantly increase the overall availability of quality affordable housing by leveraging our deep industry and supply chain expertise, and working with cross-sector partners to unlock the ability to build housing more efficiently and at scale to serve all income levels, building types, and geographies.

We can accomplish this by

- increasing the overall understanding and acceptance of wood as one of the most sustainable, versatile, and cost-effective building materials in the world

- updating building codes to support new techniques and material innovations

- expanding the definition of "home" by lending our resources to key initiatives to develop quality sustainable, nontraditional home-building initiatives

- partnering with mass timber producers and the design community to drive innovation and the development of wood-based products to replace steel and concrete

Together, we will show that sustainable working forests and wood products can increase the overall quality, availability, and affordability of housing for everyone. Join us!

PUTTING NUMBERS TO 'IT DEPENDS'

EMILY DAWSON
AIA, LEED AP

A look at cost trends emerging from a decade of mass timber projects in the US

Mass timber is attractive to designers and builders for so many reasons: "It makes us more collaborative!" "The environmental benefits are inspiring!" "It looks amazing!" "It even smells good!" However, answering the seemingly straightforward question "How much does it cost?" is anything but simple.

Cost-conscious clients drift back toward traditional methods and materials upon hearing "it depends." So—even though it does!—being able to answer them with as much clarity as possible is crucial. We decided to ask another tough question: with examples of over 1,500 mass timber projects in the last decade in the US alone[1] and with a growing community of designers and builders who have completed multiple projects, are cost trends emerging?

What if we zoomed out from the many details that make a mass timber project successful? Would we see patterns?

For answers, we asked architects, engineers, and builders with a depth of experience with mass timber projects to share statistics from their portfolios.[2]

As difficult as it is to compare apples and oranges, it is particularly valuable to understand cost differentials in relation to other primary structural materials: concrete, steel, and light timber or steel framing. When mass timber replaces concrete and steel construction, it usually generates greater savings than when it replaces light framing. The overall trends are similar for all three structural materials, however, so they are grouped together in this analysis.

What was immediately clear is that there generally is a premium for a mass timber project, up to 15 percent. But the median project premium was less than 2 percent, and the gap continues to shrink as teams and markets become more experienced. These figures do not take into consideration mass timber buildings' additional potential to capture more in lease rates and lower tenant turnover (see chapter 8 for more) or the advantage to the building owner's return that results from shortened schedules. These calculations will not be apparent in a builder's cost estimate, and the building owner can only investigate them accurately within their overall pro forma.

That said, understanding construction cost is foundational to any feasibility analysis. To gain insights on where project successes and struggles were occurring, we grouped cost information into the three macro systems that make up every building: (1) the superstructure, all above-grade structural components; (2) the substructure, all below-grade structural components and foun-

---

1 https://www.woodworks.org/resources/u-s-mass-timber-projects/
2 The companies who participated reported on commercial projects in the United States.

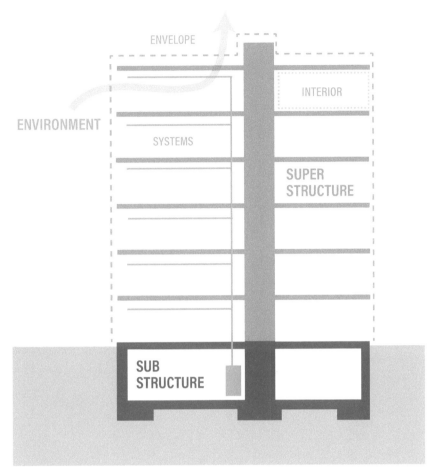

dations; and (3) the environment, which groups the building envelope, systems (mechanical, electrical, plumbing and fire protection (MEPF)), and interior finishes. Mass timber offers distinct advantages, challenges, and potential in each of these three categories.

Superstructure: The greatest cost savings are found in the superstructure's construction schedule. The total construction schedule can be reduced significantly, up to 25 percent. Resulting cost reductions include overhead, carrying costs, earlier occupancy, and reduced risk. Contractors report significant cost savings in general conditions, even with increased levels of coordination.

In fact, increased coordination is exactly what creates the greatest savings in the field.

Notably, these savings are often missed in a hard cost analysis of materials and labor. If the estimator understands labor savings, however, the findings can make an impact on early cost models. In a study of 100 mass timber buildings in the United Kingdom, Waugh Thistleton Architects found a 50 percent to 70 percent reduction in site staff for structural framing. The choice of lateral systems matters as well, and it can often drive the overall material and labor premium. Concrete cores may slow the overall schedule, for example, because the mass timber framing has to pause while the core is constructed. The fluctuation of

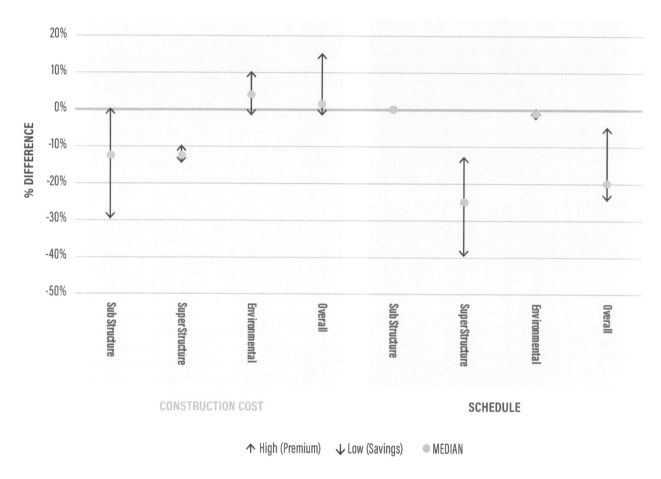

↑ High (Premium)   ↓ Low (Savings)   ● MEDIAN

FIGURE 2: COST AND SCHEDULE DIFFERENCES BETWEEN MASS TIMBER AND OTHER STRUCTURAL MATERIALS

the lumber commodity market presents another material cost challenge; tracking when to procure material can make a difference between an overall premium or savings. This is especially challenging when timber suppliers and fabricators are flooded with demand.

Substructure: Savings in foundations, when they occur, are seen primarily in hard costs. Because a smaller amount of concrete requires similar excavation, formwork, labor, and curing times as a greater amount, these savings are not likely to move the needle on a project with straightfor-ward soils conditions. However, because a timber building on average weighs only 20 percent as much as a steel or concrete structure,[3] the outcome can be quite promising when soils conditions are more complicated. Significant savings occur when a much lighter structure allows for less complex and costly foundation solutions. In these cases, total overall construction costs are likely to be lower than buildings with heavier structural systems. The savings are maximized for projects in high seismic zones, where the lighter mass timber structure translates to lower seismic forces that must be resisted by the foundations.

---

3   https://www.thinkwood.com/blog/4-things-to-know-about-mass-timber

Environment: The vast amount of installed material that follows the construction of the superstructure creates the environment that makes a building comfortable to inhabit. Every project takes a different approach to the building's envelope, MEPF systems, and interior finishes. Respondents' cost reports in this category ranged from "usually more" to "often less" when compared to other structural systems. Although more exposed structural surfaces can mean savings on finishes, cost increases commonly stem from additional acoustic treatments and higher appearance criteria for drywall detailing and exposed mechanical components. Timber buildings over 12 stories may find no savings from exposing the structure because of the way fire protective encapsulation requirements are written into the code.

However, the building environment category may hold the most promise for the future of cost comparisons with other structural systems. When paired with a highly coordinated construction team, prefabricated enclosure, systems, and finish elements can take advantage of the superstructure's rapid assembly superpower. In fact, highly modular projects can expect an overall schedule savings of up to 50 percent.[4] As mass timber and modular industries mature, options for prefabricated finish and environmental systems components will multiply.

Taking a step back from the complexity of specific projects allowed us to see cost trends emerging. A 20 percent reduction in overall schedule is now the norm, driven by a 25 percent median schedule reduction in the superstructure. The slight overall cost premium seen across projects disappears when substructure and environment savings are also realized.

Builders reported that cost margins are trending closer to negligible as the industry matures. Indeed, experienced teams more often reported cost neutrality or savings; premiums were more likely to occur with inexperienced partners. Another promising indicator that cost concerns may soon be a thing of the past is that many respondents reported in-progress affordable housing projects. Several also mentioned repeat clients and replicated projects, a true testament to project success. At this point, it is easy to imagine that "it depends" will soon be replaced with "Yes, it's true—mass timber will save you time and money." ◉

---

4   https://content.aia.org/sites/default/files/2019-03/Materials_Practice_Guide_Modular_Construction.pdf

MASS TIMBER'S MAINSTREAM FUTURE: TRAINING, KNOWLEDGE, AND SKILLS DEVELOPMENT

PETER MOONEN

National Sustainability Manager,
Canadian Wood Council

Cross-Laminated Timber (CLT) debuted in North America in early 2009, but it had been in Europe since the early 1990s. Although the first projects on this side of the Atlantic used materials imported from Europe, manufacturing began in 2010 when Nordic Structures in Quebec started providing structural mass timber panels.

Since then, the interest in and demand for mass timber products, especially CLT, has surged among designers, engineers, developers, and contractors. A structural material that could simultaneously serve as a finished surface and reduce environmental impact was well received.

But even the most attractive and well-designed building needs know-how throughout the value chain. The construction sector is, obviously, a crucial component. But mass timber construction was new, and at the start, the expertise came from craft sectors like log and timber frame crews.

Heavy timber buildings have historically been one-off structures constructed on the building site using logs, sawn timber, and, for the last century or so, engineered wood like glulam and nail-laminated timber (NLT). Workers were skilled in processing and installing the wood elements. Whether it was a temple in Asia, a log home in Maine, or a warehouse in Toronto, crews hand-built the structure, often hewing the material on-site.

Timber construction expertise came from working on-site and learning from trial and error. Over time, more formalized apprenticeship programs led to the accreditation of journeymen carpenters and master builders. This system remains in place today throughout much of North America, but mass timber construction skills are not a big part of it.

Scores of carpentry training programs are housed in colleges, trade schools, and technical institutions across North America. Most, however, are focused on the light-frame construction methods typical in residential home construction, low-rise commercial and institutional buildings, and increasingly in mid-rise projects up to 6 stories.

Very few programs in North America provide even a foundation in mass timber construction. There are some, but more are needed.

THE EUROPEAN EXPERIENCE

In Europe, training specific to mass timber has been incorporated into apprenticeship programs, mostly through on-the-job experience. Students at schools like the Bern University of Applied Sciences at Biel, for example, can get hands-on experience and a master of science degree in wood technology.

The university prepares wood industry professionals for a wide range of specialist and managerial functions through a mix of theory and practice,

THE TRAINING OFFERED BY THE MID-AMERICA CARPENTERS REGIONAL COUNCIL PROVIDES A SOLID FOUNDATION IN MASS TIMBER SYSTEMS, PRACTICES AND SAFETY AT THEIR FACILITY IN ROCKFORD, ILLINOIS.

Photo Courtesy of Craig Triplett, Mid-America Carpenters Regional Council

with experienced lecturers in an attractive educational environment. These new specialist skills, interdisciplinary teamwork, and a broad network throughout Switzerland lay the foundation for careers in fabrication, construction, and design.

Through apprenticeships at Höhere Fachschule Holz Biel, carpenters, timber construction specialists, sawyers, forest wardens, and other professionals in the timber trade expand their specialized knowledge in an application- and practice-oriented manner. As a result, they become sought-after specialists. The courses are continuously developed in cooperation with professional associations, commissions, and business partners, and are recognized nationally and internationally.

Another long-standing wood education program is in Rosenheim, Germany. Established in 1925,

Fachschule Rosenheim has a long tradition of training wood technicians and merchants. Over time, what started as a technical school developed into a globally recognized training center. It is now a state school.

Both Bern University and Fachschule Rosenheim are key European participants in the International Wood Building Forum held annually in Innsbruck. The program has become a must-do for serious designers and builders of mass timber structures.

In addition to a long-standing tradition of institutional education, the professional carpentry trade in Europe has a strong and consistent apprenticeship program that includes mass and heavy timber construction skills. Most crews working in the mass timber construction sector are well versed in mass timber manufacturers' software. Crews can work directly with panel design teams and manufacturers to provide detailed shop drawings, reducing time between design and manufacturing, and increasing the productivity of construction teams and manufacturers. Manufacturers can thus handle larger numbers of smaller jobs while still supplying large projects. One manufacturer in Europe produces mass timber panels for 1,100 projects every year.

UNITED KINGDOM

The Structural Timber Association (STA) represents the collective interest of its members by providing confidence in the use of structural timber across the construction industry. It works to influence legislation and regulation, supporting the collective objectives of its sector.

The association's principal objective "is to promote the use of structural timber in construction as timber presents our best opportunity for meeting the UK's net-zero commitments by 2050."

With this objective in mind, the association recognizes that the quality and standards of timber construction must be the highest. To achieve that, the association has developed both a training regimen and an accreditation system to show contractors, financial institutions, and insurance companies that its companies are held to high standards.

Training and accreditation taken under the quality assurance plan reassure the construction community that the association's members meet or surpass legislative and regulatory requirements. This accreditation is recognized by warranty providers, insurers, and other key stakeholders.

The 3-tiered accreditation program requires that 66 percent of the workforce of a contractor or installer of mass timber be certified as competent under the STA timber frame competency criteria.

The training program improves timber frame erectors' skill levels and acknowledges the competencies of existing timber frame erectors. The program sets industry wide standards for erectors and installers of structural timber frames. As part of the STA Assure quality initiative, members are required to complete three workbooks and an online test to examine practical and theory-based knowledge, which takes up to 1 year to complete.

CANADA

Carpentry is a voluntary trade in Canada, except in the province of Québec. Nonetheless, it consistently appears among the top 10 of more than 120 Red Seal trades in annual certificate completions. There are now over 53,000 carpentry completions in the 60-year history of the Red Seal program. (Officially known as the Interprovincial Standards Red Seal Program, it is a common standard for tradespeople and a partnership between the federal government, provinces, and territories). None of the programs requires expertise in mass timber. Only a few of the training institutions provide, or plan to provide, mass timber construction training.

BRITISH COLUMBIA

All apprentice and training programs in British Columbia (BC) are under the direction of the Industry Training Authority (ITA), a provincial crown corporation established in 2004 that is responsible for occupational training, recognition of credentials, and funding. Thirteen postsecondary institutions have an estimated total of 2,000 "seats" in carpentry programs.

Of special interest is the introduction of a microcredential online course called "Introductory Studies in Mass Timber Construction" at British Columbia Institute of Technology (BCIT). The fee was fully funded by government, and the course was advertised to carpenters, ironworkers, quantity surveyors, construction managers, 3D modelers, developers, manufacturers, and designers. The fully online 5-credit course is open for continuous entry and takes 8 weeks to complete.

The course provides foundational training and covers introduction to mass timber construction, including cost estimating, digital project delivery, construction management, erection, installation of building envelope and services, performance, and visualization

In addition, in August 2022, BCIT launched a mass timber installer course. It grants an associate certificate in construction of mass timber structures. This program comprises 4 online courses and an in–person course at a new erection center at BCIT. Courses cover construction planning and rigging for mass timber; installation of mass timber structures; installation of building enclosures; installation of interior components and services; and a practicum on construction of mass timber buildings.

The BCIT course, like many mass timber training programs, is optional and not a requirement for a Red Seal (journeyman) accreditation. In BC, apprentice training decisions are dominated by the ITA. Mass timber is not yet part of the criteria, but BCIT's new mass timber introductory program may attract the ITA's attention and ensure mass timber becomes a future requirement.

ONTARIO

In Ontario, the College of Carpenters and Allied Trades delivers construction skills courses under full-scale, site-simulated conditions in its state-of-the-art facilities in Woodbridge. The mass timber program had its first cohort in fall 2019. COVID-19 put the program on hiatus, but it is now back in operation.

This full-time, 4-week (20 days) mass timber course is an in-depth training program focusing on building with mass timber. The course includes an in-class component focusing on the characteristics of wood, and the forces applied, such as shear, compression, and tension. The course explores the advantages of using wood with a focus on sustainable building materials, carbon sequestering, fire resistance because of charring, and its other unusual characteristics. CLT, glulam, NLT, and other building options are introduced and discussed. Students study screws and fasteners, including the understanding of ductility, and determining fastener selection and placement from the drawings of the CLT modules. The rigging/signaling component takes 5 days and is also hands-on, working with a mobile crane and operator.

Tony Currie, director at Carpenters Union, has been involved from the beginning. Demand for mass timber is growing rapidly, but the number of skilled installers cannot keep pace.

"We need at least at least 100 trained journeymen. These are people that can lead the crew, not necessarily run the whole job, but oversee an installation crew," said Currie. "To do that, a

LEFT — MASS TIMBER CONSTRUCTION CONNECTIONS SYSTEMS ARE INCREASINGLY MORE COMMON — AND DIVERSE. HANDS-ON TRAINING FOR BEAMS, COLUMNS AND PANELS IS CRITICAL FOR ACCURATE AND EFFICIENT CONSTRUCTION.

RIGHT — SPECIALIZED EQUIPMENT IS OFTEN PART OF THE MASS TIMBER INSTALLERS TOOLBOX, BUT IS NOT ALWAYS INCLUDED IN TRADITIONAL CARPENTER TRAINING PROGRAMS — YET..

Photos Courtesy of Craig Triplett, Mid-America Carpenters Regional Council

worker needs to understand wood, the mass timber, the assembly system, the connections, safety, water, etc. And that's what we provide."

The 50,000-square-foot training facility can handle hundreds of students over the course of a year, but not enough people are taking advantage of this program. "Every trade is facing labor shortages," said Currie, "but if mass timber is going to grow, we have to invest in these programs and in our tradespeople to give them the necessary skills. And for that, we need to work together to get more students to go into the construction trades."

ALBERTA

The Southern Alberta Institute of Technology (SAIT) in Calgary has developed a certificate of competencies in mass timber construction management and sustainability. The program, which

is under development, will provide 120 hours of training and include an option for hands-on lab practice, including assembly of mini-mass timber structures.

SAIT is also developing a program for existing practitioners, including these 3 microcredentials (MC):

MC 1: Mass timber products and building systems

- Module 1 – Mass timber as a building material

- Module 2 – Mass timber building systems

MC 2: Sustainable mass timber construction project management

- Module 3 – Sustainability and mass timber construction

- Module 4 – Construction management of mass timber projects

MC 3: VDC and AR in mass timber construction projects

- Module 5 – Mass timber construction in Virtual Design and Construction (VDC)

- Module 6 – Mass timber system assembly Virtual Reality (VR) or lab

UNITED STATES

TallWood Design Institute

The TallWood Design Institute (TDI) is a collaboration of educational, industry, and labor organizations that seek to expand the understanding, knowledge, and construction skills necessary to increase the use of wood in construction.

The Oregon-based institute has developed a certificate program in mass timber manufacturing and construction, a modular training program in mass timber manufacturing intended to help workplace and professional learners acquire the skills to understand and succeed in the sector. The program was spearheaded in large part by regional trade organizations with support from WoodWorks.

Although most of the course modules are designed for manufacturers, a few are relevant to both the design and construction of mass timber buildings.

Like many programs, it includes an online and an in-person component, enabling greater outreach to practitioners and students remote from the training center and reducing time away from work.

TallWood has built relationships with some community colleges, again to reduce travel demands on students. Participants can take 1 or more modules based on their individual interests or learning needs, or they can complete the entire program to earn the certificate.

The courses offer introductory elements, such as the technical characteristics of different mass timber products and the ways they are best used; and more advanced components, including examining software used in manufacturing, design, and construction, and how mass timber construction processes differ from traditional. The program also includes key elements of efficiency, safety, and success.

Iain MacDonald, director at TDI, is cautiously optimistic about mass timber. "Looking 5 years down the road, I see a lot of opportunities for mass timber construction. However, the degree and speed of adoption of mass timber from its current niche status to mainstream is yet to be determined," he said.

MacDonald thinks the sector will need to have a diversity of project types that can serve as reference points for developers and contractors. "The sector will grow much faster if we can address the 2 big issues—fiber supply and workforce skills and numbers," he said. "The easier we can make it for the industry to find and retain interested workforces, the better off it will be."

MID-AMERICA CARPENTERS REGIONAL COUNCIL APPRENTICE AND TRAINING PROGRAM

As interest in mass timber construction grew in the Midwest, the Mid-America Carpenters Regional Council Apprentice and Training Program partnered with WoodWorks to provide mass timber installer training to construction professionals in Greater Chicago. Intended to serve as a model for training across the US, the program is helping ensure the availability of experienced construction professionals to meet increasing demand for buildings made from CLT and other mass timber products.

The program includes an introduction to mass timber concepts, with an emphasis on CLT. Topics include materials introductions, project planning, equipment safety and signaling, total station/e-drawings integration, site layout, rigging and handling, fall protection and safety, bracing and shoring, and making connections. The intent was to establish a knowledge base that equipped installers to work with CLT, Mass Plywood Panels (MPP), and glulam. Mock-up assemblies include 3 common joint types (lap, butt, spline), and training aligned with industry practices in rigging, connection hardware, and screw fastener installation. Virtual training for union contractors is available upon request.

Craig Triplett oversees the program out of the council's office and training center in Rockford, Illinois. He's also been involved in setting up more than 20 "train the trainers" programs—each 4 days long—across the country.

But even then, key barriers to mass timber installer training exist. "It is still a niche market, but as buildings come into the market, the contractor in that market will contact training centers. But if a training center is not close to where their project is, they can't afford to send people to take the course. It seems only the large national contractor companies can undertake the training otherwise," Triplett said.

"A lot of contractors don't yet know how to do things with mass timber. And if they don't know what they are doing, they cannot bid properly. Getting trained up and knowledgeable allows them to be more competitive in bidding," he said.

INDUSTRY PROGRAMS

In the absence of a comprehensive and available training network, many companies have undertaken their own internal training.

In 2010, when CLT first sparked interest in the construction sector, there weren't a lot of experts. Aside from educational institutions, most contractors had to learn from their mistakes and the experiences of others. But those first days of head scratching are paying off now for some of the early adopters in the construction sector.

Brendan Kelly, now field operations manager with Timberlab in Oregon, said he hit the mass timber experience wall early. "I didn't know what mass timber was 5 years ago when we got our first project," he said, "and there wasn't a training program anywhere.

"I had 18 years' experience as a formwork carpenter and had to take my knowledge of vertical and concrete deck buildings. It was a hard job—little experience or knowledge. All in all, quite frustrating."

Kelly took his experience with many of the elements—cranes, braces, and practical knowledge

ON THE JOB EXPERIENCE IS A CRUCIAL SUCCESS FACTOR AND A NATURAL EXTENSION OF CLASS ROOM AND LAB TRAINING.
WoodWorks

of general construction—and applied it to mass timber. "Over the last 6 years, we've really refined our skills. It's quite possible I may not even be doing it the right way, but it works for us. There's a million ways to skin these cats, and we learn something on every job.

"On a mass timber project you are exposed to some of the most dangerous elements of construction—height, heavy equipment, and cranes. It's not just how the building goes together, but we have to make sure our crew is safe.

"We also have to figure out what questions to ask. Since mass timber projects can be so fast, a safety event causes a big productivity loss. Our crews have to be very aware. When you are building fast, you can also get into trouble really fast."

One of the problems Kelly faced was designers' lack of understanding of actual mass timber construction practices. While the WoodWorks programs in

Canada and the US have elevated the awareness and skills of architects and engineers, much is still to be learned across the whole value chain.

"One of the big challenges early on with these buildings was working with designers who may be designing things that cannot be built or are difficult to put together. That's changing, but as more designers take an interest in mass timber, their learning curve is going to be steep—just like ours was.

"We all screw up in our career, and we get experience from that. You don't know what you don't know. If you don't have experience messing up, you're going to."

Swinerton/Timberlab have a crew of about 30 people.

Job safety training is the primary objective. The secondary objective is to develop experienced people who can be project supervisors on future jobs. "I want every single person advancing their career—from apprentice to journeyman to supervisor to replacing me! Having consistency of crews is paramount. We need to share our knowledge and experiences from every job."

Scott Cameron, general superintendent and mass timber specialist at Turner Construction Company, one of the largest general contractors in North America, agrees, saying, "We have to invest today in the training of the people who will be building tomorrow's mass timber buildings.

"Mass timber is demonstrating it is the next big thing in construction, and we need to allocate resources to build the capacity. And that means all of us—carpenters, contractors manufacturers, educators, government. We are all in it."

Cameron believes mass timber has proven itself to be good for the construction sector and good for the communities in which these buildings are being built. "Construction is quieter, is faster, has a smaller footprint on communities, The noise is less; site time is less. Our teams would be 1/3 the size of a concrete crew. And all of that matters when you are a builder or developer."

He sees knowledge exchange as crucial to the success of the entire mass timber community. "The mass timber community includes designers and architects. It needs to include carpenters, other trades, installations, developers—all with their own skill sets. Sure, it may seem like a risk to share what you think are your secrets. But we all had to learn from someone. The end results will be good for everyone—more manufacturing, more financially viable projects, more acceptance in the market, and more jobs.

"I'm hopeful that, if I can set the tone and share information from my company, it will be reciprocated at some point and a valuable information exchange can happen.

"The bottom line, from a business point of view, is a positive financial outcome. If you are the only one who knows what to do, it is not going to solve the problems a project will face when you encounter someone who doesn't understand.

"At this point in the growth of mass timber construction, the community needs to support and collaborate with each other. We need to share best practices, so that the systems become mainstream. If there are more installers and [general contractors] who understand it, the pricing will be better, and there will be more buildings."

There are consistent messages about mass timber construction:

- Knowledge sharing is essential.

- A larger and more skilled labor force is paramount.

- A strong commitment to, and investment in, training by government, educators, designers, manufacturers, and builders will bring mass timber into the mainstream the planet needs.

"I have a lot of passion for this," said Timberlab's Kelly. "My work through construction has been really good for me and my family. When you have a really good team and a good plan, you can make this stuff easy and be successful. The worst thing is trying to wing it. Training—and lots of it—is essential." ◐

LEADING BRITISH COLUMBIA'S MASS TIMBER ACTION PLAN

BY THE MINISTER OF JOBS, ECONOMIC DEVELOPMENT, AND INNOVATION, AND THE MINISTER OF STATE FOR TRADE

LEFT: Brenda Bailey; RIGHT: Jagrup Brar

This spring marks the 1-year anniversary of our government launching the Mass Timber Action Plan in British Columbia, Canada. This plan puts people first by driving clean, sustainable, and inclusive economic growth in an emerging sector.

Our province is a world leader in mass timber, a commodity that is revolutionizing the way we build worldwide by delivering up to 7 times the economic value for an in-demand forest product that helps us meet our climate goals.

As we dig into our new ministerial roles—Brenda Bailey as Minister of Jobs, Economic Development, and Innovation, and Jagrup Brar as Minister of State for Trade—we are both strongly committed to continue leading our work to grow the mass timber sector. We will leverage our building innovation and forestry expertise to seize opportunities and facilitate even more mass timber construction in our province. By doing so, we ensure we can create well-paying jobs for people in every part of our province, reduce our greenhouse gas emissions, and add value to our forests sector.

Through our Mass Timber Action Plan, we are making great progress partnering with companies and people worldwide who share our vision. We're pleased to say Minister Brar will be attending the annual International Mass Timber Conference in Portland, Oregon, with a goal of expanding our network and further showcasing the opportunities B.C. has for domestic and international partnerships.

To help more people see and understand the benefits of mass timber, we are investing in innovation and showcasing the work of designers, builders, and other experts by helping fund projects using mass timber in innovative ways. Buildings are a leading contributor to greenhouse gas emissions, and mass timber is a natural solution.

In B.C., we understand that government must play a role in moving the mass timber sector forward. That's why we created the Office of Mass Timber Implementation whose sole focus is to drive outcomes—the first such government office anywhere in the world. This is how we will stay on the forefront of this groundbreaking technology, and we are very excited to keep moving forward.

MASS TIMBER PERFORMANCE INDEX

Roy Anderson,
Vice President, The Beck Group

In **Figure 1**, we update the Mass Timber Performance Index (MTPI) that first appeared in the 2022 edition of the International Mass Timber report. The MTPI is meant to serve as a general guide to Cross-Laminated Timber (CLT) panel pricing. It's general because the values that appear in **Figure 1** are based on a financial model of a CLT manufacturing plant that projects the cost of producing mass timber panels. In other words, the prices shown in the figure are not prices reported from actual transactions between mass timber manufacturers and their customers. The data is informative, nevertheless, because it helps architects, building developers, and others interested in mass timber construction understand the approximate cost of their materials.

For about 4 years, the MTPI ranged between $20 and $25 per cubic foot. In the second quarter of 2020, however, the MTPI shot up, eventually reaching more than $45 per cubic foot in early 2021. It then plummeted in the third quarter of 2021, only to climb sharply once again in early 2022, followed by another dramatic decline. At the end of 2022, the MTPI was back in the normal historical range.

The cost of lumber is the driving factor in the observed MTPI changes. Lumber price volatility is a result of supply and demand factors that combined during the COVID-19 epidemic to increase demand for lumber and simultaneously constrain the ability to produce it. Finally, when considering MTPI values, remember they are based on the estimated average value of 3-ply CLT panels Free on Board (FOB) the manufacturer's plant with no extra costs assumed for final machining, addition of hardware, or transport to customers. The values on the left axis of the figure are the prices expressed in $/cubic meter; the values on the right axis are the prices expressed in $/cubic foot.

LUMBER PRICE VOLATILITY DISCUSSION

Softwood lumber, the main raw material used in CLT panel manufacturing, is a commodity. Like any commodity, its price is subject to the interaction of supply and demand. Between 2000 and 2020, for example, the largest year-over-year change in the average annual lumber price was a 28 percent increase in 2010 relative to 2009 coming out of the Great Recession. Lumber demand had plummeted to all-time lows and then climbed back to more normal levels in 2010. In contrast, the average lumber price increased by 52 percent in 2020 relative to 2019, followed by a 49 percent average lumber price increase in 2021 relative to 2020.

In other words, the lumber price increases observed during the height of the COVID-19 pandemic were unprecedented. Going forward, lumber price volatility, and therefore mass timber panel price volatility, likely will not reach the levels seen in 2020 and 2021. Should this prediction prove true, mass timber panel manufacturers and their customers likely will see more consistency in the pricing of mass timber panels and glulam beams. Of course, another shock to lumber supply or demand, such as another pandemic or ma-

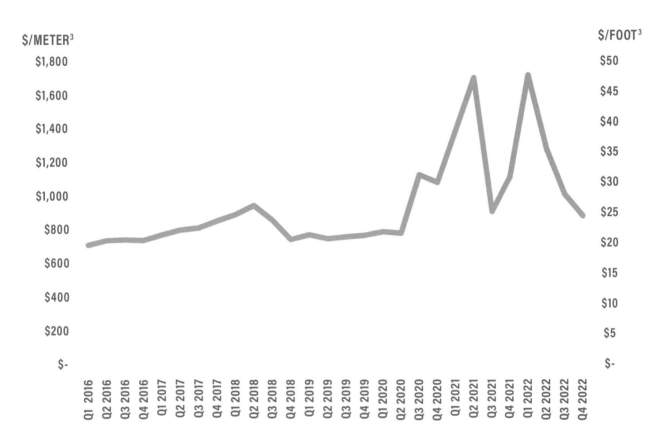

$/METER³

$1,800
$1,600
$1,400
$1,200
$1,000
$800
$600
$400
$200
$-

$/FOOT³

$50
$45
$40
$35
$30
$25
$20
$15
$10
$5
$-

Q1 2016 Q2 2016 Q3 2016 Q4 2016 Q1 2017 Q2 2017 Q3 2017 Q4 2017 Q1 2018 Q2 2018 Q3 2018 Q4 2018 Q1 2019 Q2 2019 Q3 2019 Q4 2019 Q1 2020 Q2 2020 Q3 2020 Q4 2020 Q1 2021 Q2 2021 Q3 2021 Q4 2021 Q1 2022 Q2 2022 Q3 2022 Q4 2022

FIGURE 1: MASS TIMBER PRODUCT PRICE INDEX ($/METER³ LEFT AXIS AND $/FT³ RIGHT AXIS)

jor natural disaster, could cause more dramatic price volatility than expected in the near term.

NORTH AMERICAN MASS TIMBER: LUMBER USAGE, MASS TIMBER CONSUMPTION, AND MASS TIMBER IMPORTS

Another topic of great interest to those following the mass timber industry is North American mass timber manufacturing plants' rate of production. Like mass timber market prices, little solid information is available directly from manufacturers about their production capacity and production rates. Nevertheless, this section provides estimates of North American mass timber production and lumber use from 2019 to 2022.

As shown in **Table 1,** the volume of mass timber products used in building construction each year has increased steadily, starting with a little over 280,000 cubic meters in 2019 and ending at nearly 362,000 cubic meters in 2022. Thus, growth of mass timber usage is steady, but not doubling every two years as previously projected. The table also shows a corresponding jump in lumber use in 2022, with total usage reaching more than 287 million board feet. Note that as described in chapter 4, glulam production has consumed about 300 million board feet of lumber annually in North America in recent years. The lumber consumption shown in **Table 1** is incremental to the glulam usage.

Mass timber products are still being imported into North America. Thus, some of the apparent

YEAR	PUBLICLY REPORTED NUMBER OF MASS TIMBER BUILDINGS CONSTRUCTED IN US & CANADA*	ESTIMATED BOARD FEET OF LUMBER USED IN MASS TIMBER IN NORTH AMERICA (MBF LUMBER/YEAR)	ESTIMATED NORTH AMERICAN USE OF MASS TIMBER PRODUCTS (CUBIC METERS PER YEAR)	ESTIMATED IMPORTS OF MASS TIMBER PRODUCTS INTO THE US (CUBIC METERS PER YEAR)	APPARENT NORTH AMERICAN MASS TIMBER PRODUCTION (CUBIC METERS PER YEAR)	ESTIMATED NORTH AMERICAN MASS TIMBER MANUFACTURING CAPACITY IN PANELS USED FOR CONSTRUCTION (CUBIC METERS PER YEAR)	ESTIMATED PERCENT OF PRACTICAL BUILDING PANEL MASS TIMBER MANUFACTURING CAPACITY UTILIZED
2019	143	224,500	282,900	15,000	267,900	400,000	67%
2020	168	241,300	303,500	24,700	278,800	541,000	52%
2021	170	257,300	323,800	19,300	304,500	520,000	59%
2022	200	287,500	361,900	13,000	348,900	807,000	43%

TABLE 1: ESTIMATED NORTH AMERICAN MASS TIMBER LUMBER USAGE AND PRODUCTION (2019 TO 2020)

MBF = 1,000 board feet

*Source: WoodWorks USA and WoodWorks Canada

mass timber use in North America comes from overseas and must be subtracted from the total to estimate the capacity at which the North American mass timber industry operated in 2022. As the data in the table shows, while there was an increase in mass timber production in 2022, manufacturing capacity increased more rapidly. Thus, as a whole, the industry operated at lower percentage of capacity in 2022 than 2021 (i.e., 43 percent in 2022 versus 59 percent in 2021). This is a low utilization of capacity relative to many forest products manufacturing sectors.

Estimating capacity for any industry is difficult because constraints on capacity change as various supply and demand factors shift. For mass timber, estimating capacity is especially tricky because it depends on how efficiently press capac-

ity is utilized. In addition, some producers shift their capacity between producing mass timber for building construction and for utility mats.

NORTH AMERICAN MASS TIMBER LUMBER USAGE AND CAPACITY DISCUSSION

As the data in the **Table 1** shows, the number of buildings constructed with mass timber in the US and Canada increased by about 17 percent in 2022 relative to 2021. As previously described, this continues an upward trend in mass timber building construction. See chapter 8 for additional market analysis. Many more mass timber projects are in the planning stages, and the number continues to grow. In late 2020, about 600 projects were in the design phase; in late 2021, that number had grown to 700; as of late 2022, it stood at about 767.

As a point of reference to the analysis presented here, the Softwood Lumber Board commissioned a Mass Timber Outlook[1] study, which it published in October 2020. A key finding was that by 2025, the mass timber market (glulam and mass timber panels) would experience an incremental annual gain in softwood lumber usage of 800 million board feet. Per the data in the table, the estimated annual lumber consumption from mass timber was about 241 million board feet per year at the time the lumber board released its report. An 800 million board foot increase would move annual consumption from mass timber to 1 billion feet per year by 2025. Although mass timber construction continues trending upward, the number of building projects using mass timber would need to increase significantly over the next couple of years for the board's projection to likely be a reality.

Regarding the methodology used in the analysis, estimated lumber consumption is derived from total square footage of mass timber buildings constructed per year (as publicly reported by WoodWorks); a mass timber usage factor per square foot of building; a lumber usage factor per cubic foot of mass timber; and an adjustment factor to account for mass timber buildings not included in the WoodWorks database. Regarding the estimate of capacity, the key assumption was that each North American manufacturer operates at about 65 percent of the maximum press capacity. ◓

---

1   Softwood Lumber Board. *Mass Timber Outlook*. October 2020. Accessed at: https://softwoodlumberboard.org/wp-content/uploads/2021/03/SLB-Mass-Timber-Outlook-2021-Final-Condensed.pdf

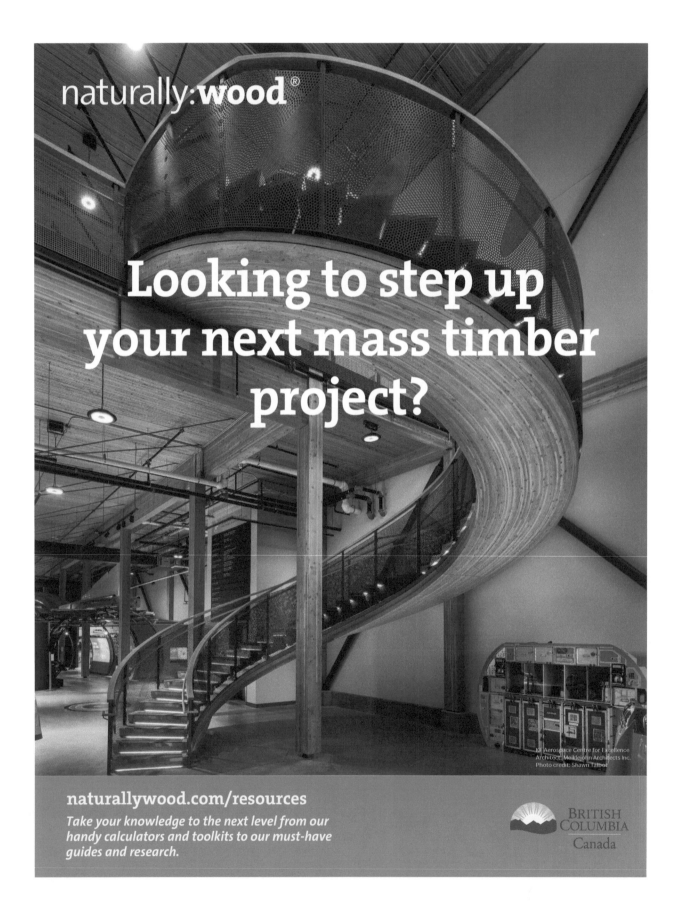

'EAT THE PROBLEM'
or a case for use of small-diameter logs in specialty mass-timber panels

LECH MUSZYNSKI,
Oregon State University

In recent years, the development of mass timber panel technology in North America has generated a daunting list of ways it is expected to transform life on planet Earth and beyond. Evaluating them all is beyond the scope of this report, though many merit in-depth discussion.

It might be time, however, to revisit one of the proposed promises: that the level of homogenization achieved in reconstituted wood elements should allow low-value lumber to be used in robust structural products. It's not a new idea, and there is a long history of practical applications in a range of engineered wood products that offer larger dimensions, greater uniformity, and more predictability of crucial performance characteristics than are found in the pieces of lumber, veneer, or strands used to produce them.

That experience has inspired hopes that mass timber panels might become a value-added outlet for lumber generated from small-diameter logs, defined as less than 8 inches (203 millimeters) at the narrow end.[1] Small-diameter logs constitute a substantial proportion of commercial harvests. That fraction may be even larger in slow-growing boreal forests, short rotation plantations, and selective harvesting operations like forest restoration programs.

The US Forest Service has adopted forest restoration programs, including thinning operations targeting smaller and lower-quality trees as an effective strategy for mitigating catastrophic wildfires and outbreaks of pests in Western forests. The goal is to restore fire resilience and improve the health and value of the remaining stands. These operations consume a substantial portion of the Forest Service budget, so the agency is seeking value-added markets for small-diameter logs and underused species generated as by-products to offset the higher costs of these programs.[2] For various reasons, the uses of small logs for pulp, energy conversion, small-diameter veneer peeling, marginal use in roundwood construction and more, fall short of that goal, so there is a pressing interest in expanding the market.

Structural engineered products, such as glulam or Cross-Laminated Timber (CLT), have been consistently proposed as potential outlets. Pilot studies provide concept-level evidence that viable structural products may in fact be constructed from low-value material generated by forest restoration programs. The use of lumber from small logs in mass timber panels is beyond proof of concept. In Northern Quebec, Nordic Structures

---

1 Magnus Fredriksson et al. "Using Small Diameter Logs for Cross-Laminated Timber Production," *BioResources* 10 no. 1 (2015): 1477-1486. https://Bioresources.Cnr.Ncsu.Edu/Resources/Using-Small-Diameter-Logs-For-Cross-Laminated-Timber-Production/

2 "Wood Innovation Program," Forest Service, US Department of Agriculture. Accessed on Sept. 15, 2022: https://www.fs.usda.gov/science-technology/energy-forest-products/wood-innovations-program

uses lumber sawn from small-diameter boreal black spruce to manufacture large glulam beams and CLT panels.[3] It should be stressed, however, that these logs harvested from slow-growing boreal stands produce high-quality lumber. A model better reflecting the reality of the US market might be Vaagen Timbers, a company operating in northern Washington State, producing successful structural CLT panels with lumber sawn from small-diameter logs selectively harvested in contract forest restoration projects and processed by its parent company, Vaagen Brothers Lumber.[4,5]

A string of research projects conducted at Oregon State University suggests that even CLT panels fabricated from low-grade materials can be used in low-rise modular housing units for rapid deployment in communities destroyed by natural disasters like wildfires, or in response to the affordable housing crisis in the region.[6,7,8,9,10,11] Turning the by-product of costly fire prevention operations in the Western region into a vehicle for reconstructing communities affected by wildfires and solving the affordable housing crunch would be a perfect example of the age-old "eat the problem" approach. Application of modular designs where a variety of building programs and functions may be achieved with a small set of repetitive prefabricated elements is expected to streamline the fabrication of mass timber panels and bring an anticipated economy of scale to an intrinsically noncommodity industry. (See the Mosaic Housing Case Study in Chapter 8)

Such development may require meeting several important prerequisites.

Improving predictability. Industry should be able to rely on the availability of small logs for local and regional sawmills, and mass timber manufacturers. In principle, the aim of forest restoration is to build the health and resilience of forests, and logs are a by-product. Typically, such programs may not be concerned with the logistics of transferring the generated materials to potential users. Forest restoration activities also vary widely across a mosaic of land ownership, making it difficult to plan long-term log procurement and financing methods.[12] Communicating long-term forest treatment schedules, a comprehensive inventory of the volume marked for selective thinning, and rough assessment of expected quality to the mass

3   "Chantiers-Chibougamau Manufacturing Plant," Nordic Structures. Accessed on Nov. 4, 2022: https://www.nordic.ca/en/projects/structures/chantiers-chibougamau-manufacturing-plant

4   Vaagen Timbers. Accessed on Nov. 4, 2022: https://www.vaagenbros.com/.

5   Vaagen Brothers Lumber. Accessed on Nov. 4, 2022: https://vaagentimbers.com/about.

6   Christina Lawrence, "Utilization of Low-value Lumber from Small-diameter Timber Harvested in Pacific Northwest Forest Restoration Programs in Hybrid Cross Laminated Timber (CLT) Core Layers: Technical Feasibility" (master's thesis, Oregon State University, 2017) 147 pp.

7   Brent Lawrence, "Utilization of Low-value Lumber from Small-diameter Logs Harvested in Pacific Northwest Forest Restoration Programs in Hybrid Cross Laminated Timber (CLT) Core Layers: A Market Response" " (master's thesis, Oregon State University, 2017) 99 pp.

8   Sina Jahedi, "Defining Project-specific Custom CLT Grade Utilizing Low-value Ponderosa Pine Lumber from Logs Harvested in SW Oregon and Northern California Forest Restoration Programs" (Ph.D. dissertation, Oregon State University, 2022) 117 pp.

9   Sina Jahedi et al. "MOE Distribution in Visually Graded Ponderosa Pine Lumber Harvested from Restoration Programs in Southern Oregon and Northern California," *Wood and Fiber Science* 54, no. 2 (2022): pp. 75-80

10   Sujit Bhandari, "Modular Cross Laminated Timber Structures Using Underutilized Ponderosa Pine" (2022) 174 pp.

11   Sujit Bhandari et al. "A Review of Modular Cross-Laminated Timber Construction" Submitted to *Journal of Building Engineering* (2023) p: 105485. In Press.

12   Chung W., N. Anderson, F. Belart, Y. Chen, R. De Amicis, J. Hogland, J. Johnson, J. Kim, K. Lyons, L. Muszyński, N. Streletskaya (2022): Smart Forestry: Paving the Way from Forest Restoration to Mass Timber. Component of Build Back Better with Mass Timber BBBRC. DOC EDA Program, Award # 07-79-07914

timber sector would reduce the uncertainties and enable long-term investment planning. Developing treatment schedules in collaboration with the industry expected to provide a market for the small logs may go even further.

Developing capacity for efficient processing of small logs. Improving the predictability of the small-logs inventory and harvesting plans in a region may create an incentive for local lumber manufacturers to invest in technology to profitably process such material. Creating a suitable profit margin is not a trivial challenge because profitability diminishes with log diameters. For diameters below 8 inches (203 millimeters) on the narrow end, yields decrease dramatically. Not many sawmills can process such material efficiently. The resulting lumber may not be competitive in commodity-oriented markets unless there is a matching capacity to use such lumber in value-added structural products.

Developing design values for lumber from small logs and uncommon species. Construction applications require lumber certified for structural uses and assigned a grade with associated design characteristics. Structural grades are commonly assigned by an assessment of visual clues, including number, size, and position of knots or slope of grain, or by nondestructive measurement of physical properties, including density, bending modules, and stress wave propagation—all with known correlations to design characteristics. Both the grading rules and design characteristics associated with lumber species or species-groups commonly available for structural uses are outlined in the National Design Specification (NDS)

for Wood Construction.[13] The North American performance standard for structural CLT panels (PRG 320) requires that the laminations in the principal strength direction, those aligned with the pieces seen on the face of the panel, are grade No. 2 or better, while the transverse laminations are No. 3 or better for species recognized in NDS.[14]

The problem is that restoration projects generate small logs in species not commonly considered for structural uses. Even for species commercially harvested for structural uses, small logs are likely to produce lumber with larger proportions of juvenile wood, which does not meet the benchmark design characteristics for their respective NDS grades. New design values specific to the material generated in restoration projects must be established before the material can be accepted in certified structural wood-based composites like glulam or CLT, even if the prototype panels fabricated from such materials demonstrate predictable quality appropriate for low-rise modular applications.

Developing a robust modular design concept (preferably open source). For many reasons, the mass timber panel industry does not follow the usual commodity pattern. The main product of the industry is *projects*, with custom panel production but a step in a complex process that begins with design and ends with the assembly of a building shell at the construction site. Currently, most such projects commissioned in North America aim at the high end of the construction market with distinct, one-of-a-kind, high-visibility structures. Such projects are an unlikely market for large volumes of lower-grade mass timber panels,

---

13 American Wood Council, *NDS Supplement National Design Specification Design Values for Wood Construction.* (Leesburg, VA, 2018)
14 ANSI/APA. *ANSI/APA PRG 320:2019 Standard for Performance-Rated Cross-Laminated Timber.* (2020).

even if a certain portion of the elements in these structures could use them. An alternative robust modular design could be replicated in substantial numbers with as much variation as the modules would allow. This concept could apply to structures capable of rapid deployment as medium-range shelters, affordable housing, businesses like hotel chains, and community-oriented buildings such as schools, offices, and medical facilities as part of community rebuilding after widespread destruction (e.g., wildfires, floods, earthquakes). They could be designed of lower-grade structural mass timber panels. Such an approach could supply a market that would better match the volumes of small logs seeking a commercial home and provide a condition for the economy of scale in the sector.

Public awareness, community support, and coordination. One striking feature of the range of challenges and opportunities described above is that at both ends, the challenges exceed the realm of pure market forces. One is aimed at mitigating the risks of destructive wildfires in the immediate future, the other at responding to recent disasters. Both are imperatives rooted in the basic human need for safety and security. Though both often concern the same community leaders and legislatures, they are rarely seen as two ends of the same fundamental problem. Thus, they are dealt with asynchronously by different agencies and budgeted separately.[15] The key to addressing these issues in an efficient way is to build awareness of the synergies of the goals of the regional Forest Service, public agencies concerned with mid- and long-term response to natural disasters, and businesses that process small logs into engineered wood products offered in service of the communities touched by destructive disasters and acute shortages of affordable housing. ◐

15 Daniel L. Sanchez et al., *Literature Review and Evaluation of Research Gaps to Support Wood Products Innovation.* Technical Report of the Board of Forestry and Fire Protection Joint Institute for Wood Products Innovation. Submitted to the California Board of Forestry and Fire Protection: Agreement # 9CA04450. (2020) 116 pp.

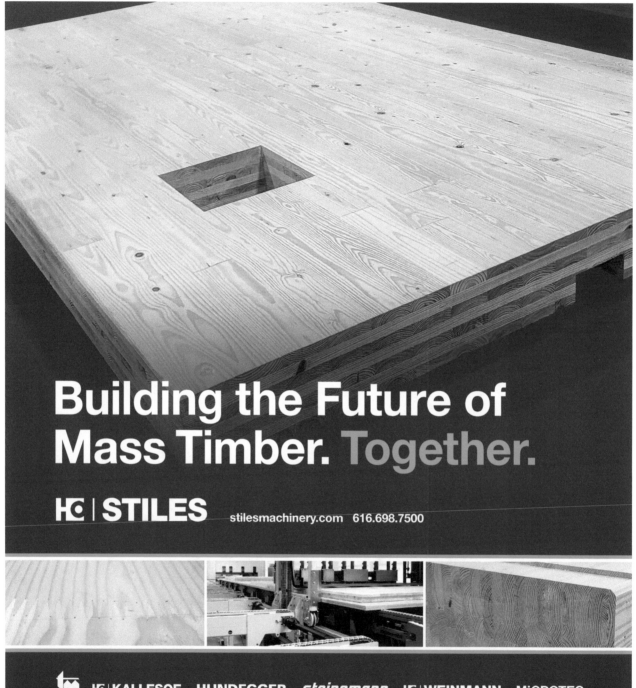

CHAPTER 1: INTRODUCTION

Historically, wood's use as a construction material, while extensive, was largely limited to low-rise and light-frame buildings. A light-frame building uses many small and closely spaced members assembled by nailing. Typical light-frame construction features 2-by-4s and 2-by-6s as wall supports, wood joists as floor supports, and rafters as a roof assembly. The application of this light-frame construction style is primarily limited to homes, smaller apartment buildings, and low-rise nonresidential structures.

Now, though, the use of wood in construction is shifting with the game-changing introduction of mass timber in North America. According to Think Wood, mass timber is inspiring innovation. "Valued for its natural beauty, strength, and versatility, wood offers endless possibilities in architecture and design. Conveying warmth and sophistication, it can be used as a load-bearing structure and an interior finish material. Mass timber construction is capturing the imaginations of leading building and design professionals, who continue to evolve and advance its potential."[1]

This report provides readers with a broad, yet deep, understanding of the North American mass timber industry in 2022. This chapter explains why the report was assembled, defines the key types of mass timber products, describes how they are used, and introduces the mass timber supply chain concept.

1.1 WHY A MASS TIMBER REPORT?

This report was developed as a companion piece to the International Mass Timber Conference (IMTC), held annually in Portland, Oregon. As evidenced by dramatic year-over-year growth in attendance, the conference has strengthened the mass timber community by providing a forum for the exchange of ideas and information, and for the development of relationships along the industry's supply chain.

Mass timber has captured widespread attention in recent years. Architects, engineers, developers, builders, the forest industry, and community leaders are excited about mass timber's revolutionary potential in building construction. And rightly so. That's because it's a technology that uses renewable resources, reduces building construction and development costs, increases versatility in building sites, is safe, and yields highly usable structures. It seems that almost every day a new mass timber article or report is released, be it a story on a new mass timber high-rise, the announcement of a new manufacturer, or news about a favorable change in building codes. Information on mass timber is being developed at a phenomenal rate. It can be overwhelming, especially when each new piece of information is specific to just one aspect of the industry. By contrast, this report is intended as a single, comprehensive, in-depth source of North American mass timber information, as it stands in 2022.

It is also important to recognize that the mass timber industry is global. The majority of the annual volume of mass timber panels produced globally

---

1   https://www.thinkwood.com/mass-timber

is manufactured overseas, mostly in Central Europe. As a result, mass timber building projects are often "exported" to destinations halfway around the globe from the manufacturing plants. Thus, this report includes comments and analyses about the global aspects of the industry.

As the industry continues to evolve, this report will be expanded and updated annually.

1.2 WHAT IS MASS TIMBER?

Mass timber is not just one technology or product. Solid wood (i.e., timber and lumber) has been used as a structural material for millennia. More recently, however, a different class of wood products has emerged. These Engineered Wood Products (EWPs) are a group of construction materials that combine wood's inherent strength with modern engineering. EWPs are manufactured by using adhesives to bind strands, particles, fibers, veneers, or boards of wood to form a composite product. The theory underlying all EWPs is that the process of disassembling wood into small pieces and then gluing them back together results in a product that is significantly stronger than a solid wood product of the same dimensions. In a solid piece of wood, strength-limiting defects such as knots, splits, checks, or decay tend to concentrate in a single area. That defective area is where the wood is most likely to fail. In EWPs, the disassembly and reassembly processes randomize the locations of defects and yield products with predictable strength characteristics. EWPs include structural building materials such as plywood, Oriented Strand Lumber (OSL), Laminated Veneer Lumber (LVL) (see **Figure 1.1**), wooden I-joists, and of particular interest in this report, mass timber products.

Mass Timber Products

Mass timber products are a distinct class of EWPs. The following sections provide descriptions of the different types of mass timber products that have been developed to date.

Cross-Laminated Timber

Cross-Laminated Timber (CLT) is a panelized structural EWP that can be used in all major building components (floors, interior and exterior walls, and roofs). It is also used as a ground mat at construction and mining sites, allowing heavy equipment to operate on unstable soils. CLT is made of 3 or more layers of lumber, each layer oriented perpendicularly to the adjacent layer (see **Figure 1.2**). The layers are then pressed together with a special adhesive. The lumber is typically preselected, so major defects such as knots and checks are removed prior to lay-up. CLT panels used for building construction are commonly 8 feet to 12 feet wide, 20 feet to 60 feet long, and 3.5 inches to 9 inches thick. Panel length is limited only by press size and highway trucking regulations.

Because the lumber is layered with an alternating grain orientation, the strength, dimensional stability, and fire resistance of CLT panels are significantly greater than for individual boards. CLT is produced in dedicated manufacturing plants with machinery for remanufacturing, finger jointing, and surfacing lumber; glue applicators and specialized panel presses; and Computer Numerical Control (CNC) routers that trim panels to size and cut openings for doors, windows, etc.

Most CLT panels are customized for a specific construction project, meaning the exact width, length, thickness (and arrangement of layers), and

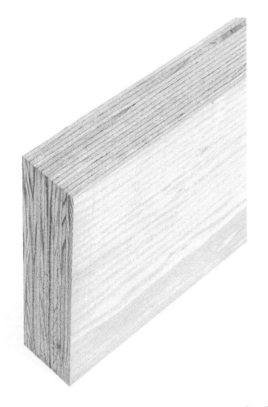

FIGURE 1.1: LAMINATED VENEER LUMBER (LVL)
Source: APA

FIGURE 1.2: CROSS-LAMINATED TIMBER (CLT) PANEL
Source: APA

other properties of each panel are tailored to one building. Openings for doors and windows—as well as openings or channels for electrical; plumbing; and heating, ventilation, and air conditioning (HVAC)—are commonly cut by the manufacturer using CNC machines. The prefabricated panels minimize the labor needed at the construction site and dramatically speed construction.

After manufacturing, CLT panels are transported to the construction site, typically by truck. Crews hoist the massive panels into place using cranes, with straps or cables attached to preinstalled "pick points," which are removed once the panel is in place.

In some cases, CLT panels are prefabricated into entire modular units (rooms and/or building sections) that can be transported by truck and installed using cranes, further reducing jobsite construction requirements.

Nail-Laminated Timber

Nail-Laminated Timber (NLT) is a century-old construction method that recently returned to favor and has been updated with new design guides and construction methods. Like CLT, NLT is a massive wood composite panel. In an NLT panel, however, the wood grain orientation does not alternate. Instead, numerous pieces of lumber are stacked face to face with the wide faces adjoining. Rather than using adhesive to bond the layers (as in CLT and glue-laminated timber, or "glulam"), the lumber is held together with nails (see **Figure 1.3**). Because it does not require the specialized presses used in CLT manufacturing, NLT can be

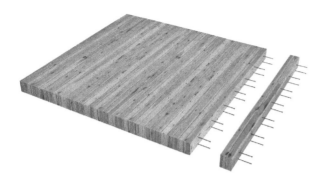

FIGURE 1.3: NAIL-LAMINATED TIMBER (NLT) PANEL
Source: StructureCraft

assembled at a temporary workshop close to the construction site or at the building site.

NLT panels are most commonly used in horizontal applications (i.e., floors and roof decks). As a result, fewer precision-machined openings, such as those required for doors and windows, are needed. One drawback is that the metal nails used in NLT can dull or damage woodworking tools such as saws, drills, and routers if the NLT panels are machined. NLT panels can be produced in any thickness common to softwood dimension lumber (e.g., 2-by-4 to 2-by-12). The width and length of the panels are limited only by the application's dimensions. NLT is recognized by the International Building Code (IBC) as being code-compliant for buildings with varying heights, areas, and occupancies.

Dowel-Laminated Timber

Dowel-Laminated Timber (DLT) is like NLT, but wooden dowels hold the boards together instead of nails (see **Figure 1.4**). In a process called friction fitting, hardwood dowels are dried to a very low moisture content and placed in holes drilled perpendicularly into softwood boards stacked on edge and side by side. (The wood grain in a DLT panel is parallel.) The hardwood dowels then expand as they gain moisture from the surrounding softwood boards. The result is a tight-fitting connection that holds the boards together. The panel sizes are like CLT and NLT (8 feet to 12 feet wide and up to 60 feet long), but the thickness depends on the width of the softwood boards being used. DLT is most common in floor and roof applications, but StructureCraft, the lone North American manufacturer of DLT, says its panels can also be used in vertical applications.

DLT is the only all-wood mass timber product. With no metal fasteners, DLT panels can be processed with CNC machinery without causing damage to the cutting tools. That's why DLT is often selected when certain profiles are needed in a panel (e.g., a design to enhance acoustics). The all-wood approach also allows building designers to select a material with no chemical adhesives.

Unlike NLT, which is commonly manufactured at the jobsite, DLT is typically fabricated in a plant, allowing the panels to be manufactured at precise dimensions and to include aesthetically pleasing patterns, integrated acoustic materials, electrical conduits, and other service interfaces.

Dowel-Bonded CLT

Dowel-bonded CLT is a massive, prefabricated, cross-laminated panel with layers of rough-sawn boards that are bonded with hardwood dowels. This is the newest of the CLT products and should not be confused with DLT, described above. The low moisture content and tight fitting of the dowels at the time of assembly ensures a durable, tight connection once the dowels swell after gaining moisture in ambient conditions. The panels are assembled in highly automated lines. Only 2

FIGURE: 1.4 DOWEL-LAMINATED TIMBER (DLT) PANEL

Source: StructureCraft

commercially successful systems are known to date: one developed by Thoma Holz100 (or Wood 100) in Austria and another developed by Swiss industrial hardware manufacturer TechnoWood AG. By mid-2019, TechnoWood had installed 8 highly automated lines in Europe. Unlike other CLT products, some layers of the dowel-bonded CLT are arranged at 45 degrees or 60 degrees to the surface layer direction.

Nail-Bonded Solid Wood Wall or Massiv-Holz-Mauer

Massiv-Holz-Mauer (MHM) is a massive, prefabricated cross-laminated panel with layers made of rough-sawn boards bonded with nails. This product should not be confused with NLT produced in North America. The nail-bonded MHM (which literally means "mass wood wall") technology might have predated the development of adhesive-bonded CLT, but the real breakthrough came with a solid wooden wall system patented in Germany in 2005. MHM is fabricated on small-scale, turnkey, 3-step Hundegger production lines. Panels may consist of 9, 11, 13, or 15 layers (each about 16.5 millimeters, or $^{10}/_{16}$ inch). The intended use of this product is as load-bearing and division walls for low-rise buildings with moderate exposure to moisture (below 20 percent) and low to moderate exposure to corrosion.

Mass Plywood Panel

A Mass Plywood Panel (MPP) is another innovative mass timber product that's produced at a single plant: Freres Lumber Co. Inc., located in Oregon. MPPs are veneer-based, rather than lumber-based, and are constructed by gluing together many layers of thin veneer in various combinations of grain orientation (see **Figure 1.5**). The uses of MPPs are similar to those of other mass timber panels, though the manufacturer says veneer-based panels can form thinner panels and/or longer, unsupported spans than are possible with lumber-based panels.

FIGURE 1.5: MASS PLYWOOD PANEL (MPP)
Source: Oregon Department of Forestry

Glulam

Glulam is another form of mass timber, an engineered wood composite made from multiple layers of lumber. The grain is oriented in a parallel direction in all layers, and the layers are bonded with adhesive to form a structural element with large dimensions (see **Figure 1.6**). Glulam, a well-established product that has been used in residential and nonresidential construction for many years, is typically used as either a beam in a horizontal application, or as a column in a vertical application, because of its high strength-to-weight ratio. Glulam use is on the rise because it is commonly used to support mass timber panels. Other less common uses are as members of massive truss systems or as large-scale utility poles.

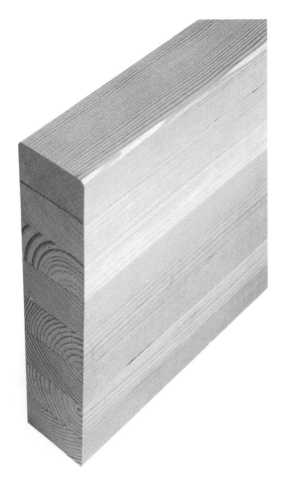

FIGURE 1.6: GLULAM TIMBERS
Source: APA

Most glulam is made from standard-dimension lumber (e.g., 2-by-4s to 2-by-12s). Thus, typical widths range from about 2.5 inches to 10.75 inches. The potential thicknesses and lengths of glulam, however, are much larger. Glulam depths range from 6 inches to 72 inches, and lengths can surpass 100 feet.

Glulam beams are typically much stronger than an equivalent-size solid-sawn beam and can be manufactured in customizable sizes and shapes, including cambered, curved, or arched structures. If glulam is to be used in applications where both structural support and appearance are consid-

erations, it is available in 4 appearance grades: framing, industrial, architectural, and premium.

Post and Beam

Post and beam is a construction method that uses large timbers in both vertical and horizontal applications to create the building framework (see **Figure 1.7**). It allows for large, open spaces within the building and flexible wall structuring. Construction using large-dimension (6 inches thick and larger) lumber has been popular in high-end homes for years, but it is now enjoying increased popularity in a variety of larger nonresidential and multifamily residential buildings (office buildings, schools, and warehouses). In these larger buildings, structural loads are typically higher than for single-family residences, so larger-dimension posts and beams and/or engineered wood composites such as glulam are of use. In many cases, post and beam frames make up the structural elements of a building frame, while nonstructural walls are commonly constructed with light wood framing.

In structures where mass timber panels are used for the floor, wooden posts and beams are often used for the supporting vertical structural elements.

Heavy Timber Decking or Jointed Timbers

Heavy timber decking is used in horizontal applications (floors and roofs) where the full engineered properties of panelized products such as CLT are not required. Heavy timber decking consists of a single layer of timbers (usually 3-by-6s or 4-by-6s) joined edgewise with tongue-and-groove profiles on each piece that lock them together (see **Figure 1.8**). The pieces may be solid-sawn or

glulam. Timber decking is more frequently used in regions where construction labor is less expensive, giving this labor-intensive application a cost advantage over other mass timber panels.

Mass Timber Hollow Core Panels and Mass Timber Ribbed Panel Assemblies

Mass timber hollow core panels use thinner (3-ply) CLT panels for the top and bottom layers, which are connected with internal glulam ribs. The hollow spaces are filled with insulation materials. Mass timber ribbed panel assemblies are another relatively new mass timber product, combining CLT decks with integrated glulam ribs connected by screws, glues, or a combination of

TOP — FIGURE 1.7: POST AND BEAM
BOTTOM — FIGURE 1.8: HEAVY TIMBER DECKING
Source: Southern Wood Specialties

FIGURE 1.9: WOOD-BASE BUILDING CONSTRUCTION SYSTEMS
Source: Fast and Epp

both on the bottom. Both products are typically used as horizontal elements (e.g., high-capacity floors with extended spans).

1.3   HOW IS MASS TIMBER USED?

Figure 1.9 illustrates how mass timber construction differs from more traditional wood construction.

Light wood-frame construction (building on the left) is the most familiar construction system. At a given site, a building is constructed using light wood materials. For example, studs form vertical wall members; joists are the horizontal floor supports; rafters provide roof supports; and plywood or Oriented Strand Board (OSB) panels sheathe the walls, floors, and roof. This style is most commonly used in single-family homes and multifamily low-rise housing.

Post and beam construction (center building) involves the use of large, heavy timbers in either sawn or roundwood form. The timbers used as horizontal beams in this style of construction transfer structural loads to other timbers aligned vertically. Diagonal braces between the horizontal and vertical elements provide even more rigidity to the structure. This style allows for an open design because all load-bearing members are fixed points instead of an entire wall.

Mass timber panel construction (building on the right) involves the use of large, solid wood panels for the roof, floor, and walls. Mass timber allows for the construction of wooden buildings that are much taller than light wood-frame construction. There are many forms of mass timber panels, including CLT, NLT, DLT, and MPP. The term "mass timber," as used in this report, refers to all of the preceding forms.

1.4 DEFINING THE MASS TIMBER SUPPLY CHAIN

A mass timber supply chain is rapidly developing in North America, and examining the components of that supply chain offers a way to organize and think about this industry. It is important to note that most mass timber products are not standardized commodities. Rather, the fabrication of mass timber products is perhaps best thought of as a step in an integrated process of producing a finished building—the actual final product. Accordingly, the supply and value chains of the mass timber panel industry represent an integrated combination of what is typical for manufacturers of structural EWPs and for the design-engineering-construction sector.

The supply chain starts with the forest resource and flows all the way through to the occupants of a mass timber building (see **Figure 1.10**). In this report, we assess the state of each link in the supply chain, and we address issues such as sustainability, economics, and technology. In short, this report analyzes how people and policies impact mass timber and what that might mean for its development.

1.5 MEASUREMENTS AND CONVERSION FACTORS

Wood products—including logs, lumber, and mass timber products—can be measured and labeled in a variety of ways, some of which can be confusing to those not familiar with common industry practices. This section discusses the terminology, measurement, and conversion conventions used in this report.

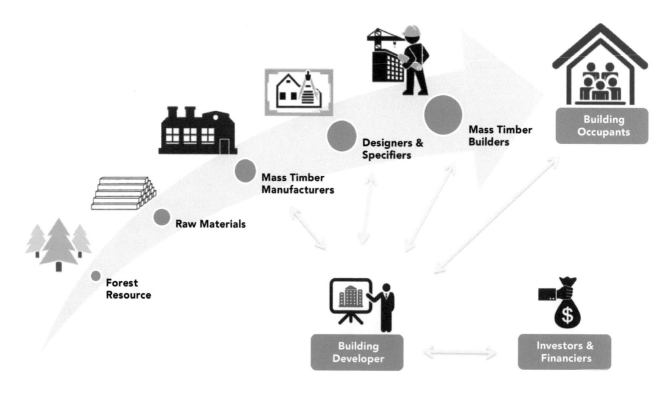

FIGURE 1.10 MASS TIMBER SUPPLY CHAIN

Log Measurement

Standing timber and log volume is reported on a cubic-foot basis. Cubic feet can be converted to cubic meters using the standard conversion of 35.315 cubic feet per cubic meter. In contrast, a variety of measurement units are used when logs are sold, especially in the United States. In fact, different measurement systems are used regionally, including a variety of log scales and weight-based measurements. Analysis of these systems is beyond the scope of this report.

Lumber Measurement

In mass timber, 2 main types of solid-sawn lumber (not engineered wood or wood/glue composite) are relevant. The first is dimension lumber (most commonly 2 inches thick and 4 inches to 12 inches wide). When used in mass timber panels, multiple pieces of dimension lumber are fastened or glued together to create one larger mass of wood. Mass timber is bought and sold in cubic feet (or cubic meters). Dimension lumber is bought and sold in board feet. A board foot is defined as 1-by-12-by-12 (all in inches). Thus, a cubic foot of wood contains 12 board feet. However, a peculiarity of dimension lumber is that its volume is expressed as a nominal size that is larger than the actual finished size. For example, a 2-by-4's actual dimensions are really 1.5 by 3.5. This difference in dimension lumber's nominal and actual sizes means that a cubic foot of wood in a mass timber panel requires an estimated 22.5 board feet of lumber, after accounting for the differences between nominal and actual sizes and yield loss when converting lumber into mass timber panels.

Table 1.1 compares the board feet per piece based on nominal size with the actual cubic volume per piece of dry, surfaced framing lumber sold in North America. For consistency, 20-foot-long pieces are used for all examples. The resulting conversion factors (board feet per cubic foot, and vice versa) are shown in the 2 columns on the right side of the table.

The second type of solid-sawn lumber used in mass timber structures is heavy timber; it is used as structural support for mass timber panel systems. Heavy timbers may either be sawn to sizes similar to nominal-dimension lumber sizes ("standard-sawn") or to the full stated size ("full-sawn"). Most heavy timbers are custom-made where the buyer and seller agree on the specified sawn dimensions. For timbers that are full-sawn, the appropriate conversion would be 12 board feet per cubic foot.

Globally, lumber practices can vary. In contrast to the North American market, structural lumber in Europe and in many other regions is offered in a variety of thicknesses. Although all lumber imported to the US from overseas conforms with US standards, mass timber panels produced overseas will freely incorporate layers of various thicknesses to meet the required engineering specifications with better efficiency.

Log-to-Lumber Volumes

In the sawmill industry, lumber yield—the volume of lumber produced from a given volume of logs—is expressed in a variety of ways, with regional differences based on local conventions for measuring logs. A full description of these various lumber yield measurements is beyond the scope of this report. But to understand how lumber volumes relate to log demand and harvest, it is most useful to consider cubic yields.

NOMINAL SIZE				ACTUAL (DRY, SURFACED) SIZE				Conversion Factor (CF/BF)	Conversion Factor (BF/CF)
Thickness (inches)	Width (inches)	Length (feet)	Volume (board feet)	Thickness (inches)	Width (inches)	Length (feet)	Volume (cubic feet)		
2	4	20	13.33	1.5	3.50	20	0.73	0.055	18.3
2	6	20	20.00	1.5	5.50	20	1.15	0.057	17.5
2	8	20	26.67	1.5	7.25	20	1.51	0.057	17.7
2	10	20	33.33	1.5	9.25	20	1.93	0.058	17.3
2	12	20	40.00	1.5	11.25	20	2.34	0.059	17.1

TABLE 1.1: NOMINAL DIMENSION LUMBER SIZES VS. ACTUAL CUBIC MEASUREMENT

Cubic lumber yields (i.e., the percentage of a log's total cubic volume that is recovered as lumber) at sawmills vary depending on several factors, with the most important being the log size (diameter). In North America, typical cubic lumber yields for sawmills producing dimension lumber are in the range of 35 percent to 60 percent, meaning that 35 percent to 60 percent of the log volume comes out as finished (dry, surfaced) lumber and the balance is a by-product (chips, sawdust, and shavings), with some volume lost to drying shrinkage. The regions with the largest logs (9 inches to 11 inches average bucked sawmill-length log diameter in the US West) achieve higher cubic lumber yields, while those with the smallest logs (4.5 inches to 6 inches average bucked log diameter in Eastern Canada) are on the lower end of the range.

For a quick but rough conversion, multiply a known lumber volume by 2 to estimate the log volume required. For example, to produce 100 cubic feet of dimension lumber, a mill needs 200 cubic feet of logs.

Mass Timber Panels and Glulam

Most measurements of mass timber panels and glulam beams are expressed in terms of cubic feet or cubic meters. These figures are based on the actual size of the finished product (although cutouts and channels are typically not deducted). For example, a CLT panel that is 6 inches thick by 10 feet wide and 40 feet long would measure 200 cubic feet ([6 ÷ 12] x 10 x 40), or 5.66 cubic meters (200 cubic feet ÷ 35.315).

When considering the amount of lumber used in mass timber or glulam products, it is important to consider the nominal versus the cubic size of the lumber feedstock (see **Table 1.1**), as well as any volume lost during the mass timber manufacturing process. In CLT, DLT, and glulam, the lumber is surfaced during the manufacturing process, with about $1/16$ of an inch removed from all 4 sides (exact amounts vary by manufacturer). Also, some volume is lost when defects are trimmed from lumber feedstock, and when panels or beams are trimmed to final dimensions.

WOOD VOLUME	VOLUME OR CONVERSION FACTOR	UNIT	DESCRIPTION
Mass Timber Volume	100,000	Cubic Feet	Total CLT and glulam used in building project
	22.5	BF per CF	CLT/glulam to nominal lumber conversion
Dimension Lumber Volume	2,250,000	Board Feet	Purchased dimension lumber
	0.057	CF per BF	Conversion from nominal to cubic volume
Cubic Lumber Volume	128,250	Cubic Feet	Equivalent cubic volume of lumber used
	0.5	CF per CF	Cubic lumber yield from logs
Log Volume	256,500	Cubic Feet	Log demand from mass timber project

TABLE 1.2: SUPPLY CHAIN CONVERSIONS EXAMPLE

For typical CLT or glulam manufacturing, a total of 20 to 25 nominal board feet of dimension lumber is used per cubic foot of finished product.

Example of Mass Timber to Logs

Given all the preceding measurement and conversion conventions, it is possible to approximate the total amount of timber (logs) required for a mass timber project. **Table 1.2** follows the wood back through the supply chain to estimate the total lumber, and then the logs, required for a hypothetical building project that uses 100,000 cubic feet of CLT and glulam. This calculation is only an estimate, and it depends on several assumptions (lumber yield, size of lumber used, and CLT and glulam wood use), but it provides a reasonable indication of the wood volume at various points in the supply chain.

The results show that substantially more log volume is required than will be reflected in the finished product volume. Importantly, the material not used in the final mass timber product is not wasted. Depending on the region where the lumber and mass timber are manufactured, the by-products can be used in a variety of ways. Chips are typically used for making paper. Sawdust or planer shavings make composite panels (particleboard or medium-density fiberboard). By-products can also be made into wood pellets for heating or power generation, or combusted in a boiler to generate power and/or provide thermal energy for lumber drying or other uses.

AON

Committed to Protection and Growth

At Aon, we provide advice and solutions that give our clients the clarity and confidence to make better decisions.

By pairing our deep understanding of the mass timber industry with a track record of innovating effective and sustainable risk and risk transfer solutions, Aon can help you protect and grow your business.

Contact masstimber@aon.ca for more information.

CHAPTER 2: THE FOREST RESOURCE

GLOBAL PERSPECTIVE

 By recent estimates, about ⅔ of the global Cross-Laminated Timber (CLT) production capacity is in Europe, including more than 50 percent in Central Europe. Central Europe alone contributes more than ⅔ of the global CLT production by volume, and it is capable of exporting projects to other global markets. Even in North America—as well as across Australia and Asia—a number of projects have been executed in CLT fabricated from species harvested in Central Europe: Norway spruce, fir, larch, and/or pines.

2.1 CHARACTERIZING THE NORTH AMERICAN FOREST RESOURCE

Forests are a key component of the landscape in many regions. Accordingly, **Figure 2.1** illustrates the portions of North America with more than 15 percent tree cover. As shown by the color shadings, there are 2 main forest types including coniferous (softwood) trees in the coastal and mountainous areas of the West; mixed hardwood and coniferous trees in the US Midwest, Eastern US, and Eastern Canada; and coniferous trees in the US Southeast. Also note that the far northern regions of Canada and Alaska have vast areas of boreal forests. But, given their distance from major population centers and their generally smaller tree sizes, these forests have little commercial value for conversion to lumber. Finally, although not shown in the figure, it is worth noting that, in Central Europe, Germany and Austria are leading in production of high-performing mass

timber elements, including glulam and Laminated Veneer Lumber (LVL) made of local hardwoods, mostly beech and oak. These technologies are commercialized, and a similar development may be expected in North America, with a focus on hardwood species abundant in the US where hardwoods predominate.

As further discussed in chapter 3, lumber-producing regions are often defined by the types of softwood they commonly produce. The 5 main regions in North America are the US West, US South, US Other, Eastern Canada, and Western Canada. Forests in the US West are dominated by Douglas fir, Western hemlock, and various pine species. In both Eastern and Western Canada, forests are largely composed of various mixtures of spruce, pine, and fir (SPF). In the US South, 4 types of pine—loblolly, slash, shortleaf, and longleaf—are the leading species of note for mass timber. When sold as lumber, those 4 species are lumped into a group called Southern Yellow Pine (SYP). The US Other region includes the Upper Midwest and Northeast. These forests are more heavily stocked with hardwood trees and therefore, up to this point, have been less significant from a mass timber industry perspective.

Extent of US Forests

The total US land area is about 2.3 billion acres. As illustrated in **Table 2.1,** forests in the United States total about 822 million acres, or roughly one-third of the US land area. Note that this data is from *Forest Resources of the United States,*

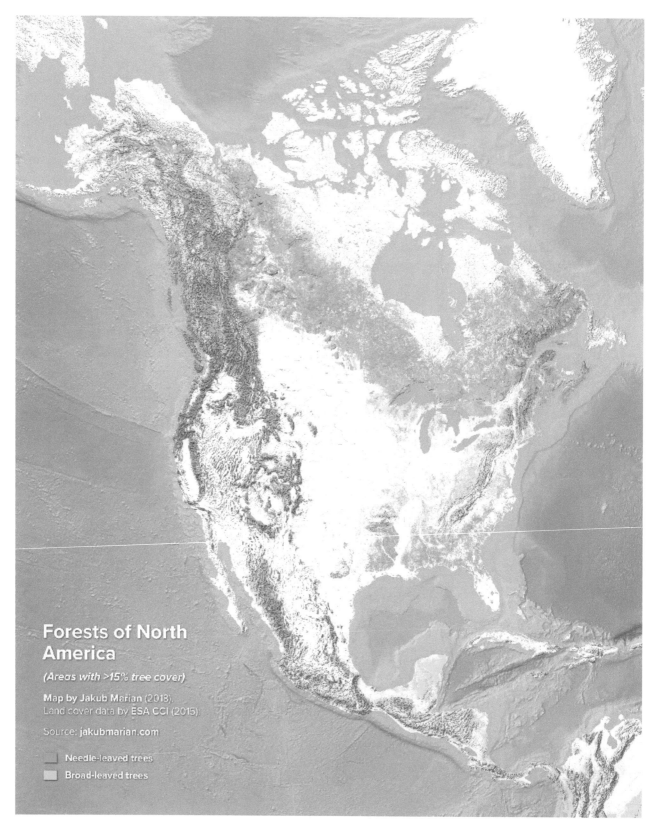

Forests of North America

(Areas with >15% tree cover)

Map by Jakub Marian (2018).
Land cover data by ESA CCI (2015).

Source: jakubmarian.com

Needle-leaved trees
Broad-leaved trees

FIGURE 2.1: EXTENT OF FORESTS IN NORTH AMERICA

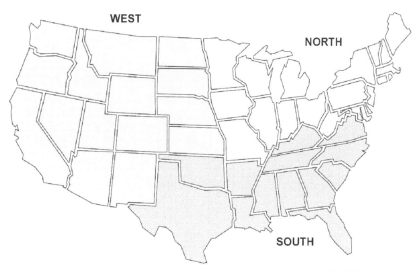

FIGURE 2.2: MAP OF US FOREST REGIONS

FOREST TYPE	NORTH	SOUTH	WEST	TOTAL
Timberland	164,894	208,092	141,437	514,423
Reserved	9,447	5,827	65,290	80,564
Other/Woodland	1,448	54,114	171,846	227,408
Total	175,789	268,033	378,573	822,395

TABLE 2.1: EXTENT OF FORESTS IN THE UNITED STATES BY TYPE & REGION (ACRES IN 1000S)

2017.[1] The total forest area increased from 766 million acres to 822 million acres in the most recent assessment. The area of forested land in the US has been stable (or increasing, per the most recent analysis) since the early 1900s, despite the US population quadrupling since 1900. Despite the massive growth in US population and the associated increase in demand for wood fiber, it's encouraging to consider that the forest area in the US has remained stable for more than 100 years.

The broad category of forested land includes several subcategories: timberland, or forests that are well stocked and capable of producing at least 20 cubic feet of wood fiber per acre per year; reserved forestland, or forests where harvesting of trees is prohibited, mainly wilderness areas and national parks; and woodland/other, where tree cover ranges between 5 percent and 10 percent, tree growth is marginal, and timber production

1   Sonja Oswalt, W. Brad Smith, Patrick D. Miles, and Scott Pugh, *Forest Resources of the United States, 2017* (2019), https://www.fs.usda.gov/research/treesearch/57903.

REGION	NATIONAL FOREST	OTHER PUBLIC	PRIVATE CORPORATE	PRIVATE NONCORPORATE	TOTAL
North	10,147	26,852	30,196	97,700	164,895
South	12,258	13,699	63,504	118,632	208,093
West	73,733	18,584	23,455	25,665	141,437
Total	96,138	59,135	117,155	241,997	514,425

TABLE 2.2: OWNERSHIP OF US FORESTS DESIGNATED AS TIMBERLAND BY REGION AND OWNER TYPE (ACRES IN 1000S)

YEAR	SAWTIMBER	POLETIMBER	SEEDLING/ SAPLING	NONSTOCKED	TOTAL
1953	201,491	170,688	94,565	42,110	508,854
1977	223,210	136,694	115,842	16,607	492,353
1987	242,864	137,981	97,413	8,057	486,315
1997	258,680	127,169	110,283	7,533	503,665
2007	280,265	128,896	96,177	8,875	514,213
2012	294,964	123,144	93,140	9,906	521,154
2017	299,716	117,637	87,395	9,676	514,424

TABLE 2.3: HISTORY OF TIMBERLAND AREA IN THE US BY STANDING SIZE CLASS (ACRES IN 1000S)

is not a priority. **Figure 2.2** shows the location of the regions listed as columns in **Table 2.2.**

Ownership of US Forests

The timberland forest classification is the most productive forest acreage in the US. **Table 2.2** categorizes it by 2 types of public owners and 2 types of private owners. As the data in the table shows, higher percentages of timberland are in private ownership in the North and South than in the West. Ownership is important because it affects how land is managed. In general, corporate timberlands are managed to maximize timber production, while public and noncorporate

private lands are managed for a broader set of objectives.

Table 2.3 shows a history of the area of US forest designated as timberland classified by tree size, including sawtimber, poletimber, seedling/sapling, and nonstocked. Note that sawtimber includes trees big enough to be sawed into lumber; pole trees are too small for use as sawlogs; seedlings/saplings are very young stands; and nonstocked is bare land that typically has yet to be replanted just after harvest. As the data shows, the area of sawtimber that could be used to make lumber for mass timber has increased by nearly 100 million acres over the last 65 years. This is an encouraging finding.

REGION	SOFTWOOD	HARDWOOD	TOTAL
North	68,278	245,926	314,204
South	149,800	227,981	377,781
West	380,794	43,232	424,026
Total	598,872	517,139	1,116,011

TABLE 2.4: US STANDING TIMBER INVENTORY ON TIMBERLAND BY REGION AND SPECIES GROUP (CUBIC FEET IN MILLIONS)

REGION	1953	1977	1987	1997	2007	2017
North	27,053	43,850	47,618	49,374	55,864	60,601
South	60,462	101,208	105,613	104,846	118,472	141,307
West	344,279	321,902	314,344	329,622	357,264	358,617
Total	431,794	466,960	467,575	483,842	531,600	560,525

TABLE 2.5: HISTORY OF US SOFTWOOD STANDING TIMBER INVENTORY ON TIMBERLAND BY REGION (CUBIC FEET IN MILLIONS)

US Standing Timber Inventory

The US Forest Service is a federal agency charged with managing nearly 190 million acres of national forests and grasslands. In addition, its Forest Inventory and Analysis (FIA) program was established nearly 100 years ago to monitor the conditions of all the nation's forests (i.e., both publicly and privately owned forestlands). A key accomplishment of the FIA was to establish more than 325,000 permanent growth plots in US forests at the initiation of the program. Thus, for about 100 years, each plot has been revisited regularly. The data collected about the trees within the plots' boundaries allows the FIA system to track changes in the forests' statuses. The FIA tracks, for example, key metrics such as species, diameter, age, and cubic volume as part of its inventory of standing trees.

Table 2.4 shows the most recently available (2019) estimate of standing timber volume in the US on timberland acres. As shown, the US has an estimated 1.1 trillion cubic feet of standing timber. The standing volume is relatively evenly split between hardwoods and softwoods. As a point of reference, and as further discussed in chapter 3, the annual harvest of softwood sawtimber associated with the US annual softwood lumber production is equal to about 1.4 percent of standing volume.

More specific to the mass timber industry is Table 2.5. It shows the history of softwood standing timber inventory by region. Note that over roughly the last 65 years, the total volume of standing timber in the US has increased by nearly 30 percent in total and by more than 230 percent in the South, both positive findings given the anticipated increased demand from the mass timber industry.

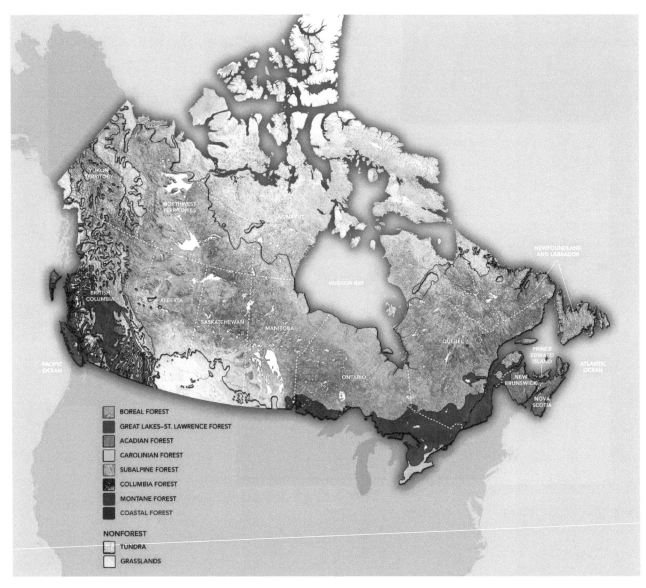

BOREAL FOREST

GREAT LAKES–ST. LAWRENCE FOREST

ACADIAN FOREST

CAROLINIAN FOREST

SUBALPINE FOREST

COLUMBIA FOREST

MONTANE FOREST

COASTAL FOREST

NONFOREST

TUNDRA

GRASSLANDS

FIGURE 2.3: CANADIAN FOREST REGIONS

Source: Natural Resources Canada. Accessed at https://www.nrcan.gc.ca/sites/nr-can/files/forest/SFM/classification/Canada_forest_regions.pdf

2.1.1 CANADIAN FORESTS

The Extent of Canada's Forests

Canada's total land area is about 2.467 billion acres. Of that total, about 857 million acres are forested. Canada and the US have roughly the same total land areas and total forested areas. Canada's forest area has been stable for decades. **Figure 2.3** shows that there are several distinct types of forest in Canada. The largest and most commercially important types include a vast boreal forest that stretches the length of the country from east to west and is composed mainly of spruces, firs, and, to a lesser extent, pines; the forests around the Great Lakes, which are primarily hardwoods, including maple and birch; the montane forests of Western Canada, which are populated with Douglas fir, hemlock, and pines; and the coastal forests in Western Canada, which are heavy with cedar, hemlock, and firs.

OWNER TYPE	PERCENT OWNED
Provincial Crown Land	75.4%
Territorial Crown Land	13.0%
Federal Crown Land	1.7%
Private	6.7%
Indigenous	2.1%
Other Misc.	1.1%
Total	**100.0%**

TABLE 2.6: OWNERSHIP OF CANADIAN FORESTS

YEAR	CUBIC FEET (IN MILLIONS)
1990	1,684,796
1995	1,682,783
2000	1,671,058
2005	1,623,808
2010	1,607,034
2015	1,594,356
2016	1,591,567
2017	1,585,493
2018	1,575,640
2019	1,573,398

TABLE 2.7: HISTORICAL TOTAL STANDING TIMBER VOLUME IN CANADA (CUBIC FEET IN MILLIONS)

Ownership of Canadian Forests

Over 90 percent of Canadian forests are publicly owned. **Table 2.6** shows a categorization by owner type that includes provincial Crown land, territorial Crown land, federal Crown land, private, and indigenous.

Canada's Standing Timber Inventory

The standing timber inventory in Canada as of 2019 was 1.57 trillion cubic feet, approximately 50 percent more standing timber volume than the United States, according to *The State of Canada's Forests: Annual Report 2021*.[2] **Table 2.7** shows that Canada's standing timber volume has de-

2   *The State of Canada's Forests: Annual Report 2021, https://www.nrcan.gc.ca/sites/nrcan/files/forest/sof2021/6317_NRCan_SoF_ AR_2021_EN_P7B_web_accessible.pdf.*

SPECIES GROUP	1 TO 20	21 TO 40	41 TO 60	61 TO 80	81 TO 100	101 TO 120	121 TO 140	141 TO 160	161 TO 180	181 TO 200	201+	TOTAL
Coniferous	8,665	31,452	70,477	139,785	312,436	224,080	105,282	50,915	33,388	24,018	205,958	1,206,457
Mixed	9,510	17,712	47,769	64,457	83,107	21,329	9,663	4,354	1,488	470	884	260,743
Broadleaf	4,857	11,009	53,038	65,236	44,725	16,482	5,892	1,856	536	33	162	203,827
Total	23,035	60,181	171,294	269,482	440,289	261,893	120,837	57,126	35,414	24,521	207,003	1,671,075

TABLE 2.8: CANADIAN STANDING TIMBER VOLUME BY SPECIES GROUP AND STAND AGE CLASS (CUBIC FEET IN MILLIONS)

clined since 1990. The causes of this are many, but 2 key factors are extensive insect outbreaks and wildfires.

Table 2.8 provides a more detailed estimate of standing timber volume, with categorizations by forest type and stand age as of 2019. As the data shows, more than 70 percent of Canada's forests are coniferous (i.e., softwoods).

2.2 FOREST SUSTAINABILITY

People across the globe are interested in access to clean air and water. Forests are key to providing access to both. Thus, assuring forest sustainability is critical to all global citizens. "Sustainability" is defined as meeting society's current needs via the consumption of natural resources without jeopardizing the ability of future generations to meet their needs through consumption of the same natural resources.

2.2.1 GROWTH-TO-DRAIN

One measure foresters use to monitor sustainability is "growth-to-drain." Growth-to-drain is a ratio of the amount of wood fiber a given area can grow annually (net of natural mortality from insects, disease, fire, etc.) to the amount of wood fiber harvested annually. A ratio greater than 1 indicates that the area is adding more wood fiber each year through net growth than is being removed by harvesting. Although many other considerations relate to sustainability, growth-to-drain is frequently a key consideration in forest management and timber harvest planning. The following sections provide an analysis of growth-to-drain for US and Canadian forests.

US Timberlands Growth-to-Drain

As described in the preceding section, so long as the ratio of growth-to-drain is greater than 1, forests can supply fiber in perpetuity. Table 2.9 provides information about historical growth-to-drain ratios in the United States. At the top of the table is data for all softwoods in the US; in the middle is information about hardwoods; and, at the bottom, softwoods and hardwoods are combined. As the data indicates, the ratio is greater than 1 in all cases.

This is a positive finding for the mass timber industry; it indicates that US forests are not being overharvested. However, the data shows a troubling trend. Natural mortality—trees dying

	1976	1996	2006	2016
Softwoods: Annual Mortality (ft³ in 1000s)	2,466,137	3,959,580	4,510,607	5,899,508
Softwoods: Annual Harvest (ft³ in 1000s)	10,020,449	10,084,714	9,883,421	8,901,491
Softwoods: Total Drain (ft³ in 1000s)	12,486,586	14,044,294	14,394,028	14,800,999
Softwoods: Annual Growth (ft³ in 1000s)	12,501,271	14,715,427	15,241,092	15,467,789
Softwood Growth-to-Drain Ratio	*1.00*	*1.05*	*1.06*	*1.05*
Hardwoods: Annual Mortality (ft³ in 1000s)	1,626,733	2,755,701	3,315,862	4,298,579
Hardwoods: Annual Harvest (ft³ in 1000s)	4,215,500	5,971,328	5,690,561	4,139,708
Hardwoods: Total Drain (ft³ in 1000s)	5,842,233	8,727,029	9,006,423	8,438,287
Hardwoods: Annual Growth (ft³ in 1000s)	9,425,003	10,232,615	11,503,274	9,541,561
Hardwood Growth-to-Drain Ratio	*1.61*	*1.17*	*1.28*	*1.13*
All Species: Annual Mortality (ft³ in 1000s)	4,092,870	6,715,281	7,826,469	10,198,087
All Species: Annual Harvest (ft³ in 1000s)	14,235,949	16,056,042	15,573,982	13,041,199
All Species: Total Drain (ft³ in 1000s)	18,328,819	22,771,323	23,400,451	23,239,286
All Species: Annual Growth (ft³ in 1000s)	21,926,274	24,948,042	26,744,366	25,009,350
All Species Growth-to-Drain Ration	*1.20*	*1.10*	*1.14*	*1.08*

TABLE 2.9: HISTORY OF US GROWTH-TO-DRAIN RATIOS FOR SOFTWOODS AND HARDWOODS

from causes such as wildfire, drought, insects, and disease—increased by 250 percent from 1976 to 2016. There is considerable debate about whether the cause is climate change or lack of management, especially in publicly owned forests in the US West. In any case, pressure on growth-to-drain ratios would ease considerably if more of the standing tree volume were used through harvesting rather than lost to natural mortality.

Also note that growth-to-drain ratios can vary dramatically by region and species. In the US South, for example, the growth-to-drain for softwoods is significantly higher than for softwoods in the entire US. **Table 2.10** shows the data that supports that statement; with both naturally regenerated and plantation stands of SYP (i.e., the overwhelming majority of softwoods in the US South), the growth-to-drain ratio is well over 1. This means that, each year, 80 percent more wood is being added to the standing volume than

	NATURAL STANDS	PLANTATIONS	TOTAL
US South: Softwood Annual Growth (ft³ in 1,000,000s)	2,886	5,972	8,858
US South: Softwood Annual Harvest (ft³ in 1,000,000s)	721	3,225	3,946
US South: Softwood Annual Mortality (ft³ in 1,000,000s)	603	323	926
US South: Total Drain (ft³ in 1,000,000s)	1,324	3,548	4,872
Growth-to-Drain Ratio	2.2	1.7	1.8

TABLE 2.10: US SOUTH GROWTH-TO-DRAIN RATIO FOR SOFTWOODS IN 2017

is being used or is dying from natural mortality. As is further discussed in chapter 3, the combination of a high percentage of privately owned lands and a large amount of excess growth is leading to extensive investment in new sawmilling capacity across the region.

Canadian Growth-to-Drain

Table 2.11 provides a 30-year history of growth-to-drain for Canadian forests. Note that total wood supply is the Annual Allowable Cut (AAC), a calculated value that projects the amount of timber that can be harvested sustainably based on the capacity of the forests to grow new fiber and their annual natural mortality. As the data shows, in all cases, the actual harvest levels have been lower than the AAC by an average factor of 1.4 for all species, 1.3 for softwoods, and 2.3 for hardwoods. This is a positive finding for the mass timber industry, as it indicates that Canadian forests are not being overharvested and could

supply more fiber if warranted by increasing market demand.

2.2.2 ENVIRONMENTAL FOREST MANAGEMENT CERTIFICATION

Many forest landowners manage with multiple objectives in mind and consider sustainability in their forest management planning and decision-making. Environmental forest management certification programs offer landowners a formal process for ensuring that their plans are consistent with sustainability objectives related to fiber production; wildlife habitat; clean water; recreation values; and the wide range of plants, animals, insects, and fungi that make up the web of life in a forest ecosystem.

Concerns about sustainability and the protection of myriad forest values emerged in the United States and Canada during the 1960s, '70s, and '80s. As a result, laws such as the National Environmental Policy Act (NEPA), Endangered Spe-

YEAR	TOTAL WOOD SUPPLY	TOTAL HARVEST	TOTAL GROWTH-TO-DRAIN	SOFTWOOD SUPPLY	SOFTWOOD HARVEST	SOFTWOOD GROWTH-TO-DRAIN	HARDWOOD SUPPLY	HARDWOOD HARVEST	HARDWOOD GROWTH-TO-DRAIN
1990	247.6	156.4	1.6	180.2	141.2	1.3	63.6	15.2	4.2
1991	246.3	154.2	1.6	180.5	138.5	1.3	62.0	15.7	3.9
1992	241.5	163.7	1.5	177.0	146.8	1.2	60.6	16.9	3.6
1993	238.2	169.6	1.4	174.7	150.5	1.2	59.7	19.1	3.1
1994	238.4	177.4	1.3	174.0	154.2	1.1	60.5	23.2	2.6
1995	234.4	183.2	1.3	171.0	157.4	1.1	59.5	25.7	2.3
1996	234.9	177.9	1.3	170.8	151.3	1.1	60.3	26.6	2.3
1997	237.4	183.6	1.3	172.2	153.8	1.1	61.4	29.8	2.1
1998	235.2	173.9	1.4	170.8	142.8	1.2	61.8	31.1	2.0
1999	239.6	196.7	1.2	175.2	162.8	1.1	61.6	33.9	1.8
2000	234.9	199.5	1.2	173.3	163.3	1.1	60.5	36.2	1.7
2001	236.1	184.4	1.3	175.2	149.9	1.2	60.7	34.5	1.8
2002	237.4	195.4	1.2	176.3	159.6	1.1	61.1	35.7	1.7
2003	239.8	181.4	1.3	177.7	143.8	1.2	62.0	37.6	1.6
2004	246.9	208.1	1.2	184.7	168.5	1.1	62.0	39.6	1.6
2005	245.0	201.3	1.2	182.2	165.2	1.1	62.7	36.1	1.7
2006	248.1	182.5	1.4	185.5	148.7	1.2	62.5	33.7	1.9
2007	252.4	162.1	1.6	189.8	134.6	1.4	62.6	27.3	2.3
2008	251.1	138.3	1.8	189.7	114.2	1.7	61.3	23.9	2.6
2009	241.8	115.8	2.1	181.8	94.3	1.9	59.9	21.4	2.8
2010	237.7	141.0	1.7	179.0	117.4	1.5	58.6	23.5	2.5
2011	232.7	147.0	1.6	174.7	121.0	1.4	57.8	25.9	2.2
2012	230.6	149.3	1.5	173.4	124.6	1.4	57.1	24.7	2.3
2013	228.0	151.1	1.5	171.6	126.0	1.4	56.5	25.1	2.3
2014	230.6	150.1	1.5	171.8	124.9	1.4	58.8	25.1	2.3
2015	228.5	155.6	1.5	168.5	128.2	1.3	58.8	27.3	2.2
2016	222.3	155.2	1.4	162.8	126.4	1.3	59.5	28.8	2.1
2017	219.9	152.4	1.4	160.7	125.1	1.3	59.0	27.4	2.2
2018	219.9	154.9	1.4	160.3	127.6	1.3	59.5	27.3	2.2
2019	218.1	139.8	1.6	159.0	114.3	1.4	58.8	25.6	2.3

TABLE 2.11: COMPARISON OF ANNUAL ALLOWABLE CUT TO ACTUAL HARVEST IN CANADA (CUBIC FEET IN MILLIONS)

cies Act (ESA), Clean Water Act, Clean Air Act, National Forest Management Act (NFMA), and others were passed. All of these laws help ensure a baseline of sustainability and accountability in forest management, especially on public lands. In the 1990s, however, concerns arose about the sources of wood from private lands and from countries where illegal logging is prevalent or where forest management practices are lax.

Those concerns, spurred by buyers of wood products who wanted assurance that their products were sourced from well-managed forests, led to the development of environmental forest management certifications. Through the Earth Summit in Rio de Janeiro and the Montreal Process meetings in the early 1990s, forest health and management criteria and indicators were developed. They were to be monitored by independent, third-party verification groups. The intent was to create a market-driven reward for complying with the criteria and indicators judged to represent sound, sustainable forest management. Wood is the only building material that has third-party certification programs in place to demonstrate compliance with sustainability principles.

In the decades since, only about 11 percent of the world's forests have been certified as complying with one of several programs, according to the *Global Forest Atlas* from the Forest School at the Yale School of the Environment. Despite accounting for only 11 percent of the certified acreage, those certified forests provide an estimated 29 percent of global timber production. More than 92 percent of all certified forestland is in the northern hemisphere, with the US and Canada accounting for more than half that total. The acreage of certified land in tropical forests is approximately 2 percent. Thus, even though cer-

tification was conceived as a means of stopping deforestation—primarily a tropical forest issue—little forest management has been certified among the world's tropical forests. Note that the species and lumber products produced from tropical forests are not used in the production of mass timber products. Thus, the mass timber industry has little direct impact on tropical forest management and deforestation.

Forest Certification in the US and Canada

Across the US and Canada, more than 480 million acres of forestland, or roughly 28.5 percent of all non-reserved North American forests, have been certified under various third-party forest certification programs. The 4 main certification programs operating in North America are listed here:

- American Tree Farm System (ATFS): ATFS is managed by the American Forest Foundation and is designed to serve relatively small family forest ownerships. Currently, there are about 74,000 members who manage a collective 19 million acres of forestland. ATFS is endorsed by the Programme for the Endorsement of Forest Certification (PEFC), a global umbrella organization that endorses a variety of national forest certification systems. Through ATFS's association with PEFC, ATFS-certified landowners have global certification status. See additional information here: https://www.treefarmsystem.org/.

- Forest Stewardship Council (FSC): FSC was initiated in 1993 and is a global forest certification program. As of 2022 (the most recent annual report), nearly 533 million acres have been certified globally. In North America, FSC certificate holders include publicly owned

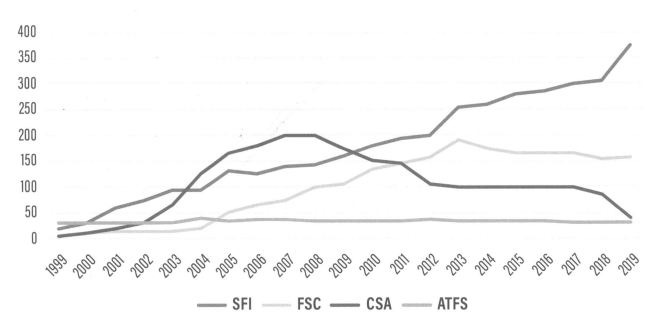

FIGURE 2.4: HISTORY OF ACRES CERTIFIED IN NORTH AMERICA BY FOREST CERTIFICATION PROGRAMS

forests, native forest enterprises, family forest trusts, and industrial timberlands. Roughly 158 million acres are FSC-certified in North America. See additional information here: https://www.fsc.org.

- Sustainable Forestry Initiative (SFI): SFI was started in 1994 and primarily serves large industrial forest landowners. It is endorsed by PEFC. As of 2022, about 370 million acres of North American forestland have been certified to the SFI standard. See additional information here: https://www.forests.org/.

- Canadian Standards Association: CSA Group is the Canadian standards system established in 1996. Like SFI and ATFS, CSA is PEFC-endorsed. See more information here: https:// www.csagroup.org.

Figure 2.4 shows the history of the acres certified in North America under each program. Note that data in the figure was interpolated by the author team from a figure included in the *2020 SFI Annual Progress Report*.[3]

Certification of Public Lands in the United States

Most federal land in the United States—including national parks, national forests, Bureau of Land Management (BLM) lands, and wildlife refuges—is not certified to the standards of any of the above programs. Rather, federal laws guide management planning and activities. Large areas of federal land have been permanently set aside from timber harvest. These include wilderness areas, national parks, and inventoried roadless areas. Such reserved areas play an important role in sustainability by providing habitat conditions

3   *https://www.forests.org/progressreports/*

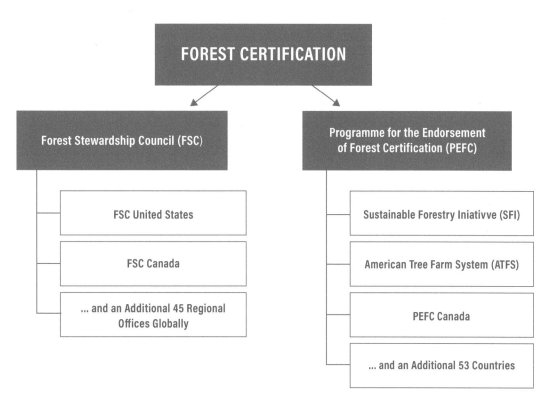

FIGURE 2.5: RELATIONSHIPS AMONG FOREST CERTIFICATION PROGRAMS

not always found on forestlands managed for timber production.

Generally, state and municipally owned lands are managed to generate sustained revenue from the harvest of timber and the use of other resources. Revenue from management activities often supports school systems and other rural, local government needs. Unlike federal lands, several states and municipal governments have enrolled in one of the above forest management certification programs. Landowners who have not pursued third-party certification are guided by state and municipal laws and/or best management practices (BMPs) that govern or guide forest management within a jurisdiction. The nature and extent of these laws vary considerably across the US. Common to all, though, are principles designed to assure clean water and long-term sustainability.

Thus, at a minimum, end users can be assured that forest management in the US overwhelmingly complies with local, regional, and federal forest management laws.

Certification of Public Lands in Canada

Most Canadian forestland is publicly owned. However, a tenure system allows private companies to carry out sustainable forest management on public lands. Under the tenure system, the right to harvest a public resource (timber) is transferred to a private entity. Although details vary from province to province, the basic concept is that a company signs a long-term agreement with the Canadian government. The agreement encompasses a designated forest acreage and dictates certain forest management guidelines (i.e., applicable forestry laws, regulations, and policies) with which the company must comply. In addition to those standards, about 420 million acres of forest in Canada have been certified by third parties, including FSC, SFI, and CSA. Canada also has 59 million acres reserved from harvest in the form of parks and other protective designations. The reserved areas represent about 6 percent of Canada's forests.

Future of Forest Certification

A report[4] released by Dovetail Partners, a nonprofit that provides authoritative information about the impacts and trade-offs of environmental decisions, analyzes what the future of forest certification might look like. A key takeaway is that competition among forest certification programs may hinder the ability of forest certification to continue having a meaningful impact on forest management. **Figure 2.5**, adapted from the Dovetail Partners report, shows the divergence among forest certification programs: the FSC program stands alone while the PEFC program acts as an umbrella organization for numerous global programs.

Key drivers cited as threats to the programs are the steady growth within supply chains of private- and public-sector alternative approaches to forest certification, technological innovation,

4   Dovetail Partners, *Forest Certification Update 2021: The Pace of Change* (January 2021), https://www.dovetailinc.org/portfoliodetail.php?id=60085a177dc07.

Godfrey Hall (1898)

Andy Quattlebaum Outdoor Education Center (2019)

Samuel J. Cadden Chapel (2021)

from past to present
Clemson's structural roots are in timber

The Wood Utilization + Design Institute (WU+D) is a multidisciplinary engine of innovation at Clemson University advancing mass timber research and utilization.

Clemson.edu/WUD   @wudclemson on

and government policies. The report offers ways to ratchet down competition, including the suggestion that supply chain influencers adopt either a neutral position about material sourced from the different programs or rank their choice to sourcing certified fiber in order of preference. According to Dovetail Partners, ranked choice is an alternative to the all-or-nothing approach that is apparently a common practice among some sectors of end users.

2.3 FOREST DIVERSITY

Species richness, the number of unique species in an area, is frequently used as a measure of forest sustainability. In the US, there are many different ecological zones, translating into numerous species of trees. During US Forest Service FIA timber cruises in 2017, cruisers identified nearly 1,000 unique species. Most abundant were red maple, loblolly pine, balsam fir, sweetgum, and Douglas fir. However, when considered on the basis of biomass rather than tree count, Douglas fir makes up the largest portion, accounting for about 1 percent of all the aboveground biomass.

Almost all US forests are native species, and most are naturally regenerated, with planted forests accounting for just 10 percent to 15 percent of the total. In the past 25 to 30 years, government agencies and nonprofit groups have warned that some forest types—and the plant and animal species associated with them—are in decline. Coalitions were formed to reverse the declines. In the Eastern US, they include longleaf pine and shortleaf pine restoration efforts. In the West, restoration projects have focused on Western white pine, whitebark pine, quaking aspen, and ponderosa pine. These groups recognize the desirability of restoring native forests and their associated species. Similarly, a parallel program resulted in restocking Central European forests with native hardwoods (earlier replaced by monoculture softwood plantations). The efforts to find a high-end market for these species resulted in commercialization of the high-performance hardwood mass timber products (mainly beech and oak glulam and beech LVL). In Canada, most forests are made up of native species. A little over half of the harvested acreages are replanted, while half rely on natural regeneration. Canada boasts several different forest types.

2.4 FOREST HEALTH

What is a healthy forest? The answer is nebulous, but the primary disturbance agents are clear: insects, disease, and wildfire. How landowners view the impacts of those disturbance agents differs depending on their management goals. If the forest is reserved (i.e., wilderness or a national park) and the purpose is to manage for natural processes, the definition of "healthy" is different than that for land managed by a publicly traded company seeking a return on investment for shareholders. A noncorporate family forestland manager with diverse goals will provide yet another definition. The answers reflect different objectives. What is healthy also varies by forest ecosystem, requiring different management practices.

In reserved forests, insect outbreaks, wildfires, and chronic endemic diseases lead to patterns of high natural mortality followed by natural regeneration. While disastrous from a wood utilization viewpoint, these patterns may be considered healthy from other vantages because they are part of a forest's natural processes. Dead trees, for example, become habitats for birds, plants, mammals, and insects. These natural agents of change

FIGURE 2.6: EXAMPLE OF A HIGH-INTENSITY FOREST FIRE

can be considered desirable in some forests and undesirable in others—for example, where they destroy valuable timber, damage a municipal watershed, or spoil scenic vistas.

The owner of a forest managed for timber production wants to manage tree mortality to reap an economic benefit and provide a renewable product that supports society's need for human habitat in the form of homes, shops, and offices. Some timberlands are managed to blend different objectives. As described earlier, many family forests and public lands are managed for a mixture of goals, so some mortality from fire, insects, and diseases may be acceptable and even desirable. Even so, severe die-offs are not desirable. Maintaining a balance is an important part of managing the forest.

2.5 FOREST FIRE RESILIENCE

Forest fires and the smoke they generate once again filled the news in 2021. Wildfire risks are driven by 2 synergistic factors. As the climate warms and wildfire seasons lengthen, the risk of "megafires" increases. The problem is exacerbated by limited management activity on some ownerships and by 100 years of aggressive wildfire suppression. Forests that once burned frequently now have abnormally large quantities of green and dead trees, and thickets of brush. The fuel buildup is particularly acute in western North America. High-intensity wildfires are ever more common, with proportionately severe consequences (see **Figure 2.6**).

Many land managers, scientists, wildfire managers, and increasingly, the public are calling

FIGURE 2.7: THE EFFECT OF FOREST MANAGEMENT ON FIRE BEHAVIOR

USDA Forest Service, How Fuel Treatments Saved Homes from the Wallow Fire, https://www.fs.usda.gov/Internet/FSE_DOCUMENTS/stelprdb5318765.pdf.

for action to mitigate these risks. Two common treatments are thinning (removal of forest fuels, including some trees and underbrush) and controlled burning (intentional burning with a low-intensity fire to reduce ground fuel buildup without damaging the overstory of large trees). Many of the forests in need of treatment are not traditional industrial forestlands. More often, they are public lands and family forests where the public's tolerance for cutting or burning trees is low. Some treatment areas are in municipal watersheds with reservoirs that serve domestic and agricultural water users.

Thinning and prescribed burning are both costly because the cost of removing smaller trees is almost always greater than their commercial value. However, when thinning and burning costs are weighed against the immense cost of firefighting and the associated loss of lives, property, and resources, these forest health treatment projects may make sense economically. There are many examples around the country where proactively treating forests saved property, lives, and even communities. For example, **Figure 2.7** shows how forest management affected the Wallow Fire in Arizona. High on the ridge (upper portion of the photo), the fire killed the trees as it burned with high intensity through the tree crowns. Lower on the ridge (middle portion of the photo), the forest had been thinned before the fire, and when the flames reached that area, the fire dropped from the tree crowns and became a much lower-intensity ground fire that allowed the trees to survive and firefighters to prevent the loss of several homes and structures (foreground of the photo).

Thinning can be accomplished with mechanical harvesting equipment, by crews sawing trees and piling them for burning, or with planned low- to moderate-intensity burns completed under prescribed conditions. Often, thinning and burning are used in conjunction with each other for greatest efficacy. Some trees in need of removal can be used for forest products, including mass timber. When such markets exist, it becomes considerably more affordable to manage forests for the desired outcomes.

The increased use of mass timber products can expand markets for some small and medium trees that should be thinned to reduce the risks of wildfires, insect outbreaks, and diseases. The use of more wood in commercial buildings helps create new demand, leading to more logging and manufacturing capacity. In addition to the forest health benefits, the increased activity can lead to new jobs in the forest and at manufacturing plants, especially in rural communities with limited opportunities for building viable economies.

sustainable management as a major component of meeting the world's climate change goals. Chapter 9 is devoted to outlining the 3 S's of carbon management—sequestration, storage, and substitution—and their interaction.

2.6 FOREST CARBON

Forests are a key component of the Earth's natural carbon capture and storage system. The Intergovernmental Panel on Climate Change (IPCC) has identified forests and wood products from

CHAPTER 3: RAW MATERIALS

Mass timber is widely viewed as a potentially significant market for North American softwood lumber producers as the number of buildings constructed with mass timber continues to increase. However, mass timber also represents a somewhat unusual market for sawmillers because the lumber must be dried to a lower moisture content than lumber used in other applications. Kiln-drying is often the bottleneck in a given sawmill's annual lumber output capacity. Therefore, the sawmiller's ability and willingness to do "extra" drying is an important factor in mass timber's raw material supply chain. Those interested in mass timber will find it helpful to understand the key features of these raw materials. Accordingly, this chapter includes a technical analysis of the specifications for use in mass timber, a look at the production capacity among raw material manufacturers (e.g., sawmills), and an estimation of the demand for raw materials that mass timber's development could create for suppliers.

3.1 RAW MATERIAL SPECIFICATIONS

The following sections summarize the specifications for sawn lumber and Structural Composite Lumber[1] (SCL) used in mass timber products. More detailed information is available in the design standard reference specific to each product type.

FIGURE 3.1: ILLUSTRATION OF A MASS TIMBER PANEL'S MAJOR (PARALLEL OR LONGITUDINAL) AND MINOR (PERPENDICULAR OR TRANSVERSE) STRENGTH DIRECTIONS

3.1.1 CROSS-LAMINATED TIMBER

Before launching into a technical discussion about how lumber can be used in mass timber, we'll first discuss the terminology. Every Cross-Laminated Timber (CLT) panel has major and minor strength axes. The major axis is the direction with the greatest number of layers of wood grain in a parallel orientation. For example, **Figure 3.1** shows a 3-layer panel. The grain of the wood in the 2 outer layers is *parallel*, and thus the longest axis of the panel is the major strength direction. Sometimes, the parallel axis is also called the *longitudinal* axis. The wood grain in the middle layer is oriented *perpendicular* to the adjacent layers. Because there is only 1 perpendicular (or *transverse*) layer, it is the panel's minor strength direction. The following technical sections reference these italicized terms.

The Engineered Wood Association (APA) developed a standard that addresses the manufactur-

---

1   Structural Composite Lumber (SCL) is a family of engineered wood products that includes Laminated Veneer Lumber (LVL), Parallel Strand Lumber (PSL), Laminated Strand Lumber (LSL), and Oriented Strand Lumber (OSL). These products are created by combining wood veneers, wood strands, or wood flakes with moisture-resistant adhesives to form blocks of material known as billets. The billets are then sawn into sizes roughly analogous to sawn lumber.

ing, qualification, and quality assurance requirements of CLT panels. It's called *ANSI/APA PRG 320–2019: Standard for Performance-Rated Cross-Laminated Timber.* The most recent edition was approved by the American National Standards Institute (ANSI) on January 6, 2020.

Section 6, subsection 6.1 of *ANSI/APA PRG 320* is the portion of the standard that specifies the characteristics of sawn lumber and SCL approved for use in CLT panels. The following list summarizes key aspects; see the PRG 320 report for full details.

Species

Specific to the North American mass timber market, lumber from any softwood species[2] or species combination (e.g., hem-fir; fir-larch; or spruce, pine, fir (SPF) recognized by the American Lumber Standards Committee (ALSC) under PS 20 or by the Canadian Lumber Standards Accreditation Board (CLSAB) under CSA-0141 with a minimum published specific gravity of 0.35 is permitted. Any given layer (lamination) in a CLT panel shall be made from lumber of the same thickness, type, grade, and species or species combination. Adjacent layers in a CLT panel can be made from differing thicknesses, types, grades, and species or species combinations. If SCL is made from any species with a specific gravity greater than 0.35 and meets the standards of ASTM[3] D5456, it is permitted. Finally, note that strict enforcement of species and grade restrictions in panels imported

from overseas manufacturers as integral project parts may not be practical or even desirable.

Lumber Grade

The distinction between major and minor strength axes is important because differing lumber grades are required, depending on whether they are in a longitudinal or transverse layer. Lumber is graded in 1 of 2 ways: (1) visually—where strength/grade is estimated from a visual inspection, or (2) machine stress rated (MSR)—where pieces of lumber are measured for resistance to bending and assigned a strength rating. In a CLT panel's longitudinal layers, the lumber grade must be visual grade No. 2 (or better), or MSR grade 1200f-1.2E. Perpendicular layers must be at least visual grade No. 3 or the equivalent. Any proprietary lumber grades meeting or exceeding the mechanical properties of the approved CLT lumber grades can be used if they meet an approved agency's qualifications.

Thickness

The minimum thickness of any lumber layer in a CLT panel is ⅝ inch (16 millimeters) at the time of gluing. Maximum thickness is 2 inches (51 millimeters) at the time of gluing. Thickness must be consistent across each individual layer. Thickness consistency is defined at the time of bonding as plus or minus 0.008 inch (0.2 millimeters) across the width of the layer, and plus or minus 0.012 inch (0.3 millimeters) across the length of the layer. Per PRG 320, any bow or cup present in lum-

---

2   The higher a species' specific gravity, the more dense the wood; and generally, the more dense the wood, the greater its strength properties. Douglas fir, larch, Western hemlock, Southern Yellow Pine (SYP), lodgepole pine, Norway pine, various spruce species, and various true firs are common North American softwoods that have good strength properties.

3   ASTM International, formerly known as the American Society for Testing and Materials, is an international standards organization that develops and publishes voluntary consensus technical standards for a wide range of materials, products, systems, and services.

LONGITUDINAL LAYERS				TRANSVERSE LAYERS			
Nominal Size (inches)	Actual Thickness (inches)	Actual Width (inches)	Ratio (Actual Width to Actual Thickness)	Nominal Size (inches)	Actual Thickness (inches)	Actual Width (inches)	Ratio (Actual Width to Actual Thickness)
1x2	0.75	1.5	2	1x2	0.75	1.5	2
1x3	0.75	2.5	3.33	1x3	0.75	2.5	3.33
1x4	0.75	3.5	4.67	1x4	0.75	3.5	4.67
1x6	0.75	5.5	7.33	1x6	0.75	5.5	7.33
2x2	1.5	1.5	1	2x2	1.5	1.5	1
2x3	1.5	2.5	1.67	2x3	1.5	2.5	1.67
2x4	1.5	3.5	2.33	2x4	1.5	3.5	2.33
2x6	1.5	5.5	3.67	2x6	1.5	5.5	3.67
2x8	1.5	7.25	4.83	2x8	1.5	7.25	4.83
2x10	1.5	9.25	6.17	2x10	1.5	9.25	6.17
2x12	1.5	11.25	7.5	2x12	1.5	11.25	7.5

TABLE 3.1: ALLOWABLE AND UNALLOWABLE THICKNESS-TO-WIDTH RATIOS FOR LUMBER USED IN CLT PANELS

Any cell in red font is a lumber size with a thickness-to-width ratio that renders that size unacceptable for use in CLT panels.

ber "should be small enough to be flattened out by pressure in bonding." Many overseas national or regional lumber markets offer much broader selections of thicknesses. The overseas CLT manufacturers take advantage of that variety by offering panel lay-ups more efficiently adjusted to project requirements. Some CLT manufacturers in Central Europe utilize laminations as thin as 0.4 inches (10 millimeters). These lay-ups would not meet the PRG 320 minimum lamination thickness requirement.

Width

For longitudinal layers, the net lamination width for each board shall not be less than 1.75 times the net lamination thickness. For transverse layers, the net width of a board shall not be less than 3.5 times the net thickness of the board. **Table 3.1** illustrates the thickness-to-width ratios for the longitudinal and transverse layers of common lumber sizes. Note that it is common practice for CLT manufacturers to plane about 1/16 inch off all 4 sides of a piece of lumber prior to panel lay-up. Thus, the thickness-to-width ratios of a board's final dimensions may differ slightly from those shown in the table. Notably, 2-by-4, a common size in North America, cannot be used in transverse layers. Exceptions to these thickness-to-width ratios are allowed if the pieces in a layer are both face- and edge-glued. Laminations made from SCL are permitted to be full CLT width.

Moisture Content

The moisture level of lumber used in CLT panels must be 12 percent, plus or minus 3 percentage points (i.e., 9 to 15 percent), when the panel is manufactured. Because lumber shrinks or swells as it loses or gains moisture, the lumber's moisture content is a key focus area for mass timber manufacturers. It is also an important part of the manufacturing process because the majority of lumber is sold after it has been kiln-dried. The grading rules require that lumber be dried to 19 percent moisture content or lower. Given these circumstances, sawmills may be reluctant to reduce kiln capacity by running batches of "mass timber lumber" for longer-than-normal drying cycles when demand for lumber is strong. This issue is further discussed in section 3.4 and from the perspective of the mass timber panel manufacturer in chapter 4.

Surfacing

Any sawn lumber used in a CLT panel must be planed or sanded—at least on any surfaces to be bonded—and the planed or sanded surface must not have any imperfections that might adversely affect the bonding process (e.g., raised grain, torn grain, skip, burns, glazing, or dust). ANSI and the APA, noting the intricacies of bonding the layers in a CLT panel, state that the bonding surfaces on some species need to be planed within 48 hours of the bonding process. Planing or sanding of face-bonding surfaces of SCL used to make CLT panels is not required unless it's needed to meet thickness tolerances.

3.1.2   NAIL-LAMINATED TIMBER

The International Building Code (IBC) recognizes Nail-Laminated Timber (NLT) as a structural material and provides guidance on structural design and fire safety. No product-specific ANSI standard has been developed, but design guides are available for both the US and Canada, and they can be downloaded for free at www.think-wood.com. NLT is commonly manufactured at the building site by nailing pieces of lumber together after they have been arranged so that their wide faces are touching. Almost any properly graded softwood dimension lumber can be used to make NLT. However, considerations such as cost, availability, species, structural performance (grade), and aesthetics come into play when selecting material. Most NLT panels manufactured to date use No. 2 grade dimension lumber in 2-by-4, 2-by-6, and 2-by-8 sizes. The lumber's moisture content must be below 19 percent before fabrication.

3.1.3   DOWEL-LAMINATED TIMBER

The structural design of each lamination in a Dowel-Laminated Timber (DLT) panel is covered by both the IBC and the National Building Code of Canada (NBC). The *International Code Council Evaluation Service Report ESR-4069*, published in November 2020, provides guidance on the use of DLT, given the material's structural and fire-resistance properties. The report evaluates DLT's compliance with the 2018, 2015, 2012, and 2009 IBC and the 2018, 2015, 2012, and 2009 *International Residential Code*. Additionally, StructureCraft, a North American mass timber manufacturer of DLT, has developed a design guide.

Species and Grades

DLT panels are made from SPF, Douglas fir, and hem-fir species or species groupings. Panels made from other species are available on request. The structural grades include select structural, No. 2 and better, 2400f-2.0E MSR for Douglas fir, and 2100f-1.8E MSR or 1950f-1.7E MSR for SPF.

Moisture

Lumber must be kiln-dried to 19 percent or less moisture content at the time of manufacture. Note that the hardwood wooden dowels used to join the DLT laminations are at a much lower moisture content at the time of manufacture. When the drier dowels are exposed to the wetter softwood laminations, they gain moisture and swell, thereby forming a tight connection between laminations.

Thicknesses and Widths

From a global perspective, in Europe, Massiv-Holz-Mauer (MHM) and dowel-bonded CLT favor thinner (nominal 16 millimeters to 25 millimeters, equivalent to ⅝ inch to 1 inch) and wider (200 millimeters and more, equivalent to 8 inches). Both technologies can, however, accommodate rough (undressed) lumber. MHM uses rough-sawn boards rather than nominal 2-by stock. The surface is not considered for visual quality. That means there should be greater potential for using lower-quality lumber than that required for adhesive-bonded CLT. The process favors wider laminations (200 millimeters and more, equivalent to 8 inches). Laminations are grooved on one side along the grain to increase thermal insulation. The final thickness of grooved laminations is about 16.5 millimeters (⅝ inch). Dowel-bonded CLT also uses rough-sawn lumber in core layers, but it needs dressed lumber for the face layers, which often are meant to be visible in structures. Also, bonding with dowels requires wide-face lumber (likely more than 200 millimeters, or about 8 inches) to form 2 rows of success-

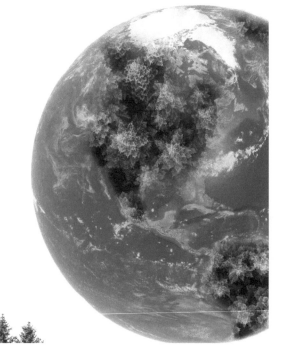

CLIMATE SMART
FORESTRY

SUSTAINABLE FORESTRY INITIATIVE
SFI-00001

Forests play a critical role in addressing climate change and storing carbon.

Mass timber certified to SFI standards provides assurance that forests remain forests for future generations.

Learn more: forests.org

GRADES	PREMIUM	SELECT	STANDARD	INDUSTRIAL
COMMON APPLICATION	Residential; Hotels; Feature Walls	Residential; Libraries; Schooles; Museums; Offices	Offices	Nonvisual; High Ceilings
SPECIES	SPF; Douglas fir; (other species available)			
COATINGS	Upon request, a penetrating clear sealer and tinted top coatings can be shop-applied to exposed side of panel. Our team focuses on working with designers to determine the best coating system for durability and ease of maintenance.			
WANE*	Width < or = 1/4"; Length < or = 2'; No bark	Width < or = 3/8"; W/O bark length < or = 5'; W bark length < or = 2'; Max 1 in every 5 boards	Width < or = 1/2"; W/O bark length < or = 10'; W bark length < or = 7'; Max 1 in every 4 boards	Permitted
KNOTS	No open knots; tight knot permitted	Open Smooth < or = 3/4" diameter; Open Jagged < or = 1/2" diameter; Tight knot permitted	Permitted	Permitted
BLUE STAIN	Max 1 every 10 boards; Up to 10% surface area; No dark/black coloring	Max 1 every 7 boards; Up to 15% surface area; No dark/black coloring	Max 1 every 5 boards; Up to 20% surface area; No dark/black coloring	Permitted
CHECKS IN STRAND EDGE	Nonpermitted	Width < or = 1/16"; Length < or = 12"	Width < or = 1/16"; Length < or = 24"	Permitted
CHARACTERISTICS DISTRIBUTION	Distributed	Distributed	Some distribution	No redistribution required
PANEL SURFACE	Deviation on board-to-board elevation < or = 1/8"		Deviation on board-to-board elevation < or = 1/4"	Deviation permitted
UNNATURAL BELMISHES	Except for Type 4 (Industrial), the underside of the DLT panel shall be free of "unnatural" characteristics, e.g., black marks, scuffs, damage, and glue. Such blemishes shall be sanded/required as needed.			
CHARACTER OF WOOD	All wood, as a natural material, will exhibit characteristics such as knots/holes, wane, grain, checks, coloration, etc. The intent of the above appearance grading is to provide a degree of predictability/limitation to these characteristics. However, some variations in the visual appearance will be apparent.			

TABLE 3.2: LUMBER CHARACTERISTICS ALLOWED WITHIN STRUCTURECRAFT DLT PANEL GRADES

Wane is the presence of bark or lack of wood fiber along the edge of a piece of lumber.

ful dowel bonds in each surface layer. This likely limits the prospect of using small logs.

Lumber Size

DLT panels come in thicknesses ranging from 4 inches to 12.17 inches. Lumber widths are available from 2 inches to 6 inches (nominal).

Appearance

StructureCraft has developed 4 grades of DLT panels: premium, select, standard, and industrial. **Table 3.2** specifies the lumber characteristics of each of StructureCraft's grades.

SPECIES GROUP	SPECIES INCLUDED IN GROUP
ALASKA CEDAR	Alaska Cedar
DOUGLAS FIR-LARCH	Douglas Fir, Western Larch
EASTERN SPRUCE	Black Spruce, Red Spruce, & White Spruce
HEM-FIR	California Red Fir, Grand Fir, Noble Fir, Pacific Silver Fir, Western Hemlock, & White Fir
PORT ORFORD CEDAR	Port Orford Cedar
SOUTHERN YELLOW PINE	Loblolly Pine, Longleaf Pine, Shortleaf Pine, Slash Pine
SPRUCE-PINE-FIR	Alpine Fir, Balsam Fir, Black Spruce, Engelmann Spruce, Jack Pine, Lodgepole Pine, Norway Pine, Norway Spruce, Red Spruce, Sitka Spruce, White Spruce
SOFTWOOD SPECIES	Alpine Fir, Balsam Fir, Black Spruce, Douglas Fir, Douglas Fir South, Engelmann Spruce, Idaho White Pine, Jack Pine, Lodgepole Pine, Mountain Hemlock, Norway Pine, Norway Spruce, Ponderosa Pine, Sitka Spruce, Sugar Pine, Red Spruce, Western Larch, Western Red Cedar, White Spruce

TABLE 3.3: SOFTWOOD SPECIES (OR SPECIES GROUPINGS) COMMONLY USED IN GLULAM TIMBERS

3.1.4 GLULAM

ANSI A190.1-2017, Standard for Wood Products—Structural Glued Laminated Timber and *ANSI 117-2020, Standard Specification for Structural Glued Laminated Timber of Softwood Species* are the 2 documents published by the APA that describe the specifications of lumber to be used in glulam timbers.

Key specifications include the following:

Species

The *ANSI A190.1-2017* standard states that any softwood or hardwood species is approved for use in structural glued laminated timber if stress indices and knot distributions are established as described in *ASTM D3737*. The *ANSI 117-2020* standard is more specific about allowable species or species groupings, as shown in **Table 3.3**.

Moisture Content

The moisture content of lumber used in glulam timbers shall not exceed 16 percent at the time of bonding.

Wane

Wane is a defect in a piece of lumber characterized by bark or insufficient wood at a corner or along an edge. For dry-service conditions (i.e., when lumber in use is not regularly exposed to moisture), wane up to one-sixth the width at each edge of interior laminations is permitted in certain grade combinations. When that is the case, the basic shear design value shall be reduced by one-third. When wane is limited to one side of a member, the basic shear design value is reduced by one-sixth. Other instances of wane are allowed, but the circumstances are complicated. See *ANSI 117-2020* for details.

Grade

Lumber used in glulam timbers is graded visually or mechanically, and it is identified by grade before bonding. Rules approved by the Board of Review of the ALSC or written laminate grading rules apply to visually graded lumber. Rules approved by the Board of Review of the ALSC or special rules that conform with the ANSI A190.1 standard apply to mechanically graded lumber. An accredited inspection agency oversees the qualification of proof-graded lumber, subjecting it to full-size tension tests as set forth in the American Institute of Timber Construction (AITC) test 406. A number of more specific grading rules apply, depending on the position of the piece in the glulam timber, its species, whether the lumber is ripped prior to bonding, and other factors. See *A190.1-2017* for details.

Bonding

All bonding surfaces—including face, edge, and end joints—are smooth and, except for minor local variations, free of raised grain, torn grain, skips, burns, glazing, or other deviations that might interfere with the contact of sound wood fibers.

Thickness

Laminations are not to exceed 2 inches in net thickness, unless a gap-filling adhesive is used for face and edge bonds.

Dimensional Tolerances

At the time of bonding, variations in thickness across the width of a lamination shall not exceed plus or minus 0.008 inches (2 millimeters). Variations in thickness along the length of an individual piece of lumber or along a lamination shall not exceed plus or minus 0.012 inches (3 millimeters).

3.1.5 POST AND BEAM

Traditionally, post and beam construction uses timbers of at least 6 inches in nominal width and thickness. Less guidance is available for the specification of lumber (timbers) for this category of mass timber than for others. Nevertheless, the *Code of Standard Practice for Timber Frame Structures* developed by the Timber Framers Guild (TFG) (www.tfguild.org) in 2018 does provide some. A few specifications follow:

Grade

Grades are select structural, No. 1, or No. 2. All structural timbers are to be graded by an approved lumber grading agency, certified grader, or an individual who has completed a timber grading training course. The lumber grader is to provide a grade stamp or a certificate of grade for each piece of timber. Knots and other natural timber features shall not be construed as defects unless their magnitude exceeds the limits prescribed in the applicable lumber grading rules. Checks are a natural feature resulting from ordinary timber drying and seasoning. Checks that develop after the timber frame has been raised are not construed as defects.

Species

Acceptable species include Douglas fir, Eastern white pine, red oak, white oak, Southern Yellow Pine (SYP), and Alaska yellow cedar.

Moisture

Timbers are to be dried to a maximum moisture content of 19 percent.

Size

Timbers 8 inches by 12 inches and smaller are to be Free of Heart Center (FOHC). Timbers larger than 8 inches by 12 inches are to be boxed heart. All timber sizes are nominal (actual dimensions are typically ½ inch smaller than the nominal size in both thickness and width). Pith is the center of a tree that extends along its long axis. The wood around the pith typically is not as strong as wood nearer to the bark. Therefore, a quality factor for smaller timbers is that the pith (heart center) should not be included in the timbers, or that the pith be "boxed" in the center of the timber on larger timbers.

Surfacing

Timbers may be surfaced four sides (S4S), rough-sawn, or hewn. "Surfaced four sides" refers to timbers that are planed smooth on all 4 sides; rough-sawn is timber that has been sawn but not planed; and hewn timbers have been shaped using an axe or other similar tool.

3.1.6 HEAVY TIMBER DECKING

Specifications for heavy timber decking are less prescriptive than other mass timber products. Some guidance is provided in *Heavy Timber Construction,* published by the American Wood Council (AWC). Key excerpts include the following:

Grading

The lumber used in heavy timber framing and decking must be graded in accordance with the rules customarily used for the species. These are generally regional grading agencies, including the Northeastern Lumber Manufacturers Association (NELMA), California Redwood Inspection Service (RIS), Southern Pine Inspection Bureau (SPIB), West Coast Lumber Inspection Bureau (WCLIB), Western Wood Products Association (WWPA), and Canadian National Lumber Grades Authority (NLGA).

Sizing

The decking used in heavy timber floor decks is to be of sawn or glued laminated plank, splined, or tongue-and-groove planks not less than 3 inches (nominal) in thickness or of planks not less than 4 inches (nominal) in width when set on edge. Splining and tongue-and-groove refer to protrusions and indentations on the sides of lumber pieces so that adjacent lumber pieces can be interlocked. For roof applications, the timbers are to be sawn or glulam, splined, or tongue-and-groove plank not less than 2 inches (nominal) in thickness or of planks not less than 3 inches (nominal) in width when set on edge.

3.1.7 VENEER

Veneer-based mass timber products are ANSI/APA PRG 320-certified and include mass plywood panels up to 11 feet 10 inches wide, 12 inches thick, and 48 feet long. Freres Lumber Co. Inc. can also manufacture beams and columns made from veneer up to 12 inches wide, 72 inches deep, and 48 feet long that are ANSI/APA PRG 320-certified.[4]

The veneers are first formed into Laminated Veneer Lumber (LVL) billets (an LVL plank of standardized size) that are then made into Mass Plywood Panels (MPP). Because the veneers are first formed into LVL billets, certification of MPP falls under the classification of SCL, which includes LVL and is covered under *ASTM D5456*.

More specifically, the manufacturer uses wood veneers to make LVL billets. These billets are 1.6E, 1.55E, or 1.0E Douglas fir LVL as recognized by the APA in the product report *PR-L324*; the billets also are in accordance with custom lay-ups of ANSI/APA PRG 320 that employ product qualification and mathematical models that use principles of engineering mechanics. The LVL billets can range in thickness from 1 inch to 24 inches and in width from 1.5 inches to 72 inches. Depending on the billets' dimensions and MPP design needs, the billets are parallel laminated, bonded with qualified structural adhesives, and pressed to form a solid panel (i.e., MPP).

Freres uses Douglas fir veneers classified by moisture content and a grade (G1, G2, G3) that's dependent on their strength, as measured by Ultrasonic Propagation Time (UPT) testing, which correlates the time it takes for sound to pass through wood veneers with key strength determinants, such as specific gravity and modulus of elasticity (ratio of stress to strain). Freres is also a manufacturer of veneer and plywood and thus controls the raw material supply for its MPP

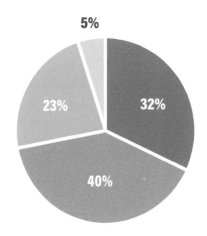

■ Residential Construction   **■ Nonresidential**
■ Repair & Remodeling   **■ Industrial**

FIGURE 3.2: LUMBER CONSUMPTION BY END-USE MARKEET SEGMENT (2017 TO 2021)
Source: Forest Economic Advisors

manufacturing operations from standing timber through the finished product.

3.2 NORTH AMERICAN LUMBER SUPPLY

As the number and sizes of mass timber construction projects grow, the capacity of sawmills to supply lumber is of considerable interest. Thus, this section focuses on softwood lumber production and use in North America.

3.2.1 END USES FOR SOFTWOOD LUMBER

Historically, softwood lumber has been used in 4 key end-use market segments: residential construction, repair and remodeling, nonresidential

---

4   The equipment Freres uses to make the columns and beams can handle widths up to 24 inches. Freres is working to achieve APA certification for the larger widths. Additionally, columns and beams can be produced up to 60 feet in length, but current production of longer beams is limited by the length of Freres's press.

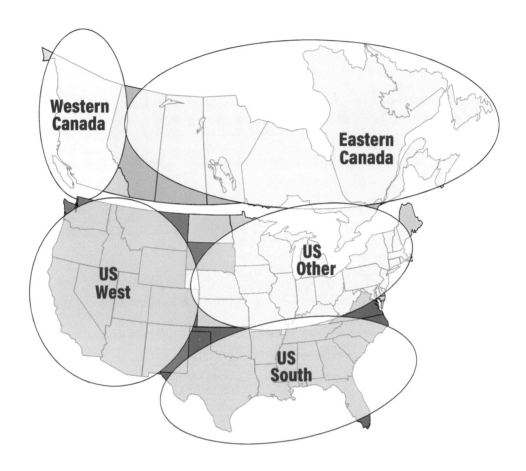

FIGURE 3.3: NORTH AMERICAN SOFTWOOD LUMBER PRODUCING REGIONS

construction, and industrial/other. **Figure 3.2** shows the average portion of softwood lumber consumed by each end-use market segment in the US from 2017 to 2021. As the data shows, for those 5 years, on average, 40 percent of all softwood lumber consumed was for repair and remodeling, followed by nearly 32 percent for residential construction. Thus, historical demand has been tied to either new home construction, or the repair and remodeling of existing homes. The industrial/other end-use segment is lumber typically used for applications such as packaging, pallets, and furniture, which utilize the lower grades of lumber. The advent of mass timber and the new demand it places on softwood lumber is the focus of the remainder of this chapter.

3.2.2 WHERE SOFTWOOD LUMBER IS PRODUCED IN NORTH AMERICA

Softwood lumber in North America is produced in 5 geographical regions: US West, US South, US Other, Western Canada, and Eastern Canada, as shown in **Figure 3.3.** Note that in the US South, 4 species of pine (loblolly, longleaf, shortleaf, and slash) are commonly manufactured into lumber and sold as a species grouping designated as SYP. In Eastern Canada and Western Canada, the predominant lumber grouping is SPF, but the makeup of species within the SPF lumber grouping differs. In the US West, the predominant lumber species

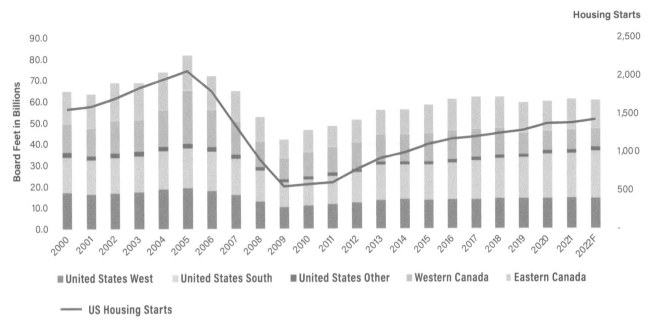

FIGURE 3.4: HISTORICAL UNITED STATES AND CANADIAN SOFTWOOD LUMBER PRODUCTION BY REGION (BOARD FEET IN BILLIONS) & HOUSING STARTS

Source: Western Wood Products Association

or species groupings are Douglas fir, Douglas fir-larch, and hem-fir.

The volume of softwood lumber produced in each North American region from 2000 to 2022 as reported by the WWPA (2022 is a forecast based on the first 7 months of the year) is shown in **Figure 3.4.** Note that there are some differences in lumber production and consumption (i.e., some lumber produced hadn't been sold when data was collected). To simplify the discussion, we treat production and consumption as being equal because the volume in inventory is typically a small portion of the total annual production.

Several things to note about the data in the figure:

• North American softwood lumber production peaked in 2005 at more than 82 billion board feet. At that time, Western Canada was the top producing region with nearly 25 billion board feet. At the time, the US West and US South were nearly equal in production, with about 19 billion board feet each.

• Lumber production across North America decreased dramatically during the Great Recession, with totals in 2009 dropping to about 50 percent of the 2005 peak. Note that North American lumber production has historically been driven by the level of housing starts in the US. This is shown in the figure by the line that corresponds to the right-hand axis of the graph; lumber production is highly correlated to the annual level of US housing starts.

• After the low in 2009, North American lumber production increased steadily through 2017 but has since been relatively flat.

- There are several regional issues of note:

Western Canada

One of the most dramatic changes is that Western Canada went from producing about 30 percent of North America's lumber in 2005 to producing only an estimated 14 percent in 2022. That change was mainly driven by reductions in the annual allowable cut of timber in the interior region of British Columbia. In that region, a massive mountain pine beetle epidemic affected nearly 45 million acres and killed nearly 60 percent of the standing pines. The outbreak started in the 1990s, and during the 2000s, timber harvests were significantly increased to salvage the dead timber.

The salvage efforts are complete, but current and future harvests have been significantly reduced to allow the forest to grow to a standing inventory that will once again allow for higher levels. Rebuilding is a long process, meaning reduced timber harvest rates will remain in place for the foreseeable future. The sawmill industry built up during the salvage period, and the existing capacity became too large for the available log supply. As a result, many sawmills have permanently closed.

More recently, the province of British Columbia, in partnership with First Nations, announced plans to defer timber harvests on nearly 50,000 hectares of forests identified as old-growth that were not already set aside from logging. Those plans will further reduce lumber production in the region.

US South

Perhaps equally dramatic are the changes occurring in the US South. Before the Great Recession, the US South and the US West produced roughly equal amounts of lumber each year. Since the Great Recession, however, the US South has bounced back while the US West has been flat. For example, in 2022 the US South's production climbed to over 22 billion board feet, which is more than 3 billion board feet higher than US South production in the peak North America-wide production year of 2005. A key driver was the 30-year timber harvest rotation brought about by improved forest practices (e.g., genetic improvement of seedlings, and extensive planting and thinning operations). The result was higher volume yields per acre. Thus, during the significant yearslong drop in lumber production during the Great Recession, a massive amount of sawtimber inventory built up "on the stump." In addition, about 85 percent of the timber in the US South region belongs to private landowners. This means that sawtimber harvest levels are largely dictated by economic drivers, rather than by regulatory drivers. These conditions have spurred massive capital investment in new sawmilling capacity through upgrades to existing mills and greenfield (i.e., new mill at a new site) sawmill development. Nearly 5 billion board feet of capacity has or will come online by 2023, driven by $2.5 billion of capital investment in new and upgraded sawmilling infrastructure in the region. The nearly 5 billion board feet of new/upgraded capacity and associated capital investment are a "first wave." This is because, despite the increased capacity, there are still regions with excess sawtimber supply. Thus, companies are planning further investments in sawmilling capacity in the US South.

FIGURE 3.5: HISTORY OF US FOREST SERVICE TIMBER SALES FISCAL YEAR 1940 TO FISCAL YEAR 2021 (ANNUAL VOLUME BOARD FEET [LOG SCALE] IN BILLIONS)

Source: https://www.fs.fed.us/forestmanagement/products/cut-sold/index.shtml

US West

Lumber production in the US West decreased by about 300 million board feet in 2022 compared to 2021 after reaching a post-Great Recession high of 14.7 billion feet of production in 2021.

A long-standing issue in the US West constraining lumber production is that log supplies are a function of who owns the timberland. Privately held timberland accounts for about 70 percent of the total harvest. Industrial timberland owners manage their timberlands intensively and generally harvest near the maximum allowable sustainable rates. Thus, harvests on industrial lands cannot increase without beginning to deplete the supply of standing timber. Small private timberland owners hold significant acreage and contribute a considerable portion of the annual harvest. This segment, however, is made up of many thousands of individuals and families. As a group, these landowners typically do not act in sync because individuals have a variety of management objec-

tives and timber production is not always a top priority. They could supply additional logs, but because they do not act collectively, their supply is constrained. The balance is under public ownership: the US Forest Service, the Bureau of Land Management (BLM), and miscellaneous states, counties, and municipalities. About 70 percent of all timberland acres are publicly owned, a high percentage relative to public ownership in the US South. For about the last 30 years, forest management policies on federally owned public lands have constrained log supplies across the US West and limited lumber production.

For nearly 4 decades starting in the mid-1950s, the US Forest Service sold 10 to 12 billion board feet of logs each year. The passage of the Endangered Species Act (ESA) required changes to federal policies, resulting in the listing of the northern spotted owl, various salmon species, and the marbled murrelet. That led to a dramatic decline in the annual volume of timber sold since 1988, as shown

REGION	% DIMENSION (2"NOMINAL)	ESTIMATED 2022 PRODUCTION OF DIMENSION (BBF)	% SMALL TIMBERS (3"–5")	ESTIMATED 2022 PRODUCTION OF SMALL TIMBERS (BBF)	% LARGE TIMBERS (6"+)	ESTIMATED 2022 PRODUCTION OF LARGE TIMBERS (BBF)	% OTHER	ESTIMATED 2022 PRODUCTION OF ALL OTHER SIZES	TOTAL 2022 PRODUCTION (BBF)
US West	55%	7.9	5%	0.7	5%	0.7	35%	5.1	14.4
US South	80%	17.8	10%	2.2	5%	1.1	5%	1.1	22.3
US Other	20%	0.3	n/a	n/a	n/a	n/a	80%	1.4	1.7
Western CA	75%	6.4	n/a	n/a	n/a	n/a	25%	2.1	8.6
Eastern CA	50%	6.8	n/a	n/a	n/a	n/a	50%	6.8	13.6
North America Total		39.3		3.0		1.8		16.5	60.6

TABLE 3.4: ESTIMATED NORTH AMERICAN SOFTWOOD LUMBER THICKNESS MIX IN 2022 (BOARD FEET IN BILLIONS)

in **Figure 3.5.** US Forest Inventory and Analysis (FIA) data suggests that, despite the massive tree mortality from the many wildfires in recent years, federal lands are growing 3 times more wood fiber than is being removed by harvesting and natural mortality. That suggests timber harvests could be increased significantly without endangering the sustainability of the resource. In the meantime, increased lumber production is largely held in check by limited log supply.

Eastern Canada

As in other North American regions (except the US South), lumber production in Eastern Canada between 2016 and 2021 was relatively flat, hovering around 15.0 billion board feet per year. However, in 2022, Eastern Canada's production dropped to 13.6 billion board feet. This is surprising since, unlike Western Canada, where timber supply is constrained by the lingering effects of the mountain pine beetle, standing timber is read-

ily available. However, parts of Eastern Canada are a long distance from markets, and the average small tree size in those parts increases sawmill manufacturing costs because productivity is constrained by a small average piece size. In general, larger mills enjoy economies of scale, allowing for lower manufacturing costs. Historically, Eastern Canada has concentrated on pulp and paper mills that produce newsprint. Those pulp mills were largely supplied with residue from sawmills. As demand for newsprint dwindled, producing lumber from small logs has become more difficult economically, constraining milling capacity.

The smaller tree sizes also mean that lumber tends to be narrower and shorter. To produce a reasonable annual lumber volume, the mills must operate their lines at very high throughput rates (i.e., a large number of logs through processing equipment per unit of time), and because of limited ability to increase feed speeds and still main-

REGION	% ABOVE #2	ESTIMATED BBF ABOVE #2	% OF #2	ESTIMATED BBF OF #2	% OF #3	ESTIMATED BBF OF #3	% BELOW #3 AND OTHER	ESTIMATED BBF OF BELOW #3 & OTHER	TOTAL PRODUCTION OF DIMENSION (BBF)
US West	35%	2.8	55%	4.4	5%	0.4	5%	0.4	7.9
US South	40%	7.1	40%	7.1	10%	1.8	10%	1.8	17.8
US Other	10%	0.0	55%	0.2	20%	0.1	15%	0.1	0.3
US Total		9.9		11.7		2.2		2.2	26.1

TABLE 3.5: ESTIMATED US SOFTWOOD DIMENSION LUMBER GRADE MIX IN 2022 (BOARD FEET IN BILLIONS)

tain good lumber quality, they likely have little ability to increase those rates.

3.2.3   2020 NORTH AMERICAN SOFTWOOD LUMBER PRODUCTION DETAILS

As described in section 3.1, mass timber product standards specify the use of certain lumber sizes and grades. Thus, the grades and sizes of lumber produced are also important. **Table 3.4** shows lumber production by thickness, based on the WWPA's estimated North American softwood lumber production volumes for 2022. The percentages of production by size values are estimates from sawmill industry benchmarking data collected by the Beck Group. Of the estimated 60.6 billion board feet of lumber produced in North America in 2022, about 65 percent is nominal 2-inch-thick dimension lumber (i.e., boards nominally 2 inches thick and 8 feet to 20 or more feet long). Of the remainder, only small portions are made into thicker timbers, and another 25 percent or so are in other, mis-

cellaneous sizes. Note that most of the volume in the "other" category is stud-grade lumber. It is the same thickness as dimension lumber, but it is produced only in 4-inch and 6-inch widths, and mainly in lengths of less than 12 feet. Most stud-grade lumber is used as vertical structural components in wall systems for homes. The balance of the "other" category includes industrial and common boards (i.e., nonstructural lumber), and miscellaneous products.

Similarly, it is useful to understand the grade mix, as shown in **Table 3.5**. Using the WWPA's 2022 production estimates and the Beck Group's sawmill benchmarking data, the table shows that nearly 85 percent (21.6 billion board feet out of 26.1 billion board feet) of dimension lumber production in the US is No. 2 grade or better. Data for Canada is not included because the information was not readily available, but the grade yields are likely similar.

REGION	% 2-BY-4	ESTIMATED 2-BY-4 PRODUCTION (BBF)	% 2-BY-6	ESTIMATED 2-BY-6 PRODUCTION (BBF)	% 2-BY-8	ESTIMATED 2-BY-8 PRODUCTION (BBF)	% 2-BY-10	ESTIMATED 2-BY-10 PRODUCTION (BBF)	% 2-BY-12	ESTIMATED 2-BY-12 PRODUCTION (BBF)	TOTAL 2020 DIMENSION PRODUCTION (BBF)
US West	40%	3.2	30%	2.4	10%	0.8	10%	0.8	10%	0.8	7.9
US South	25%	4.5	30%	5.4	20%	3.6	15%	2.7	10%	1.8	17.8
US Other	40%	0.1	30%	0.1	10%	0.03	10%	0.03	10%	0.03	0.3
US Total		7.8		7.8		4.4		3.5		2.6	26.1

TABLE 3.6: ESTIMATED US SOFTWOOD DIMENSION WIDTH MIX IN 2022 (BOARD FEET IN BILLIONS)

Finally, **Table 3.6** displays the estimated width mix. As the data shows, about 30 percent of all dimension lumber is estimated to be 4 inches wide, followed by another 30 percent that is about 6 inches wide. A significantly higher percentage of 2-by-4s is produced in the US West than in the US South. Lumber width is a significant consideration for mass timber manufacturers, as prices vary among widths, and productivity improves when wider pieces of lumber are used.

3.2.4   SOFTWOOD LUMBER PRICING

The purchase of raw material is the single largest cost associated with the manufacture of mass timber products, accounting for more than 50 percent of a plant's total operating cost. Lumber pricing, therefore, is a key focus area for manufacturers. In the US over the past 10 years, demand for lumber in the residential construction and repair and remodeling market segments has ranged from a low of 20.8 billion board feet per year to a high of 40.0 billion board feet per year. The associated swings in supply create considerable volatility in lumber prices, a phenomenon that is unusual in the rest of the world because, in many countries, lumber is less commonly used to construct homes.

Price volatility was in full swing in 2021, ranging between a second-quarter high with average prices approaching $1,300 per thousand board feet to third-quarter prices just under $500 per thousand. 2022 started out much the same, with prices in the first quarter again averaging over $1,200 per thousand board feet but then trending steadily downward through the remainder of the year to finish around $500 per thousand.

For a longer-term perspective, for about the past 25 years, the price of dimension lumber in North America has averaged roughly $350 per 1,000 board feet. The low point occurred in 2009, in the depths of the Great Recession, when dimension lumber was selling for around $200 per thousand board feet. The high point had been in mid-2018, when prices approached $600 per thousand board feet. In 2021, however, driven by a COVID-induced increase in demand in the home repair and remodeling sector and by a constrained ability to produce lumber because of COVID-related labor shortages and other supply constraints related to shipping, prices skyrocketed to all-time highs. During different periods in 2021 and 2022, dimension lumber prices in North America approached levels nearly 4 times the long-term average price.

3.2.5 ENVIRONMENTAL CERTIFICATION OF SOFTWOOD LUMBER

In chapter 2 of this report, we explained how forested land is certified when managed under certain protocols that have been judged to represent sustainable forest management. Such forest management programs also offer chain-of-custody certification to participants in the supply chain. Chain-of-custody is the process of certifying that, as products move from the forest to the end user, material originating from certified forests is identified or kept separate from noncertified material. Chain-of-custody certification generally involves detailed logistics and materials-handling protocols, inventory management, batch processing, filings, and third-party audits.

Forest management and chain-of-custody certification fulfills the end users' desire for assurances that the products they are using are from well-managed forests. This is especially true for developers seeking to certify a building under Leadership in Energy and Environmental Design (LEED) and similar programs. In addition, large

tech companies, like Google and Facebook, that have expressed interest in mass timber are keenly interested in using environmentally certified raw materials. But it isn't yet clear which environmental certification programs these large and influential mass timber users will prefer.

Forest landowners and wood product manufacturers who follow the forest management and chain-of-custody guidelines can market their products as being environmentally certified. It is difficult to track the volume of lumber (and veneer/plywood) sold annually in North America that is environmentally certified because a high percentage of these forest products could be environmentally certified under one or more of the programs. But frequently they are not marketed in that manner, and thus there is no well-documented record of their sales volumes.

One of the main reasons these sales are not well-tracked is that, for most consumers, this attribute is relatively unimportant. Considerations such as price, quality, species, and grade are much more important. In addition, landowners and manufacturers must expend considerable effort and money to acquire and maintain these certifications. Given the limited market demand and the expense, many landowners and manufacturers decide not to certify their products, even though they could. Others elect to certify their material on a case-by-case basis as dictated by customer expectations. A small number of producers choose to certify as much of their product as possible, regardless of the level of demand from customers.

For producers of mass timber products, this means that market demand for environmentally certified materials—aside from mass timber products—is relatively low. Therefore, finding environmentally

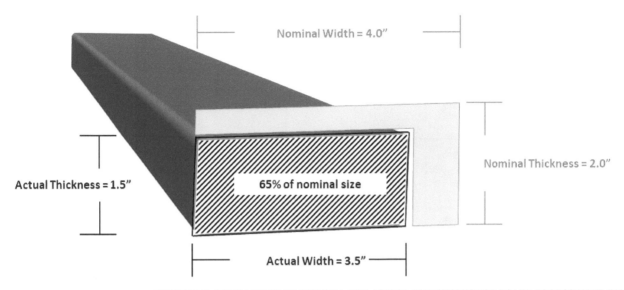

Nominal Width = 4.0"

Nominal Thickness = 2.0"

Actual Thickness = 1.5"

65% of nominal size

Actual Width = 3.5"

FIGURE 3.6: COMPARISON OF NOMINAL AND ACTUAL DIMENSIONS FOR BOARD FOOT LUMBER TALLY

Source: The Beck Group

certified material may be a challenge, but likely it is not a roadblock. In interviews with the Beck Group, the general feeling of mass timber producers is that only a small portion of their demand is for certified mass timber products, and when those orders need to be filled, they can usually oblige. It may cost more, however, to acquire certified lumber. As previously noted, a big wild card is whether one of the large tech companies will announce plans for a large mass timber project (or projects) and give preference to raw materials from a given environmental certification program. Such an event would likely trigger a rise in the price of environmentally certified raw materials until the supply chain is able to adjust to the increased demand.

3.3   THE MASS TIMBER INDUSTRY'S ESTIMATED DEMAND FOR RAW MATERIALS IN 2022

Definitive data about lumber consumption among mass timber producers is not readily available. However, an analysis completed by the Softwood Lumber Board[5] suggests that, in the near term, lumber demand associated with mass timber can reach about 1 billion board feet per year and could grow to nearly 5 billion board feet per year by 2035. This topic is analyzed in further detail in chapter 4.

3.3.1   NOMINAL VERSUS ACTUAL LUMBER SIZES

As described in chapter 1, an estimated 22.5 board feet (nominal tally) is needed to produce 1 cubic foot of finished mass timber panel. Some readers may be thinking that 22.5 board feet per

5   Softwood Lumber Board, *Mass Timber Outlook (2020)*, https://softwoodlumberboard.org/wp-content/uploads/2021/03/SLB-Mass-Timber-Outlook-2021-Final-Condensed.pdf.

Lumber Size (Thickness x Width)	ACTUAL			NOMINAL			Actual Fiber % (Actual/ Nominal)	Air Space %
	Actual Thickness (Inches)	Actual Width (Inches)	Cross-Sectional Area (Inches Squared)	Nominal Thickness (Inches)	Nominal Width (Inches)	Cross-Sectional Area (Inches Squared)		
2-by-4	1.5	3.5	5.25	2	4	8	65.60%	34.40%
2-by-6	1.5	5.5	8.25	2	6	12	68.80%	31.30%
2-by-8	1.5	7.25	10.88	2	8	16	68.00%	32.00%
2-by-10	1.5	9.25	13.88	2	10	20	69.40%	30.60%
2-by-12	1.5	11.25	16.88	2	12	24	70.30%	29.70%

TABLE 3.7: COMPARISON OF THE PERCENTAGE OF ACTUAL FIBER TO AIRSPACE AMONG LUMBER SIZES FOR NOMINALLY TALLIED LUMBER

cubic foot seems like too much lumber input per cubic foot of finished panel. Such thoughts likely stem from the knowledge that a board foot is defined as 1 inch thick by 12 inches wide by 12 inches long. Thus, it may seem that 1 cubic foot of mass timber should be equal to 12 board feet.

This is not the case for several reasons. First and most importantly, softwood lumber in North America is bought and sold on a nominal board foot basis. For example, a common lumber size is 2 inches thick by 4 inches wide. Those dimensions, however, are nominal, meaning in name only. The actual dimensions are 1.5 inches thick by 3.5 inches wide. As shown in **Figure 3.6**, this means that about 35 percent of the area in a 2-inch by 4-inch space is air. Because so much of a tally is airspace, more than 12 board feet of lumber will be needed to produce a cubic foot of mass timber panel. Additionally, about 8 to 10 percent of a board's thickness is planed away before it is glued up. Planing activates the wood

surface for the adhesive to bond it. Also, during finger-jointing, a portion of the incoming lumber becomes waste as defects are cut out with a chop saw. Finally, a portion of a mass timber panel is lost to trim around the perimeter and cutouts for windows, doors, and other openings.

The percentage of airspace decreases as lumber width increases, as shown in **Table 3.7**. Nevertheless, a significant portion of the board foot tally for every piece of lumber is airspace.

3.4 SUPPLYING THE MASS TIMBER MARKET: SAWMILLER PERSPECTIVES

Conceptually, sawmillers are always interested in developing new markets for the lumber they produce. However, dimension lumber is a commoditized product in North America. As such, prices are volatile as various supply and demand factors ebb and flow. Regardless, manufacturers face the constant discipline of producing at a low cost. Thus, many sawmillers tend to operate their mills in a manner that emphasizes high productivity and minimizes distractions that slow production without adding significant value.

For the mass timber market, there are 2 parts of the manufacturing process where the sawmiller's mindset has had an impact. The first is that there appears to be a market opportunity to produce thinner mass timber panels for certain applications where strength requirements aren't as stringent. Taking advantage of this opportunity would require the availability of structural-grade lumber sawn to thinner dimensions (e.g., 1 inch or less thickness). However, doing so has several disadvantages for sawmills that are also producing dimension lumber. First, the mills would lose a tally advantage they enjoy when producing dimension lumber. In other words, dimension lumber finishes at 1.5 inches thick, but the mills get credit for the lumber being a full 2 inches thick. A second factor is that sawmill productivity is greatly reduced when sawing 1-inch-thick lumber (or less) because many of the processes in a sawmill (e.g., primary breakdown, edging, planing, etc.) are linear in nature. When pieces are thinner, there is less volume per piece for pieces of the same length. For all of these reasons, sawmills are reluctant to produce thinner lumber.

The second is lumber drying. As previously stated, the specification for lumber used in mass timber is 12 percent, but the grading rules for kiln-dried dimension lumber only require drying to 19 percent moisture. Thus, lumber destined for mass timber manufacturing must receive extra drying at the sawmill, or the mass timber manufacturer must have a means of further drying the lumber at their facility.

From the perspective of the sawmiller, lumber drying is often the "bottleneck" in the manufacturing process. In other words, the output of the entire operation (i.e., sawmill and planer mill) is limited by the capacity of the lumber drying kilns. Taking extra time to dry lumber to a lower moisture content, therefore, is a decision that must be carefully considered because it takes extra time in the kilns, and the yield of lumber of the appropriate sizes and grades must be considered. In other words, not all the lumber in any given batch sent through a kiln will meet mass timber's grade and size specifications. That lumber is known as downfall (i.e., material that cannot be used for mass timber manufacturing). Thus, some percentage of the lumber that receives the additional time and expense of extra drying cannot be sold to mass timber manufacturers and must be used in other, less stringent applications.

The strategies for dealing with this issue are evolving. In one approach, sawmilling companies have contracted with mass timber manufacturers to provide lumber that meets their moisture content specifications. Such contracts likely include a significant above-market premium on the price to account for the extra drying time and downfall. Data isn't available on the premium, but it is likely in the range of $50 to $100 per thousand board feet. During lumber market cycles when prices are high, as they were during parts of 2020 and 2021, numerous sawmilling companies are unwilling to slow their process, regardless of any premium.

In another emerging strategy, mass timber manufacturers are purchasing "ordinary" kiln-dried lumber that may have air-dried during shipment and storage to an acceptable range for mass timber manufacturing. Such an approach requires that the manufacturer have an in-line moisture meter in their manufacturing process, allowing the sorting of boards that can be used from those that have too much moisture. The "wet" boards are then set aside. They can be diverted to an on-site controlled drying process or an off-site custom drying service, or they can be set aside for more air-drying, an uncontrolled process.

Each has advantages and disadvantages, as described below:

- **On-site controlled kiln-drying:** Some mass timber manufacturers have invested in their own kilns, so the moisture content issue can be addressed in a controlled manner and with their own equipment. The advantage of this approach is that it allows for the best control over product quality. The disadvantage is that expenses increase. They include the up-front capital expense of kilns, the ongoing operating costs of the kilns (both labor and energy), and the potential yield loss from any material that degrades during the kiln-drying process (e.g., case-hardening, bowing, cupping, warping) to the point it can no longer be used for mass timber. Plus, an experienced kiln operator is needed. Some mass timber manufacturers report that they are experimenting with dehumidification kilns, which operate at much lower temperatures, meaning less likelihood of degradation. The drawback is that drying takes longer at the lower temperatures. Early results indicate that, because relatively little moisture needs to be removed from lumber already kiln-dried to 19 percent moisture, the slow drying issue is mitigated.

- **Off-site custom kiln-drying:** Some mass timber manufacturers have used the services of off-site custom kiln-dryers. The advantage of this, like on-site, is that it allows for the drying of lumber under controlled conditions. The disadvantages are the costs for handling the wet lumber, paying the kiln-drying service, and transporting the lumber to and from the custom kiln-drying site. In addition, the availability of custom kiln-drying services differs by region.

- **Uncontrolled air-drying:** Lumber will lose or gain moisture depending on ambient air conditions. Thus, lumber simply left to further air dry may lose enough moisture to be used in mass timber panels. There is no energy cost, but this uncontrolled process depends on weather conditions. Thus, it may work only during certain times of the year and in certain regions where ambient conditions generally allow for drying. Also, for best results, the lumber should be placed on stickers (i.e., spacers between layers of lumber that allow air flow and, in turn, drying). The labor and time associated with the handling increase the expense.

In yet another approach, some mass timber manufacturers are part of vertically integrated companies that have sawmilling, kiln-drying, and mass timber manufacturing capacities. This trend applies particularly to the mass timber panel industry and is not specific to North America but observed in many other mass timber-producing regions. The advantage from a mass timber manufacturer's perspective is that the material is controlled—often from the tree in the forest (when timber is either owned or purchased standing)—through the manufacture of a mass timber panel. Assuming kiln-drying capacity is not a bottleneck at such operations, the issue of moisture content is less problematic. As seen during the lumber market conditions experienced in 2020, vertically integrated operations are better able to "hold the line" on raw material costs in the production of mass timber panels, but they must recognize that doing so comes at the opportunity cost of selling lumber in an extraordinarily hot market at prices never before seen in the softwood lumber industry.

3.5 CARBON CONSIDERATIONS

The September 2017 issue of *Forest Products Journal* included an article[6] that analyzed the carbon impact associated with the production of softwood dimension lumber in the Pacific Northwest and Southeastern US. Key conclusions from the study were that the global warming impact indicator is that 129 pounds of carbon dioxide equivalent was released for each cubic meter of lumber produced in the Pacific Northwest, and 179 pounds of carbon dioxide equivalent for each cubic meter of lumber produced in the Southeastern US. An additional key finding was that, in the Pacific Northwest, nearly 1,900 pounds of carbon dioxide equivalent is stored per cubic meter of lumber produced, and in the US South, nearly 2,100 pounds of carbon dioxide equivalent is stored per cubic meter of lumber. Thus, there is a net carbon benefit of nearly 1 ton of carbon dioxide equivalent associated with wood use for the duration of the product's useful life.

These findings are a stark contrast to other common building materials (e.g., steel and concrete) that do not store any carbon dioxide equivalent during their useful life and that require considerable energy and associated carbon emissions be expended in their manufacture. The study also notes that, in lumber production, well over 90 percent of the global warming impact arises from the process of manufacturing (e.g., sawing,

planing, kiln-drying, and packaging). Only a very small percentage of the impact arises from the energy expended in log processing and transport (i.e., forest operations).

---

6   Michael Milota and Maureen E. Puettmann, "Life-Cycle Assessment for the Cradle-to-Gate Production of Softwood Lumber in the Pacific Northwest and Southeast Regions," *Forest Products Journal* 67, no. 5/6 (2017).

Finding a better way has been *our* way for a long time. It's why we're committed to stewarding healthy forestlands. To treating our employees like family, and giving back to the places we call home. It inspires us to develop the sustainable building materials of the future. So, while a lot is new at Freres, we're proud to say that the most important things will never change.

INNOVATION IS OUR TRADITION

FRERES
ENGINEERED WOOD

Welcoming the next 100 years with a new look.
frereswood.com

100

CHAPTER 4: MASS TIMBER PANEL MANUFACTURING

- Following COVID-related slowdowns in building projects during 2020 and 2021, there has been a significant uptick in mass timber building projects in North America during 2022 with more than 220 new projects completed through September 2022 and nearly 750 projects in design, according to WoodWorks.

- Mass timber manufacturers continue to refine their services and means of bringing product to market, including increasing Computer Numerical Control (CNC) machining capacity to cut finished panels to final dimensions and create cutouts for electrical and mechanical components, etc. The capacity to finish panels after they've been laid up is frequently cited as the bottleneck in mass timber manufacturing. Additionally, mass timber manufacturers continue to add staff with timber engineering/design expertise, establish partnerships up and down the supply chain, develop design guides, and create supporting businesses that better link the mass timber manufacturing and building construction communities.

This chapter focuses on mass timber panel manufacturing. Included is a review of the manufacturing processes for key mass timber panels; a list of North American manufacturers and their production capacities, products, and services; and a discussion of strategic and technical mass timber manufacturing issues.

GLOBAL PERSPECTIVE

The Cross Laminated Timber (CLT) sector in Central Europe, which includes Austria, Switzerland, Germany, Northern Italy, and Czechia, produced about 1.1 million cubic meters (m³) of CLT in 2021,[1] the last year for which complete data is available, according to a biannual summary published by Timber-Online.net, the online version of the respected Austrian trade journal *Holzkurier*. That number does not include companies in other parts of Europe, but it is equivalent to 9 percent growth over 2020.

At the time of publication (November 2022), the Central European region was on track to produce 1.3 million m³ of CLT by the end of 2022. In addition, *Holzkurier* estimated that new construction and announcements of new production capacity in Central Europe between 2020 and 2022 might soon add another million cubic meters per year.

This tally does not account for development in the rest of Europe and elsewhere in the world. In 2022, two large-scale CLT plants were launched in Sweden, and one new plant started production in New Zealand. The expansion came about despite the combined disruptions to the global supply chain caused by the pandemic and the war in Ukraine.

---

1   Gunther Jauk, "Sustained Strong Growth: Production of Cross-Laminated Timber to Set a New Record: +17% to 1.3 Million M³," Timber-Online.net, Nov. 7, 2022, https://www.timber-online.net/wood_products/2022/11/sustained-strong-growth.html.

4.1 MASS TIMBER PANEL TYPES

There are 2 basic types of mass timber panels: those for use in buildings and those for use as industrial matting. Each is described in more detail in the following sections.

4.1.1 BUILDING PANELS

Manufacturers have developed 2 common building panel grades based on appearance rather than strength: architectural grade, for use when a panel surface will be exposed to the building's occupants; and industrial grade, for use when a panel surface will be covered or will not show. Either grade can be PRG 320[2] certified, if needed. Each manufacturer offers an array of finishes; in most cases, the finishes can be customized.

Architectural-grade panels are designed to ensure that the lumber is of the proper grade and species for visual exposure. The panels may require special sanding, epoxy finishes, stains, or coatings, and the filling of holes, gaps, or knotholes. In addition, lumber grain orientation may be varied. The panel's face layer typically does not include physical defects; to accomplish that objective, an appearance-grade layer of lumber (hardwood or softwood) may be laminated on. Each manufacturer offers its own set of architectural-grade finishes.

Industrial-grade panels are likely to have the same strength characteristics as comparable architectural-grade panels, but they may not meet the same aesthetic standards because the surface of the panel is usually covered when it's installed. Visual defects on the face layer of industrial-grade panels may include unfilled voids on the edge of laminations, loose knotholes on face layers, or wane (lumber pieces that are not fully square-edged on all 4 corners). Industrial-grade panels are typically less expensive than architectural-grade panels because the costs of materials, labor, and machining are lower.

In addition, the panel's application plays a significant role in its grade type. A floor may have architectural grade on the bottom side to serve as an exposed ceiling in the room below but industrial grade on the top side because a floor covering will be installed over the top side. Similarly, many exterior walls will be covered with a siding; therefore, only one face of the panel may be architectural grade. Mass timber panels used in roofs and elevator shafts are typically industrial grade.

4.1.2 MATTING

Matting panels are intended not for use in buildings, but to protect the environment and for other industrial uses. These mats typically are placed on the ground to form temporary roads to prevent environmental degradation caused by the heavy machinery used in mining, drilling, pipelines, utility right-of-way maintenance, and remote construction. Traditionally, mats are made of lower-value hardwood timbers nailed or bolted together. CLT mats are becoming more common because they offer superior value. They are lighter and have longer useful life spans. CLT mats also may include built-in hardware—making them easier to lift and place using a forklift, excavator, or crane, and thereby reducing setup time. Matting panels and their uses are described in more detail in section 4.6.

---

2   *ANSI/APA PRG 320: Standard for Performance Rated Cross-Laminated Timber,* https://www.apawood.org/ansi-apa-prg-320.

4.2   MASS TIMBER PANEL MANUFACTURING PROCESS DESCRIPTIONS

Each of the following subsections describes the basic manufacturing steps for key mass timber panels.

4.2.1   CROSS-LAMINATED TIMBER

CLT is produced in an industrial-scale, dedicated manufacturing facility. Although CLT is an innovative product, the major steps in its manufacturing process use well-established technologies borrowed from other segments of the wood products industry, although some (like lay-up and pressing) are performed on assemblies of unprecedented scales. Though many major variations are being practiced, the basic manufacturing process typically includes the following:

Raw Material Receiving

Lumber is received into inventory at the mass timber manufacturing facility.

Raw Material Preparation

Lumber is sorted by grade, width, and species; and moisture content is checked to ensure that the variation among pieces is not too great. Pieces that are too wet are separated for additional drying. Excessive defects (e.g., knots, wane) on the lumber pieces designated for the manufacturing process are removed using a crosscut/chop saw.

Finger Jointing

Once free of excessive defects, the pieces of lumber are glued together end to end, using a machine that cuts finger joints into the lumber ends and applies an adhesive to the joint to securely bond the pieces.

In processes that use different grades or thicknesses of materials for alternating layers, the materials flow for the longitudinal and transverse layers has to be split. As a result, many plants have parallel finger-jointing, cross-cutting, and surfacing lines that join at the layup station.

Cutting to Length

The finger-jointing process creates a "continuous" piece of lumber that can be cut to any length that is called for by the dimensions of the mass timber panel. These range from 4-foot to 12-foot lengths for the panel's transverse axis and 30-foot to 60-foot lengths for its longitudinal axis.

Surfacing

This process, also known as "planing," removes a small amount of material (typically about $\frac{1}{16}$ inch) from all 4 sides of the piece of lumber. This gives all pieces the same dimensions and activates their surfaces to ensure good absorption and bonding of the adhesive used to glue the panel layers together. In particular, the thickness has to be within a 0.2-millimeter tolerance of adjacent pieces to avoid bridging over thinner laminations in cross-laminated lay-ups. Such bridging will result in an inadequate pressure and poor bond integrity in that location.

Panel Lay-Up

The finger-jointed, surfaced, and cut-to-length lumber pieces are assembled into a panel one layer at a time. In a 3-layer panel, for example, all the long pieces that make up the longitudinal axis are assembled. Next, a glue spreader travels over them, applying a layer of glue to the wide surfaces (note that, for some panels, glue is applied to all 4 sides). Then the short pieces are assembled into the layer making up the panel's transverse axis. Another layer of glue is applied. And finally, the long pieces making up the second major axis layer are assembled. In a global perspective, some manufacturers apply adhesive on the narrow edges of laminations as well and include pressure in 2 or 3 directions to produce effective edge-bonding. A substantial volume of panels fabricated by a few major manufacturers in Europe begin the process with edge-bonding the layers before they are used to build lay-ups ready for face-bonding.

Pressing

After the adhesive has been applied and the lumber has been formed into a lay-up, it is pressed while the adhesive cures. Several variations on the adhesive and pressing technology affect the press time and the amount of energy consumed. The majority of the processes use glue that does not require heat to cure, which makes the press times longer. Some processes use glue that needs heat to activate, which reduces press time. Heated presses use radio frequency waves to penetrate the panel and cure the glue. Since adding radio wave energy complicates the process, these types of presses typically cure the lay-up piecewise, one segment at a time.

Final Manufacturing

When the mass timber panels come out of the press, their edges are typically irregular and over-run by adhesive that has bled out between the layers. In addition, the "raw" panels are slightly oversized. All of this means that the panel is cut to its final dimensions in a secondary process. Typically, the final manufacturing is accomplished with robotic CNC machine centers. They can add the necessary connection nests on panel perimeters, and cut openings for windows and doors, as well as plumbing, HVAC, and electric networks. Many CLT plants use a sander to surface the visible face of the panel if an architectural finish is required.

Packaging and Shipment

The final step involves the placing of "pick points," metal hardware that allows cranes at the construction site to pick up a panel and place it in the building. For shipping, panels are assembled into a sequence, so that, when they are delivered to the construction site, they can be moved directly into place rather than having to be unloaded and stored. That requires precise management and timing of the production and transportation sequences, and manufacturers often synchronize with the contractors or the assembly teams.

The equipment needed to complete the preceding tasks includes the following:

- **Moisture meter:** Tests the moisture content of each piece of lumber, ensuring that any lumber not meeting the target range (12 percent +/- 3 percentage points) is rejected.

- **Optical-grade scanner:** Photoelectric sensors, also known as "photo eyes," that identify any lumber with unacceptable defects (rot, splits, wane).

OR

- **Stress grading machine:** A piece of high through-put equipment, where resistance to the bending of pieces of lumber moving at high speeds is measured in flight to assign a machine stress rated (MSR) value.

- **Defect trim saw:** Cuts out the short, linear sections of lumber identified for removal by grade scanning.

- **Finger jointer:** Cuts finger joints in the ends of each piece of lumber, applies glue to each joint, and presses the pieces together, making one continuous piece.

- **Crosscut saw:** Cuts the finger-jointed lumber to lengths appropriate for the final size of the CLT panel. The only limits on the length of a CLT panel are size of the press and the highway/truck restrictions on the delivery of panels from the manufacturer to the building site.

- **Planer or molder line:** Removes a thin layer of wood from the surface of the lumber to ensure all pieces are of uniform thickness and to "activate" it so it can react to the glue. This step must be completed less than 48 hours before applying the glue.

- **Panel lay-up station:** Arranges pieces of lumber into layers in accordance with the CLT panel design. Glue is applied to each layer at this step. The level of automation varies greatly between operations.

- **Pressing**

  - **Hydraulic press:** Uses hydraulic pressure on the face and sides to hold a panel in place as the glue cures. Press time varies based on glue formulation and panel lay-up time.

  - **Vacuum press:** Uses a clamshell and silicone blanket to encapsulate a panel and then sucks out the air to tighten gaps between boards.

- **CNC finishing center:** Uses computer-controlled saws and router heads to precisely trim the edges of each panel and cut openings as needed for doors, windows, utility channels, etc.

- **Sanding machine:** Puts a smooth finish on the surface of the panel.

- **Overhead crane(s) and high-capacity conveyor system(s):** Handles integrated panels that might weigh up to 6 tons each.

4.2.2 DOWEL-LAMINATED TIMBER PANEL MANUFACTURING

Dowel-Laminated Timber (DLT) is produced in a dedicated manufacturing facility. As with CLT, incoming lumber is checked for grade and product consistency, and defective sections are removed. The lumber is then finger jointed, cut to the desired lengths, and molded/planed to the desired thicknesses. The cut-to-length boards are assembled into a panel, holes are drilled along the edges, and dowels are pressed into the holes. The entire panel is surfaced to ensure the dowels are not protruding. In the final steps, panels are finished on a CNC machine, packaged, and shipped. Unlike CLT, all the lumber in a DLT panel is oriented in the same direction. This orientation means that the DLT panels do not have the same shear strength properties as those derived from cross-lamination.

4.2.3 NAIL-LAMINATED TIMBER PANEL MANUFACTURING

Unlike CLT and DLT, Nail-Laminated Timber (NLT) can be manufactured either at a building site or at an industrial-scale production facility. The layout of an NLT panel is similar to a DLT panel, with all the lumber oriented in the same direction. The lumber is stacked on its side with randomly staggered joints, or it can be finger jointed to create continuous layers over 20 feet long. The boards are then nailed together in various lay-up configurations to create panels.

Industrial-scale makers of NLT employ jigs to guide the lumber through the saw blades and maintain panel dimensions and straightness. The jigs can be made from pony walls, back and end stops, and fences. Boards are joined using a pneumatic-powered nailer, and the process is repeated until the panel is complete. Like CLT, the panel is then cut to length and fabricated to match shop drawings. Nail placement is crucial, as nails will negatively impact cutting tools, such as saws and drills.

4.2.4 MASS PLYWOOD PANELS MANUFACTURING

Mass Plywood Panels (MPP), a recent addition to the list of mass timber products, are a veneer-based engineered wood product. The first step in its manufacture is to produce appropriately sized and graded veneer of an appropriate species. Freres Lumber Co. Inc. produces its own veneer for use in MPP and is considered the only MPP manufacturer in the world. Note, however, that in fall 2022 Boise Cascade introduced a veneer-based panel to the market, but it is categorized as CLT. The MPP is created in a 2-stage process. First, billets of Structural Composite Lumber (SCL), each 1 inch thick by 4 feet wide and up to 48 feet long, are created from multiple plies of veneer. The number of plies, their grain orientation, and the grades of veneer used to create the billets vary depending on the desired strength. In the second stage, the SCL billets are assembled into larger and thicker MPPs, with dimensions and strength engineered to meet the requirements of a given project.

Scarf joints (i.e., a joint connecting 2 billets in which the ends are beveled so that they fit over each other while maintaining a flat surface across the billets) are used to join the SCL billets, irrespective of the size of the MPP. These joints are staggered throughout the panel, so they do not create weak points. A 6-inch-thick MPP, for example, is made up of six 1-inch billets, each made of 9 plies of veneer. Thus, the total panel is made of 54 veneer plies. Throughout the manufacturing process, the entire MPP and each 1-inch SCL billet are engineered to specific strengths. In principle, different adhesives may be used to bond veneer plies in the SCL billets and to bond SCL billets in one MPP panel.

4.2.5 SOLID WOOD WALL (MHM)

MHM is a massive, prefabricated cross-laminated panel with layers made of rough-sawn boards that are bonded with nails. This product should not be confused with NLT, described above. MHM is fabricated on small-scale, turnkey 3-step Hundegger production lines. The lines consist of specialized molders to produce longitudinal grooves on one side of the laminations, an automated lay-up and nailing station, and a CNC finishing center. Relatively short, fluted aluminum nails that penetrate 3 layers do not interfere with cutting tools. Panels may consist of 9, 11, 13, or 15 layers (each about 16.5 millimeters or $^{10}/_{16}$ inch). Typically, a thick bitumen paper layer would be integrated in the lay-up to provide air tightness.

4.2.6 DOWEL-BONDED CLT

Dowel-bonded CLT is a massive, prefabricated cross-laminated panel with layers of rough-sawn boards bonded with hardwood dowels. It should not be confused with DLT, described above. The panels are assembled in highly automated lines. The dowels are arranged in a carefully designed pattern and inserted in the lay-up by CNC equipment. Low moisture content and tight fitting of the dowels at the time of assembly ensure a durable, tight connection when the dowels swell as they gain moisture in the ambient conditions. Only 2 commercially successful systems are known to date: (1) one developed by the Thoma Holz100 (or Wood 100) company in Austria; and (2) one developed by Swiss industrial hardware manufacturer TechnoWood AG. By mid-2019, TechnoWood had installed 8 highly automated lines in Europe. Unlike other CLT products, some layers of the dowel-bonded CLT are arranged at 45 or 60 degrees to the surface layer direction. The lay-ups may also include a thick bitumen paper layer integrated between the layers of lumber to provide airtightness.

4.3 NORTH AMERICAN MASS TIMBER PLANTS

This section provides an assessment of mass timber manufacturing capacity. Manufacturer information was collected through personal communication with manufacturers, publicly available research, information compiled by industry experts, and company profiles from websites and other published information sources. Please note that the status of manufacturing operations is constantly changing, with shifting operating schedules, some plants reaching completion, and other plants getting underway. The information that follows was current as of December 2022.

4.3.1 NORTH AMERICAN MASS TIMBER PLANTS' CAPACITIES AND OPERATIONAL STATUSES

In 2022, the North American mass timber manufacturing industry resumed its year-over-year upward trajectory in manufacturing capacity after a slight contraction in 2021. As shown in **Table 4.1**, at the time of this writing (late 2022), 15 companies were operating 19 facilities in North America with a combined estimated annual production capacity of 1.767 million cubic meters per year. This is an increase of about 100,000 cubic meters over 2021's estimated capacity, during which 11 companies were operating 15 facilities. Applying the rule of thumb of a 65 percent practical production factor to the maximum capacity results in an estimated practical annual production capacity of about 1.15 million cubic meters per year among North American mass timber panel manufacturers. The 3 plants identified in 2022 as being potential producers remain in that status as of late 2022. Thus, in total, there are 23 known operating or potential mass timber manufacturing plants in North America, as summarized in **Table 4.1**.

Several key changes since 2022 are that Mercer International reopened the former Katerra CLT Factory in Spokane, Washington. Also, DR Johnson, one of the first US CLT manufacturers, discontinued CLT manufacturing but remains a glulam manufacturer. Also, in October 2022, Boise Cascade achieved PRG 320 certification as a CLT producer. Their material is manufactured in their engineered wood product plant in White City, Oregon. Interestingly, the material is made

COMPANY	LOCATION	STATUS	ESTIMATED MAXIMUM ANNUAL PRODUCTION CAPACITY OF OPERATING PLANTS (M3/YEAR)
binderholz	Live Oak, FL, US	Potential Plant Site	
binderholz	Enfield, NC, US	Potential Plant Site	
Boise Cascade	White City, OR	Operating	
DR Johnson	Riddle, OR, US	Idled	
Element5 #1	Ripon, QC, CA	Operating	
Element5 #2	St. Thomas, ON, CA	Operating	
Euclid	Heber City, UT, US	Small Scale - Operating	
Freres	Lyons, OR, US	Operating	
International Timberframes	Golden, BC, CA	Small Scale - Operating	
Kalesnikoff	South Slocan, BC, CA	Operating	
Mercer International	Spokane, WA, US	Operating	
Nordic Structures	Chibougamau, QC, CA	Operating	
Smartlam North America	Dothan, AL, US	Operating	
Smartlam North America	Columbia Falls, MT, US	Operating	
Sterling Lumber	Lufkin, TX, US	Operating	
Sterling Lumber	Phoenix, IL, US	Operating	
Stoltze Mass Timber	Columbia Falls, MT, US	Planned	
StructureCraft	Abbotsford, BC, CA	Operating	
Structurlam	Okanagan Falls, BC, CA	Operating	
Structurlam	Conway, AR, US	Operating	
Texas CLT	Magnolia, AR, US	Operating	
Timber Age	Durango, CO, US	Small Scale - Operating	
Vaagen Timbers	Colville, WA, US	Operating	
Total			1,767,500

TABLE 4.1: CURRENTLY OPERATING NORTH AMERICAN MASS TIMBER PRODUCTION PLANTS

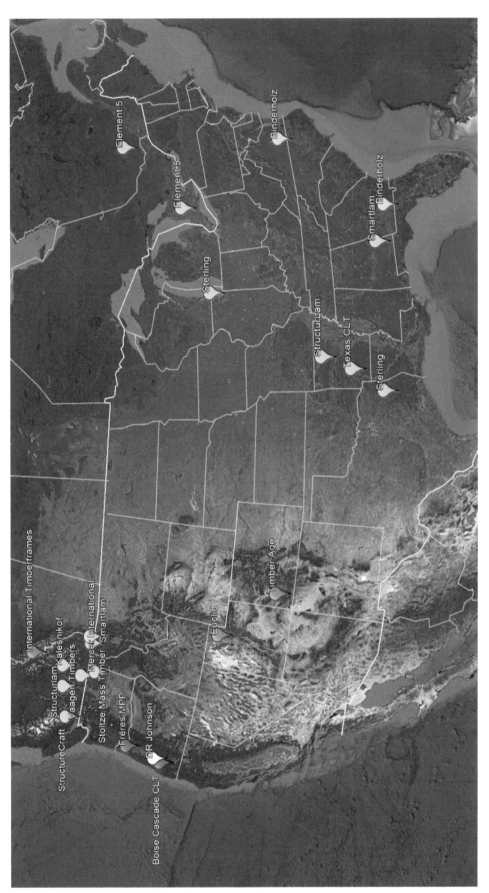

FIGURE 4.1: LOCATION OF NORTH AMERICAN MASS TIMBER MANUFACTURING FACILITIES

Source: The Beck Group

from veneer but is considered a CLT product. Another significant change over the last year is that Sterling Structural, the largest mass timber manufacturer in the world, obtained PRG 320 certification. This allows the company, which has historically focused on producing matting panels, the ability to also produce panels for use in buildings.

At the time of this writing (late 2022), no new publicly announced mass timber plants were under construction in North America. Unchanged from last year, Stoltze Timber continues to plan to develop a mass timber manufacturing operation in Columbia Falls, Montana. Also unchanged from last year is that many industry observers believe the binderholz Group will eventually develop mass timber manufacturing capacity at either or both of 2 Southern Yellow Pine (SYP) sawmills the company purchased in 2020. One is in Florida and the other is in South Carolina.

Figure 4.1 shows the location of North American mass timber plants. Some are clustered in the Western regions of the US and Canada, where there is a mix of available species, including Douglas fir, Western larch, hemlock, spruce, and various true firs. The rest are in Eastern Canada, where the available species are spruce, pine, and fir; and in the US South, where the available species is SYP (a mix of longleaf, loblolly, slash, and shortleaf pines). There is still no mass timber manufacturing facility in California, despite its large timber resource and its significant sawmilling industry. It is also one the largest building construction markets in North America. Finally, Euclid Timber Frames LC and Timber Age Systems Inc. are included. Both are small-scale mass timber manufacturers whose businesses were

featured as case studies in the 2022 International Mass Timber Report.

4.3.2 NORTH AMERICAN GLULAM PLANTS' CAPACITY AND OPERATIONAL STATUSES

New to the report this year is the inclusion of North America's glulam manufacturers. While many of the mass timber panel manufacturers can also produce glulam beams, adding the companies that focus on glulam-only production is an important addition since many mass timber buildings use designs that combine glulam beams and columns in combination with mass timber panels. **Figure 4.2** shows the location of the North American glulam manufacturing plants. Note that most of the mass timber panel manufacturers also have the ability to manufacture glulam, but the plants in the figure are glulam-only.

There are several things to note about the North American glulam manufacturers. First, since 2017, their aggregated annual output has averaged about 300 million board feet (MMBF) per year. As a point of reference, a single large softwood sawmill in North America typically produces about 300 MMBF of lumber per year. Thus, the current output of the whole glulam industry is equivalent to the output of a single large sawmill. Just prior to the Great Recession, North American glulam production reached nearly 500 MMBF per year. Second, a significant portion of the annual glulam output is dominated by 2 companies that specialize in making stock beams (i.e., standardized sizes, lengths, etc.). These include Rosboro, which operates 2 plants in Oregon in the Western US, and Anthony Forest Products (owned by Canfor), which operates 2 plants in the US South (one in Arkansas and another in

FIGURE 4.2: LOCATION OF NORTH AMERICAN GLULAM MANUFACTURING PLANTS

Source: The Beck Group

Georgia). Each company operates under a vertically integrated model. This means that company-owned sawmills produce lamstock, the lumber raw material used in glulam manufacturing, for the laminating plants. In contrast, the balance of the glulam manufacturers tend to be smaller operations that specialize in manufacturing custom-made glulam beams. These operations typically purchase their lamstock on the open market from various sawmill producers. **Table 4.2** provides a list of the North American glulam manufacturers, the locations of their plants, the lumber species they commonly use, and, if available, information about the sizes (lengths, widths, depths) of beams they can produce.

4.4 MASS TIMBER MANUFACTURERS: COMPANY AND FACILITY DETAILS

The companies entering the mass timber market have diverse experience levels and strategic orientations. In North America, some firms are vertically integrated on the supply side, with sawmills and/or glulam manufacturing plants located near their panel manufacturing operations. Others are vertically integrated on the building and development end of the supply chain. Still others are stand-alone businesses. **Table 4.3** captures some of the diversity among current manufacturers by illustrating the products they offer, the status of their design guides, their brand names, etc.

4.5 NORTH AMERICAN MASS TIMBER MANUFACTURER SERVICES

Mass timber is distinct from most other wood building materials because its manufacturers tend to work closely with architects and engineers during building design regarding product specifications such as size, thickness, strength, and appearance. An important, but frequently overlooked, section of the mass timber supply chain is the additional support services that mass timber manufacturers can provide their customers. The following bulleted list briefly describes a number of these services. Note, however, that this is a rapidly evolving portion of the supply chain, as companies that provide those support services are emerging.

It remains to be seen which will become dominant: the model adopted by pioneering North American mass timber manufacturers—providing a one-stop, turnkey solution for their clients; or the more recent move to specialization—acting as middlemen among manufacturers, architects/designers, construction firms, and developers. Or there might always be a mix of both.

The following lists a variety of "details" required to move building projects from concept to reality.

4.5.1 ARCHITECTURAL DESIGN AND PROJECT SUPPORT

Design assist: Mass timber manufacturers assist architects with their design, including how best to incorporate mass timber into their building.

Engineering services: Many manufacturers employ engineers who help building designers review structural, mechanical, electrical, seismic, acoustic, fire, and other aspects of a building as they relate to the properties of mass timber products.

Modeling work: Most manufacturers assist in an array of construction documentation. Com-

COMPANY	CITY	STATE	SPECIES	LENGTH (FEET)	THICKNESS AND WIDTH (INCHES)
Alamco Wood Products LLC	Albert Lea	MN	SYP, DF, AC, POC	up to 110'	
Anthony Forest Products Company - Eldorado Laminating	El Dorado	AR	SYP	8' to 60'	3.125" to 5.5" wide and 11.25" to 28.875" deep
Anthony Forest Products Company - Washington Laminating	Washington	GA	SYP	8' to 60'	3.125" to 5.5" wide and 7.25" to 28.875" deep
Arizona Structural Laminators	Eagar	AZ	DF, SYP		
Art Massif Structure De Bois Inc.	Saint Jean Port Joli	QC	SPF		
Boise Cascade	Homedale	ID	DF/L, AC,	Up to 60'	3.125" to 14.25" wide and 6" to 48" deep
Boozer Laminated Beam Co. Inc.	Anniston	AL	SYP	6' to 54'	3.125" to 28.875" wide and 8.75" to 28.875" deep
Diversified Wood Resources (dba American Duco Lam)	Drain	OR	DF, SYP, AC, POC	Up to 130'	up to 16.25" wide and 72" deep
Diversified Wood Resources (dba American Laminators)	Swiss Home	OR	AC, WRC, DF, HF, POC	Up to 130'	
Enwood Structures	Morrisville	NC			
Fraser Wood Industries, Ltd.	Squamish	BC			
Goodlam, Division of Goodfellow Inc.	Delson	QC	DF, SYP, SPF		
Gruen-Wald Engineered Laminates Inc.	Tea	SD	SYP, SPF		
Harrison Industries (Structural Wood Systems)	Greenville	AL	SYP	8' to 20'	
Mississippi Laminators	Shubata	MS	SYP	up to 52'	4.0" to 8.0" wide and up to 39" deep
QB Corporation	Salmon	ID	DF, SYP, WRC, AC		
Riddle Laminators (dba DR Johnson Wood Innovations)	Riddle	OR	DF, AC, POC, SYP	up to 135'	
Rigidply Rafters	Richland	PA	SYP, DF, AC, POC		
Rigidply Rafters	Oakland	MD	SYP, DF, AC, POC		
Rosboro	Springfield	OR	DF	up to 72'	3.25" wide by 4" deep to 8.75" wide by 40" deep
Rosboro	Veneta	OR	DF	up to 100'	3.125" to 6" wide and 8" to 18" deep
Shelton Lam and Deck	Chehalis	WA	DF		
Stark Truss Company Inc.	Canton	OH	SYP, SPF		
Starwood Rafters	Independence	WI	DF	6' to 56'	
Timber Technologies Inc.	Colfax	WI	DF, SPF, SYP	8' to 62'	
Unadilla Laminated Products (Unalam)	Unadilla	NY			
Western Archrib	Edmonton	AB	DF, SPF, AC	up to 150'	3.125" to 25.25" wide and 4.5" to 84" deep
Western Archrib	Boissevain	MB			
WFP Engineered Products	Vancouver	WA	DF, SYP, AC, POC		
WFP Engineered Products	Washougal	WA	DF, SYP	up to 95'	
Zip-O-Laminators	Eugene	OR	DF, AC	8' to 115'	

TABLE 4.2: CURRENTLY OPERATING NORTH AMERICAN GLULAM MANUFACTURERS

COMPANY	WEBSITE	PANEL BRAND NAME	DESIGN GUIDE	PRODUCTS	SPECIES	PANEL TYPES	PANEL THICKNESS	MAX WIDTH	MAX LENGTH	ENVIRONMENTAL CERTIFICATION
Element5 #1	https://elementfive.co/	E5 CLT & E5 Nano CLT	Yes	CLT, GLT, BOXX Panels, Nano CLT, CLIPS, and NLT	SPF	A, I	3, 5, 7, and 9 ply (or up to 15')	10.5' for visual grade and 11.48' for non-visual grade	52.5'	FSC
Freres	https://frereslumber.com/	MPP and MPL	Yes	Mass Plywood Panel, Mass Ply Lams, Plywood, Veneer	DF	A, I, M	up to 24"**	11.83'	48'	American Tree Farm System
Kalesnikoff	https://www.kalesnikoff.com/	n/a	Yes	CLT, Glulam, GLT Panels, Japan Zairai Lumber, Access Mats	SPF, DF-L, Hemlock	A, I, M	3 to 11 ply (2.00" to 15.15")	11.48'	60'	Sustainable forest certification available upon request
Nordic Structures	https://www.nordic.ca/en/home	X-Lam	Yes	CLT, Glulam, GLT Panels, I-Joists	SPF (90% black spruce)	A, I	3, 5, 7, or 9 ply (3.5" up to 10.5")	8'	64'	FSC
Smartlam North America	https://www.smartlam.com/	SmartShaft	Yes	CLT, Glulam, Elevator & Stairwell Shafts	DF-L, SPF, Hemlock, SYP**	A, I, M	3, 4, 5, 7, or 9 (4.13", 5.50" 6.88", 9.63", and 12.38")	***10', 11.25'	****51'	FSC, SFI
Sterling Solutions	https://www.sterlingsolutions.com/	Terralam	Yes	CLT	SYP	A, I, M	3, 5, or 7 ply (4.125" to 9.625")	8'	18'	No
Structurecraft	https://structurecraft.com/	DowelLam - DLT	Yes	DLT	SPF, DF, Hemlock, Sitka Spruce, Western Red Cedar, Yellow Cedar	A, I	4" up to 12.25"	12'	60.5'	FSC, PEFC
Structurlam	https://www.structurlam.com/	CrossLam CLT, GlulamPLUS	Yes	CLT, Glulam	^SPF, DF-L, SYP	A, I, M	3.43" to 12.42"	^^10', 12'	^^^40', 62'	FSC, GreenGuard glue specification
Texas CLT	http://texasclt.com/	n/a	Unknown	CLT	SYP	A, I, M	Unknown	Unknown	Unknown	Unknown
Vaagen Timbers	https://vaagentimbers.com/	n/a	Yes	CLT, Glulam, GLT	SPF, DF-L	A, I	4.13" to 9.63"	4'	60'	FSC
Vaagen Timbers	https://vaagentimbers.com/	n/a	Yes	CLT, GLT, GLT Panels	SPF, DF-L	A, I	4.13" to 9.63"	4'	60'	FSC

TABLE 4.3: SUMMARY OF NORTH AMERICAN MASS TIMBER MANUFACTURERS' PRODUCT INFORMATION

*The Mass Ply Lams (a product similar to Glulam beams/columns but made from veneer) can by up to 72" deep by 24" wide

**The Dothan, AL, plant uses SYP

***The Columbia Falls facility produces panels up to 10' wide vs. 11.5' at the Dothan facility

****Dothan can produce glulam up to 60' long

^ Conway plant uses SYP

^^ Penticton plant is 10' max, Conway is 12'

^^^ Penticton plant is 40' max, Conway is 62'

puter-aided design (CAD) services (e.g., Building Information Modeling [BIM], SolidWorks, CATIA, cadwork, AutoCAD) have played a significant role in panelizing projects and identifying building assemblies. Using these tools, manufacturers can import engineering documentation into CAD programs and develop robust three-dimensional (3D) models of the project, making mass timber part of the building's structure.

4.5.2 MANUFACTURING AND MATERIAL SUPPLY

Panel manufacturing: The manufacture of various panels at a production facility includes finger jointing lumber into mass timber panel layers (i.e., lamellas); molding/planing or surfacing the lumber; and pressing panels to the desired thicknesses, widths, and lengths.

Panel milling and finishing: This process includes additional manufacturing or CNC milling of panels to shop-specific drawings, and any architectural- or industrial-grade sanding, coating, and visual finishes. Many manufacturers list architectural and industrial finishes and can accommodate special requests for exposed elements. Some independently owned companies unrelated to mass timber manufacturers offer secondary manufacturing (CNC milling, finishing) of panels, glulam, and timbers.

Supplying connectors/hardware/fasteners: If manufacturers do not produce their own connectors and the other hardware required in mass timber buildings, they may source them elsewhere. Most manufacturing firms will provide this service.

4.5.3 CONSTRUCTION AND INSTALLATION SUPPORT

Logistics planning: Several manufacturers offer services that help with construction logistics, including just-in-time delivery of construction panels and sequencing of panel installation.

On-site: Speed and ease of installation are hallmarks of mass timber panels and key reasons for the industry's success. Because mass timber panel installation and construction are new to many building contractors, several manufacturers with construction experience provide on-site support.

4.5.4 OTHER MISCELLANEOUS SERVICES

Consulting services: Many mass timber manufacturers offer consulting services on an hourly basis. If the project requires more support to assess the practicality of mass timber elements, these companies can provide consultants during the design phase.

Steel fabrication: A variety of steel applications may be used in the construction of mass timber buildings. Some mass timber manufacturers offer in-house steel fabrication.

Renovation services and/or interior design options: Some building designs call for a complete package that includes kitchen, baths, appliances, and design elements. Some manufacturers offer such complete packages.

Environmental protection services: These focus on consultation and industrial matting, using CLT to protect specific areas from soil compaction and the impacts of heavy machinery.

Other: Most manufacturers offer shipping as a part of the package, as well as identifying any special requirements.

Global perspective: In addition to the above services, the industry segment producing structural mass timber panels may also offer general project management and assembly/construction services as part of an integrated package that results in a complete building shell. Some companies may offer packages approaching complete turnkey services for the smaller, more typical projects with which they gained experience. Assistance in all these functions may also be offered to clients who select external designers.

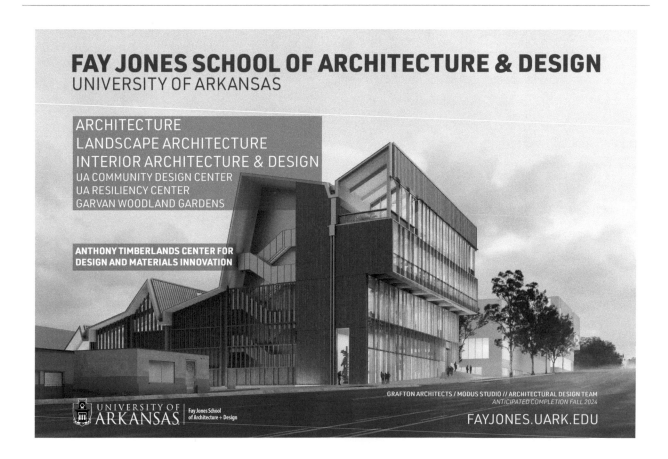

ARCHITECT'S RENDERING OF THE GRAND STAIRCASE OF THE MUSEUM.
Source: Adjaye Associates

CASE STUDY: PRINCETON UNIVERSITY ART MUSEUM

MASS TIMBER'S ELEGANT SIDE

LOCATION: PRINCETON, NEW JERSEY

OWNER: PRINCETON UNIVERSITY

DESIGN ARCHITECT: ADJAYE ASSOCIATES

EXECUTIVE ARCHITECT: COOPER ROBERTSON

STRUCTURAL ENGINEER: SILMAN

MASS TIMBER ENGINEER AND MANUFACTURER: NORDIC STRUCTURES

GENERAL CONTRACTOR: LF DRISCOLL

SIR DAVID ADJAYE'S vision for the Princeton University Art Museum took intricacy of design and construction to a whole new level. With immense V-shaped glulam beams incorporated into a hybrid structure supporting heavy roof loads, the museum showcases mass timber at its best: an elegant, sustainable material fulfilling structural and architectural roles and delivering on wood's biophilic properties.

Aside from the engineering challenges brought by the significant loads and span requirements, the engineering team at Nordic Structures also had to overcome restrictive geometric constraints to deliver a project that was true to Adjaye's design. With meticulous coordination, professionals and manufacturers considered each mechanical, electrical, and plumbing (MEP) component that penetrated the roof, and—by design—concealed them within the mass timber elements.

In addition to these challenges, the new museum had to be built on preexisting foundations. Each space's design was customized to guarantee that the new building would fit on the former founda-

tion, helping to reduce the carbon footprint and fulfill financial metrics.

Special care was also given to deflection. Each mass timber element was manufactured with consideration of the behavior of both the existing and new structures. Erection gaps would, therefore, resolve themselves after the entire building was complete, and the structure would achieve its desired final form.

The extraordinary V-shaped beams required high levels of coordination and advance manufacturing. A major part of the lifting and assembly devices, and every opening and routing required by MEP, were done at the plant, in a clean and controlled environment. That streamlined the fabrication and guaranteed a great level of care for the beams, limiting extra handling and the risk of impacting the beautiful, factory-applied finish on the mass timber elements.

Special attention was also given to transportation. Nordic Structures fabricated custom bracing devices to stabilize the beams without creating any abrasions or indentations during the 17-hour drive. The devices also kept the beams vertically oriented, which minimized the need for special rigging and lifting protocols.

TOP: V-SHAPE GLULAM BEAMS STRUCTURALLY GLUED AND SANDED PRIOR TO SEALER APPLICATION
Source: Nordic Structures

BOTTOM: ASSEMBLED AND FINISHED, THE V-SHAPED GLULAM BEAMS ARE READY FOR WRAPPING AND SHIPPING.
Source: Nordic Structures

The Princeton University Art Museum's mass timber sequesters over 800 tons of CO_2 equivalent. The wood is 100 percent Forest Stewardship Council (FSC)-certified and comes from Chibougamau in Northern Quebec, where Nordic Structures has been deeply rooted in the community since 1961. In addition to maintaining the highest of forestry standards, Nordic Structures's glulam is also on the cutting edge of sustainable development, attaining a number of environmental, health, and transparency declarations, as well as Cradle to Cradle certification, a first for the mass timber industry. ◉

FROM SEEDLINGS TO SOLUTIONS, WE MAKE TIMBER INSPIRE.

As North America's most advanced, integrated multi-species Mass Timber company, we're driven by our respect for the land, the call to carbon sequestration, and a passion to provide responsible building solutions.

KALESNIKOFF
TIMBER INSPIRES

kalesnikoff.com

CHAPTER 5: DESIGNERS AND SPECIFIERS

What is the construction industry's appetite for innovation? The US Green Building Council (USGBC) considers about 5 percent of the industry to be innovators, 20 percent to be leaders, 70 percent to be followers of current codes, and 5 percent to be lawbreakers (who do not follow codes). The 25 percent who are leaders and innovators look for ways to build modern structures focused on sustainability, efficiency, and a reduced carbon footprint. Over time, as we have seen with green building certifications and their effects on building codes, these industry leaders are likely to pull the entire building construction industry in their direction.

Mass timber is promising as an environmental solution, but it is also a disruptive technology with respect to building construction. The implications of increased off-site fabrication and more collaborative construction approaches are allowing project teams to glimpse a future with greater levels of control over materials procurement and craftsmanship. As such, many designers will find the information addressed to builders in chapter 6 is equally relevant to them as teams become more integrated, optimize design, schedule, and assess costs together in real time.

This chapter explains how to approach designing and coordinating a mass timber project from the design team perspective.

GLOBAL PERSPECTIVE

 Globally, two dominant adhesive systems are used in production of Cross-Laminated Timber (CLT). One is based on polyurethane (PUR), and the other is based on either melamine-formaldehyde (MF) or melamine urea-formaldehyde (MUF). Polyurethanes are the system of choice for about 67 percent of all existing production lines, compared with 20 percent for MF/MUF systems. Two other types—emulsion polymer isocyanate (EPI) and phenol-resorcinol-formaldehyde (PRF)—are used in about 13 percent of production lines, mostly in Japan.

PUR is used by early adopters and large manufacturers, however. So, when considering per-shift production capacities, about 80 percent of the annual global volume of adhesive-bonded CLT is produced with PUR, 16 percent with MF/MUF systems, and about 4 percent with all other systems combined.

When adhesive-bonded CLT and cross laminated products using a mechanical binder are pooled together, it turns out that mechanical binders are used by more than a quarter of all production lines. But the contribution of these mechanically bonded panels to the annual global output volume of all cross laminated products on a per-shift base is only about 5 percent.

Regional differences affect the choice of adhesive systems. About 85 percent of the production volume capacity in Alpine Europe is pressed with PUR, compared with 55 percent in the rest of Europe, 64 percent in the Asia-Pacific region, and 60 percent in North America. The proportion of the production volume capacity pressed with MF/MUF systems is 14 percent in Alpine Europe, 8 percent in the rest of Europe, and 21 percent in North America. None is used in the Asia-Pacific region.

Regional differences may be explained in part by historical developments, availability, and market preferences. In the early stages of the CLT industry in Central Europe, PUR was the only reasonably priced, commercially available system capable of creating a durable waterproof bond in a reasonable time in a cold press. It also played to the regional consumer preference for an almost transparent, "clear" bond line and zero formaldehyde content.

When the CLT industry expanded to Canada and the United States, the melamine-based systems were commercially available for large-panel production. When compared with Europeans, North American consumers do not show much preference for "clear" bond line, and the industry focused on measurable emission levels, not just on what was in the adhesive's name. On the other hand, concerns about the fire performance of the early versions of the PUR system pushed some North American adopters towards MF/MUF systems. Both systems now pass CLT fire performance tests.

5.1 ELEMENTS OF DESIGN

Wood is one of the oldest building materials. As far back as 6000 BC, humans made dwellings using wood. Wooden longhouses sheltering more than 20 people date to at least 4000 BC. To build large wooden structures, humans have long taken advantage of wood's natural strength while minimizing any weaknesses. Over the millennia, building techniques and capabilities have improved, most recently with the development of mass timber panel systems.

Panel Size

Mass timber panels are groundbreaking in the engineered wood market because their scale necessitates prefabrication and creates the potential for their use in modular construction. To maximize the benefits, building designers must consider the panel as it relates to the building's grid system in terms of overall dimensions, as well as thickness and the number of laminations. Each manufacturer has different fabrication machinery, and thus, different size limitations. In North America, a typical panel might be around 10 feet by 40 feet, or even 10 feet by 60 feet nominally, and between 3 inches and 24 inches thick. There are, however, many other options. Designers must also consider the panel's actual (versus nominal) dimensions. One of the characteristics of Cross-Laminated Timber (CLT) panels is their remarkable dimensional stability, particularly in plane. Manufacturers can finish panels for construction with submillimeter precision.

Panel sizes have also been developed around transportation requirements. The transportation and handling costs and limitations at any given building site should be considered when choosing optimum panel sizes for a project. Often, construction efficiency justifies the high cost of shipping oversized elements and assemblies.

Panel Strength

As mentioned in chapter 1, engineered composite wood products are stronger than solid wood components of the same dimensions because the natural defects in the wood are redistributed.

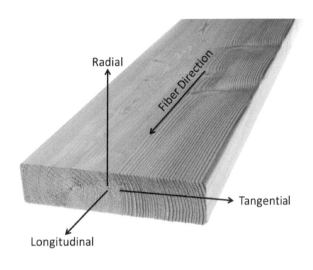

Radial

Fiber Direction

Tangential

Longitudinal

FIGURE 5.1: LUMBER STRENGTH ILLUSTRATION

Mass timber panels take advantage of the natural strengths of wood while minimizing its natural weaknesses. Wood is naturally much stronger in the longitudinal direction (aligned with the grain) than in the radial and tangential directions (across the grain), as illustrated in **Figure 5.1**. Products like CLT and Mass Plywood Panels (MPP) take advantage of wood's longitudinal strength by alternating the direction of the grain in each layer, resulting in panels that are strong and dimensionally stable in both in-plane directions.

Ongoing strength, vibration, and fire performance testing expand design opportunities on a regular basis. Because there are innumerable panel variables (number of layers, species of wood, lumber sizes and grades, adhesives versus fasteners), the testing has taken 2 approaches: (1) physically testing specific panel sizes/layers/species configurations, and (2) extending the physical test results to other untested sizes/layers/species configurations through analysis and modeling. The combination of an analytical approach and experimental testing has created a baseline for

understanding the performance characteristics of mass timber products.

For detailed information on design standards for mass timber products, refer to **Table 5.2** at the end of this chapter.

Adhesives

Adhesives are used in most engineered wood products (EWPs), including plywood, Laminated Veneer Lumber (LVL), glulam, CLT, and MPP. Standards have been established to ensure that these adhesives are structurally reliable and safe for building occupants.

Requirements for adhesives used in glulam and CLT are similar. Adhesives used in glulam must meet the requirements of the American National Standards Institute's *Standard for Adhesives for Use in Structural Glued Laminated Lumber* (ANSI 405). Guidance for CLT, under PRG 320, specifies that adhesives in CLT used in the US must also conform to ANSI 405, with 2 exceptions. First, Section 2.1.6 of ANSI 405 does not apply because it is intended to ensure glue-bond durability in exterior applications, and CLT is not recommended for exposed exterior applications. The second exception is that in the small-scale flame test under *CSA O177* (Sections 2.1.7 and 3.7 of ANSI 405), CLT must be substituted for glulam.

PRG 320 specifies that adhesives in CLT used in Canada must conform to CSA O112.10 and Sections 2.1.3, 2.1.7, 3.3, and 3.7 of ANSI 405 with the same alteration to the small-scale flame test under *CSA O177* as is required in the US. In addition, for both the US and Canada, PRG 320 specifies that CLT adhesives must conform

APEX PLAZA DURING CONSTRUCTION
Photo Credit: Prakash Patel Photography

CASE STUDY: APEX PLAZA

NAME OF PROJECT: APEX PLAZA

OWNER: APEX CLEAN ENERGY

LOCATION: CHARLOTTESVILLE, VIRGINIA

COMPLETION DATE: MAY 2022

ARCHITECT/DESIGNER:
WILLIAM MCDONOUGH + PARTNERS

MECHANICAL, ELECTRICAL, AND PLUMBING:
STAENGL ENGINEERING

STRUCTURAL ENGINEER: SIMPSON GUMPERTZ & HEGER

STARTING WITH WILLIAM McDonough + Partners' original aspiration of designing buildings like trees, Apex Clean Energy's headquarters is built with mass timber and healthy materials, while harvesting daylight and energy from the sun. The 875 roof- and canopy-mounted solar panels are expected to produce 364 megawatt hours (MWh) of energy per year. That's at least as much electricity as Apex consumes in a given year, giving the company net-positive electricity use.

DESIGN FOR DISASSEMBLY

Mass timber products bring natural beauty to occupants while allowing for transparency in materials

APEX PLAZA INTERIOR
Photo Credit: Prakash Patel Photography

sourcing, health, reutilization, and carbon management. Because mechanical fasteners were used to assemble the building, the high-value mass timber elements can be harvested from the structure at end of life, and the materials can return to the industry for their next use as part of the circular economy.

DESIGN FOR NEXT USE

What makes Apex Plaza unusual is its design for next use. In the future, Apex Plaza can be converted into residential housing. The mechanical fasteners, flexible floor plates, and mass timber column grid design allow for this. The exposed Cross-Laminated Timber (CLT) from Nordic Structures is the first Cradle to Cradle Certified mass timber product on the market, adding to the structure's circularity.

CARBON SEQUESTRATION

Carbon sequestration is an important component of building with CLT. Forests act as carbon "sinks,"

APEX PLAZA EXTERIOR
Photo Credit: Prakash Patel Photography

as healthy trees remove carbon dioxide (CO_2) from the atmosphere, release oxygen, and sequester/store carbon. Using mass timber in a building reduces the carbon footprint by storing CO_2 in the same way a healthy tree would. (One square meter of timber stores approximately one ton of CO_2.)

A faster, more economical connection than plywood.

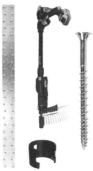

Our new **LDSS spline solution for mass timber** panel connections includes the LDSS light diaphragm spline strap, PRO300SG2 Quik Drive® tool and collated Strong-Drive® WSV screws. The steel LDSS strap attains high loads at a lower installed cost than plywood. Placed on top of CLT and other types of mass timber panels, it eliminates the need for CNC routing. The strap fastens quickly and easily with the Quik Drive tool, unique noseclip and screws. The Simpson Strong-Tie® LDSS spline strap is tested, widely available and backed by our expert service and technical support.

Switch to the LDSS spline solution for your next design. To learn more, visit **go.strongtie.com/LDSS** or call (800) 999-5099.

to Annex B of PRG 320 that sets standards for testing during elevated temperatures.

In CLT, the most common adhesives are polyurethane (PUR)-based, but melamine formaldehyde resins are also used. MPP use a phenol formaldehyde adhesive like those used in plywood and LVL. These adhesives are continually being studied and refined to be better for the environment and to better meet strength objectives desired by the industry. Some manufacturers in Europe and North America use urea formaldehyde (UF) or melamine urea formaldehyde (MUF) resins in their processes. Manufacturers in Japan use a variety of other cold-curing adhesives, though mostly in small-scale operations. The Engineered Wood Association (APA) addresses formaldehyde use in EWPs in a technical paper,[1] explaining that they "have such low emission levels that they are exempt from the leading formaldehyde emission standards and regulations."

Many mass timber products have Environmental Product Declarations (EPDs) available that demonstrate the safety of their adhesives from a health standpoint. In fact, several CLT manufacturers have achieved "Red List-free"[2] or "Red List-declared"[3] status by the International Living Future Institute (ILFI) Declare[4] EPD label, the most rigorous of the sustainable building standards.

Bio-based adhesives are an area of interest for designers and manufacturers looking for low-toxicity and low-carbon products.

5.2 CONNECTORS

As the mass timber construction market expands, so does the need for proper fasteners and connectors. Connectors are used to join the structural components and to transfer loads throughout a building. A variety of factors must be considered, including the type of joint, the materials being joined, loads carried through the joint, fire resistance, and aesthetics. Two primary families of connections have been created for wood construction: traditional joinery; and mechanical connectors, including dowels, splines, plates, and other specialized components. Traditional joinery entails cutting and joining wood together to create structural connections without the addition of other materials. Mechanical connectors are typically metal, and range from nails and screws to more complicated bracket systems. See **Figure 5.2** for examples. Some of these systems are proprietary, while others are traditional and widely available.

Connectors and fasteners must meet specific engineering requirements and be tested for performance. Two important requirements are shear strength and withdrawal strength. Shear strength is the ability of a material to resist forces that cause its internal structure to slide against itself (that is, fail) along a plane parallel with the direction of the force. Withdrawal strength, or withdrawal capacity, is the ability of the connector to resist forcible removal, or tear out, from its entry point. The National Design Specification (NDS) for Wood Construction provides design values for most dowel connectors, as well as for shear plates

---

1   Engineered Wood Products,   "Technical Note: Formaldehyde and Engineered Wood Products," no. J330E (January 2022), https://www.apawood.org/publication-search?q=J330&tid=1.

2   Structurlam Mass Timber Corporation, X-LAM Australia.

3   KLH, Element5.

4   https://declare.living-future.org/

FIGURE 5.2: MASS TIMBER CONNECTOR EXAMPLES

Top Left: Plate Connector; Top Right: Custom Connection;
Bottom Left: Concealed Beam Hangers; Bottom Right: Exposed Beam Hangers

Sources: APA, The Engineered Wood Association, Structure Craft (top right);
Oregon Department of Forestry (bottom left)

and split rings. Design values for proprietary systems are found in code evaluation reports that the manufacturer can provide.

For all connectors, it is important to know where to find their applicable design values. The International Building Code (IBC) defines the structural property requirements for connectors and fasteners of wood components. Section 2302.1 lists the sections that cover the actual stress factors required for various building applications. Sections 2304.10.1 through 2304.10.7 define the requirements for connectors and fasteners: what types of

fasteners are to be used in what situations, how many, and where they should be placed.

Joinery

Joinery uses specialized cutting techniques to form joints between wood components (mortise and tenon, dovetail, etc.). Joinery can create impressive results, both in beauty and strength. Long understood to be a time-consuming manual process that requires a significant amount of skill, joinery's possibilities have become more accessible to the building market through Com-

FIGURE 5.3: CNC JOINERY WITH PREFABRICATED
MASS TIMBER COLUMNS AND BEAMS

*Source: Emily Dawson,
Tamedia Building, Zurich, Switzerland*

 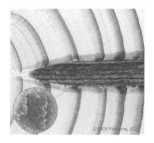

FIGURE 5.4: WOOD NAIL COIL AND LIGNIN WELDING

Source: LIGNOLOC®

puter Numerical Control (CNC) technologies (see **Figure 5.3** for an example). Designs translated into a computer model to be read by the CNC operator can be unusual, imaginative, and optimized for fabrication efficiency and installation speed. Working with a fabricator early in the design process can inform the cost-effectiveness of a joinery-based design approach.

Dowels

The most common type of mechanical fastener, dowel connectors can be made from a variety of materials. Metal dowel connectors are typically steel, and they include staples, nails, screws, and bolts. Dowel connectors transfer loads well, and they are generally easy to install and cost-effective.

Although wooden dowels can technically provide both a mechanical connection and a lignin bond (lignin is a polymer in wood's cellular structure that, with enough friction, is capable of creating a fusing effect between 2 pieces of wood), their application is analogous to metal dowel connectors. The NDS for Wood Construction allows designers and engineers to calculate the strength properties of dowel connectors. (See also NLT and DLT in chapter 1.) The benefits of wood doweling in a mass timber connection or fabrication approach are twofold: a higher carbon sequestration potential, and a more readily reusable or recyclable product at end of life. "All-wood" timber products that do not contain added metal or adhesives generate an improved Life Cycle Analysis (LCA) profile.

Recent testing at the University of Hamburg identified the phenomenon of "lignin welding," leading to the development of wooden nails acceptable for structural applications. Subsequently, a proprietary wooden nail product (see **Figure 5.4**) made from beechwood was developed in Austria, using the lignin welding effect. The German Institute for Construction Engineering (DIBt) has issued technical approval of load-bearing timber connections using these wooden nails, noting, "(T)he large amount of heat generated by friction when the nail is driven in at a high speed causes the lignin of the

wooden nail to weld with the surrounding wood to form a substance-to-substance bond."[5]

Splines

Spline connections combine joinery concepts and dowel connectors to structurally join large mass timber panels with smaller EWPs. A typical spline connection involves routing the connecting edges of 2 mass timber panels with a shallow groove, laying joinery boards within the groove, and fixing them in place with nails or screws (see **Figure 5.5**).

Plates

Custom and off-the-shelf metal plate connectors can be combined with nails, screws, or through-bolts to connect multiple elements, as shown in **Figure 5.2**. Custom welded connections can also

FIGURE 5.5: SPLINE CONNECTION MATERIAL EXAMPLES: PLYWOOD AND JOINERY BOARD

Source (Structurlam CLT and plywood splines): Emily Dawson
Source (KLH 1-inch joinery board): Scott Noble

---

5   Beck, "LIGNOLOC®," press release, September 23, 2020.

be created from plate steel to manage a variety of loads in exposed or concealed conditions. Some metal connector plates were developed to help join trusses for floors and roofs without the use of additional fasteners. These plates are usually made from sheets of galvanized steel and are die-punched to create teeth that protrude from the underside. This type of toothed metal connector plate is not suitable for most mass timber applications.

Shear Connectors

Shear connectors, or bearing connectors, include shear plates, toothed shear plates, and split rings. These connectors are designed to help wooden components handle heavier loads. Shear plates, or timber washers, are iron discs with a shallow rim on one side and a flat surface on the other (see **Figure 5.6**). This connection disperses pressure from a load across the larger radius of the plate. By contrast, a bolt spreads pressure across a smaller area. Shear plates, therefore, can handle heavier loads than bolts. Split rings are like shear plates in both form and function, but they are not as heavy-duty.

Structural Metal Castings

The free-form capability of the casting manufacturing process is ideally suited to address a variety of connection geometries with artistic creativity and structural integrity. Structural metal castings can transfer tension, compression, shear, and other loads, as well as offer increased ductility for structural systems meant to resist seismic motions. Pre-engineered, standardized castings are available off the shelf to suit an array of sizes. Custom-designed cast connections can satisfy

FIGURE 5.6: SHEAR PLATE CONNECTOR
Source: Portland Bolt & Manufacturing Co.

specific project objectives and constraints for one-off and repetitive applications (see **Figure 5.7**).

Proprietary Connector Systems

Proprietary connector systems are numerous and vary significantly in appearance, capacity, and application. These systems range from self-tapping screws with proprietary head patterns to one-off, custom-created connectors that weigh hundreds or thousands of pounds.

Self-tapping screws are among the most widely used fasteners in mass timber projects. Proprietary bracket systems are also commonly used to connect beams, posts, and panels for a variety of reasons. Some are intended to overcome limitations or weaknesses in existing systems or components. Others are created with aesthetics or ease of installation in mind.

5.3 FIRE RESISTANCE

Many mass timber products are large, thick, airtight masses of wood. These properties are in-

FIGURE 5.7 OFF-THE-SHELF STRUCTURAL METAL CAST COLUMN CONNECTIONS
TIMBER END CONNECTORS™, UMASS AMHERST INTEGRATED DESIGN BUILDING

Source: Cast Connex®; Photo Credit: Alex Schreyer

herently fire-resistant. This may seem counterintuitive because wood is regarded as a combustible material. However, tests have shown that large wooden components maintain their structural integrity during extended exposure to direct flame and intense heat. Fire ratings represent the length of time a given assembly can be exposed to high temperatures before losing crucial performance characteristics. Design teams will need to review and address flame and smoke spread classifications (as defined by the IBC) for exposed wood surfaces.

Charring

When exposed to fire, wood chars on its exterior, creating a barrier between the inner portion of the beam/panel and the flame. With continued heat, the char layer thickens at a very slow, predictable rate, and with each passing moment further insulates the wood at the core. The thickening char layer is removing oxygen from the inner depths of the wood and is, thereby, extinguishing the burning component. This enables the inner, uncharred core to remain structurally unaffected, allowing the component to retain much of its original strength.

Effective Char Rates and Char Layer Depths
(for β_n = 1.5 inches/hour)

Required Fire Resistance (hr)	Effective Char Rate, β_{eff} (in/hr)	Effective Char Layer Depth, a_{char} (in)
1-Hour	1.8	1.8
1½-Hour	1.67	2.5
2-Hour	1.58	3.2

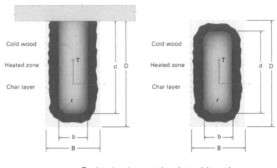

Reduction in member breadth and depth over time, t

FIGURE 5.8: CALCULATING THE FIRE RESISTANCE OF EXPOSED WOOD MEMBERS

Source: American Wood Council Technical Report, no. 10

The IBC references the NDS for Wood Construction produced by the American Wood Council (AWC) to calculate the fire resistance of mass timber elements (see **Figure 5.8**). This standard establishes a nominal design char rate of 1.5 inches per hour. "Effective" char depth includes a 0.3-inch pyrolysis zone, where the wood is not yet burned but is heated to the point of losing all moisture and is no longer structurally viable. The effective char rate per hour slows the longer the wood burns, as the char layer insulates the remaining wood from further damage.

The NDS char rate value is necessarily a conservative one. Actual char rates depend on species. Generally, denser (heavier) woods will char at lower rates, while less dense (lighter) species will char more quickly. The char rates also depend on species-specific extractives (wood molecules that are nonstructural in nature), some of which are highly flammable and may accelerate the burning process.

The design team for the Ascent tower in Milwaukee, Wisconsin, for example, demonstrated that the tall timber structure would have a slower char rating than the prescriptive code value. They tested their KLH-supplied panels at the Forest Products Laboratory (FPL) in Madison, Wisconsin, and measured a char rating of 1.29–1.31 inches per hour, saving the project the cost of almost ¼ inch of fiber from every exposed, rated wood component. This finding has excellent implications for reducing fiber and costs when design teams pursue a performance-based permitting process.

Flame and Smoke Classifications

Interior finish surfaces are classified based on a "flame spread" and "smoke-developed" index in the code with 3 levels of distinction: Class A is the most resistant; Class C, the least. Untreated wood falls into Classes B or C; designations are by species.[6] Flame spread ratings can be increased with treatments and coatings.

---

6   American Wood Council, Design for Code Acceptance 1 (DCA1): Flame Spread Performance of Wood Products Used for Interior Finish (2019).

Encapsulation

If a design requires fire resistance in addition to the values provided by the wood itself, structural encapsulation is the most straightforward approach from a code perspective. Fire safety is attained by encapsulating mass timber elements with an approved and rated assembly. The encapsulation rating is defined as the time that charring of a structural mass timber element is delayed by the "encapsulation membrane," limiting the growth and spread of fire. Gypsum board, gypsum concrete, and intumescent coatings are among the most popular encapsulation materials.

Coatings

Intumescent coatings and sealants fill gaps and protect the materials underneath them by expanding when exposed to extremely high temperatures. These treatments decrease the immediate flammability of the wood, minimizing fuel for an active fire and slowing the spread of a flame. Intumescent coatings can be costly to install, but their thinness and transparency solve some dimensional and aesthetic issues, offsetting the cost for some projects.

New fire-resistant coatings are in development, including a very thin, transparent coating invented by scientists at Nanyang Technological University, Singapore (NTU Singapore).[7] Although designers cannot always incorporate products that have not been tested under nationally recognized standards, by understanding the performance potential and current research, designers can imagine structures that would not previously have been possible.

5.4 STRUCTURAL PERFORMANCE

Foundations

Wooden structures are much lighter than buildings of a similar size made from steel, concrete, or masonry. Lighter-weight buildings transfer less load to their foundations, leading to smaller, less complex below-grade work, saving on excavation and concrete costs. This feature is particularly advantageous for building sites with poor soil-bearing pressures, and it also improves the ability to build over contaminated soils with minimum disruption. In one project that required deep foundation piles for an all-concrete building, DCI Engineers saved 30 percent in foundation costs by replacing the top 3 floors of the building with mass timber.[8]

Using less concrete is desirable for lowering a building's embodied carbon footprint, and it often has significant schedule advantages as well.

Grid Layout/Structural Bay

Mass timber panel dimensions and thicknesses, and thus, their strength and stiffness, vary by manufacturer and product. Often, vibration, a subjective value in the United States, will govern panel thickness over strength and fire resistance. A design team considering mass timber for floor panels should understand structural bay options and constraints when making early building layout decisions.

The manufacturing dimensions of various mass timber panel systems should be considered to optimize cost efficiency in plan layouts. It is advisable to bring a procurement or manufacturing partner

---

7   https://techxplore.com/news/2022-08-invisible-coating-wood-fireproof.html
8   1 De Haro, San Francisco, Dean Lewis, DCI Engineers.

TA'TALU ELEMENTARY SCHOOL
Source: Thinkspace

CASE STUDY: MASS TIMBER CONSTRUCTION IN BC'S K-12 SCHOOLS

SIR MATTHEW BEGBIE ELEMENTARY SCHOOL

OWNER: VANCOUVER SCHOOL BOARD

ARCHITECT: HCMA

STRUCTURAL ENGINEER: FAST + EPP

MASS TIMBER INSTALLER: BEAM CRAFT

WOOD SUPPLIER: STRUCTURLAM MASS TIMBER CORPORATION

MASS TIMBER PRODUCTS: CLT, GLULAM

BAYVIEW ELEMENTARY SCHOOL

OWNER: VANCOUVER SCHOOL BOARD

ARCHITECT: FRANCL ARCHITECTURE

STRUCTURAL ENGINEER: FAST + EPP

MASS TIMBER INSTALLER: KINSOL TIMBER SYSTEMS LTD.

WOOD SUPPLIER: KALESKINOFF MASS TIMBER

MASS TIMBER PRODUCTS: CLT, GLULAM

TA'TALU ELEMENTARY SCHOOL

OWNER: SURREY SCHOOL DISTRICT

ARCHITECT: THINKSPACE

MASS TIMBER PRODUCT: GLULAM

SIR MATTHEW BEGBIE ELEMENTARY SCHOOL
Source: Bright Photography, courtesy of naturallywood.com

NOW MORE THAN ever, schools need to meet a wide variety of needs: inspire students, foster well-being, remain cost-effective and environmentally sound, cut carbon, and adapt to the district's changing needs.

The *Wood Use in British Columbia Schools* report—by architects; Thinkspace, a design firm; and Fast + Epp, a structural engineering firm—highlights compelling reasons why the mass timber movement in British Columbia and beyond is growing, and it shows how the movement can help meet the above demands, especially for K–12 educational facilities.

The report explores the following:

- The benefits of wood use in schools, including impacts on learning, health and wellness, culture and tradition, speed of construction, cost effectiveness, and carbon dioxide (CO_2) emissions

- Technology advances in the mass timber and wood construction industry, including these:

  » Wider availability of mass timber products and fabrication automation of Nail-Laminated Timber (NLT)

  » Advances in structural connections and techniques, made possible through research and changes in standards and building codes; composite systems and point-supported mass timber construction increase design options

  » Building Information Modeling (BIM) and Computer Numerical Control (CNC) machining that allow projects to use suppliers' advanced automated machinery to fabricate panels, beams, or columns off-site

- How to address building codes and the need for alternative solutions in certain jurisdictions

RIGHT: BAYVIEW ELEMENTARY SCHOOL
Source: Wade Comer Photography, courtesy of naturallywood.com

- Several case studies that profile wood in structural and nonstructural applications, including Ta'talu Elementary School in Surrey, BC; and Sir Matthew Begbie Elementary School in Vancouver, BC.

Ta'talu Elementary School in Surrey will be the first 3-story, hybrid mass timber elementary school in British Columbia. The school will provide learning spaces for over 600 students, plus on-site childcare facilities. Construction materials include mass timber, light-frame wood, and steel. The predominant structure will be post and beam glulam, with light-frame wood. Load-bearing members (beams and columns) will be mass timber. Stacked floor plans allow for greater density and increased structural efficiency. A modular prefabricated design—a kit-of-parts—will make it easier to modify or add on in the future.

Sir Matthew Begbie Elementary School in Vancouver, British Columbia, is a part of the province's seismic upgrade initiative. Completed in 2022, the building took advantage of off-site prefabricated mass timber products and just-in-time delivery methods. They, in turn, improved project efficiencies, sped up the construction schedule, and offered overall cost savings. They also helped deliver the much-needed facility while reducing congestion and noise in the quiet East Vancouver neighborhood adjacent to the existing fully operational school building.

The use of locally sourced, naturally renewable timber in Bayview Elementary School fits with the Vancouver School District's commitment to sustainability. The use of mass timber means low carbon construction—delivering a net carbon dioxide (CO_2) benefit of 1,137 metric tons. ⬤

on the team as early as possible to gain the benefits of efficient material use. Also see chapter 8 for what to consider when advising building owners on contract options.

Seismic Performance

Some of the oldest wooden buildings in the world are in Japan, the most seismically active country on Earth. At over 122 feet tall, the Horyuji Temple near Osaka has survived at least 46 earthquakes of a magnitude 7.0 or greater on the Richter scale since its construction in 607 AD. Japanese scholars describe the inherent flexibility in these wooden structures by a "snake dance" theory,[9] enabling them to dissipate significant seismic energy without damage.

Building codes are the main tool for addressing seismic risks, establishing design requirements that vary by region and depend on the historical frequency and magnitude of earthquake activity. The main seismic criterion in building codes is a specification of the minimum lateral force a building must withstand to prioritize occupant safety during a seismic event. Building codes include an equation in which cyclic seismic forces are represented by a single static force, called *base shear*, that is applied to the base of a building. Designers adjust or design for variables in the base shear equation to achieve desired building performance. The variables include site seismicity, soil conditions, structural systems and building materials, building height, and building occupancy.

9   https://web-japan.org/nipponia/nipponia33/en/topic/

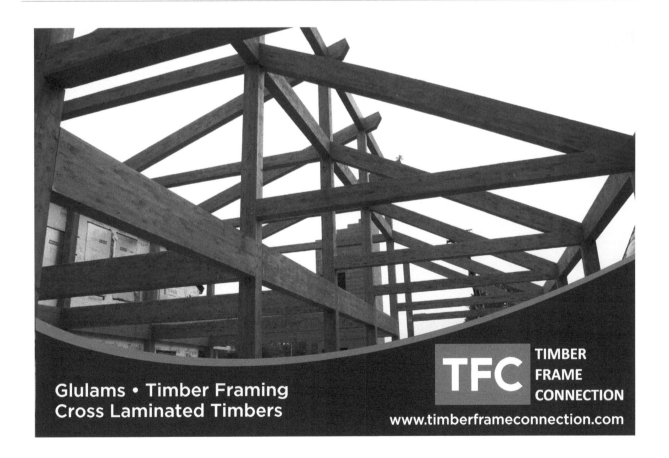

Wood, particularly mass timber, has characteristics that lead to favorable earthquake performance: weight, redundancy, and ductility.

Weight: Lighter building weight is an advantage in a seismic event because the inertial force exerted on a building is proportional to its weight, with higher inertial forces exerted on heavier buildings. Lateral systems for timber buildings are required to resist less force than heavier buildings, and as a result can be smaller and less expensive.

Redundancy: Many fasteners and connectors are used in wooden buildings to join walls, roofs, floors, beams, and columns. Each of these connections is a load path through which seismic forces can travel. The numerous connections inherent in a component-based construction approach mitigate the chance for complete structural failure if some connections fail.

Ductility is the extent to which a material or building can deform without failing. Buildings made from wood often use connection systems for joining walls, beams, and columns that further add to a building's ductility.

In high-seismic regions in the US, building codes limit the use of CLT to resist lateral forces from earthquakes, given the low ductility of CLT as a shear wall system (structural R-value of 2). The higher the structural R-value, the lower the lateral force required by the building code. Structural engineers, therefore, typically design with lateral systems having a higher R-value, such as light-frame timber plywood shear walls (up to R-7).

The design requirements of CLT shear walls and CLT diaphragms are defined in the AWC's *Special Design Provisions for Wind and Seismic* (SDPWS) 2021 edition.[10] This reference guide can be used as a basis for alternative requests to jurisdictions that do not yet recognize IBC 2021. The CLT diaphragm requirements in SDPWS 2021 are engineering-based, with no specific prescribed details. It does include a low-seismic, CLT shear wall option with a structural R-value of 1.5, as well as design details for a platform-framed CLT shear wall system, including specific connectors and aspect ratio limits for individual CLT panels. WoodWorks offers a *CLT Diaphragm Technical Guide* that includes working examples using the new CLT diaphragm requirements.

Recent research and testing of CLT shear walls have resulted in proposals to use a structural R-value of 3.0 to 4.0, depending on the aspect ratio of the CLT wall. This, however, still means designing for lateral forces roughly twice those of light-frame plywood shear walls. The R-values of 3.0 and 4.0 for the platform framed CLT shear wall system were published in *ASCE 7*, 2022 edition. Research is ongoing on higher R-value, lower design force, and shear wall systems, including mass timber rocking wall testing.[11]

Wind Loading

In regions with low seismic concerns, or in very tall buildings, wind loads may govern lateral design. Many of the seismic performance advantages of timber construction can be applied to wind loading design. However, lighter-weight buildings will require adapted shapes and/or more lateral

---

10   https://awc.org/codes-standards/publications/sdpws-2021
11   Led by Shiling Pei of Colorado School of Mines.

strengthening forces than heavier buildings to deflect or resist wind.

Hybrid Systems

Most timber structures use steel-reinforced concrete for foundations and steel components for connections. But factors such as building height, grid layout, and seismic region may lead a design team to use a full-building hybrid approach. Such projects efficiently combine multiple primary structural materials. Although wood is very strong by weight in both tension and compression, selectively incorporating concrete or steel, or a combination of both, can mitigate vibration, increase span capacity, reduce structural member dimensions, and/or increase lateral capacity (see **Figures 5.9** and **5.10**). Component-based approaches, such as hybrid slabs, are also being developed in research and in practice.

TOP — FIGURE 5.9: CONCRETE CORES AND PRECAST CONCRETE FRAME WITH TIMBER SLAB AND BEAMS

Adidas North American Headquarters, Portland, OR
Source: Lever Architecture

BOTTOM — FIGURE 5.10: HYBRID CLT AND STEEL STRUCTURE

Microsoft Campus, Mountain View, CA; Source: Holmes Structures; Photo Credit: Blake Marvin Photography

Hybrid Slabs

Some building programs require spans that are difficult to accomplish with mass timber panels alone. An efficient classroom building on a 30-foot grid, for example, might at first seem to call for solid timber floors with a thick section that's cost-prohibitive. For such projects, designers may instead consider adding beams, tension cords, or composite slabs, or they could rethink standard grid approaches developed with other construction materials. Some options for hybrid slabs have been established.

Composite concrete-timber slabs are composed of concrete and timber connected via steel components to create composite structural action; they take advantage of the properties of both materials simultaneously. A concrete diaphragm is poured over a timber slab and connected with reinforcing steel to tie the 2 materials together. Thickened concrete sections may act as beams. Reinforcing steel can take many inventive shapes, such as fasteners driven into the timber at an angle before the concrete is poured (see **Figure 5.11**),

TOP — FIGURE 5.11: COMPOSITE CONCRETE-TIMBER SLAB WITH ACOUSTIC MAT AND INCLINED SCREW REINFORCING

Peavy Hall, Oregon State University
Source: Evan Schmidt

BOTTOM — FIGURE 5.12: COMPOSITE CONCRETE-TIMBER SLAB WITH NAILPLATE REINFORCING

John W. Oliver Design Building at UMass Amherst
Source: Alex Schreyer/UMASS

perforated steel flanges added during the timber manufacturing or glued in on-site (see **Figure 5.12**), or 2-way rebar. In Europe, special types of removable anchoring systems are being developed to facilitate the deconstruction of concrete-timber

TOP LEFT — FIGURE 5.13: POST TENSIONED TIMBER BEAM

Source: 120 Clay Creative, Ankrom Moisan
Photo Credit: Ethan Martin

TOP RIGHT — FIGURE 5.14: POST TENSIONED CLT PANEL

Chibougamau terminal, Nordic Structures and EVOQ
Architecture; Photo Credit: EVOQ/Artcad

BOTTOM — FIGURE 5.15: TIMBER-TIMBER
COMPOSITE FLOOR PANEL

Catalyst, Katerra; Photo Credit: Andrew Giammarco

FIGURE 5.16: LIGHT FRAME AND MASS TIMBER HYBRID

The Canyons, Portland, OR
Source: Kaiser+Path; Photo Credit: Marcus Kauffman, Oregon Department of Forestry

slabs at the building's end of life. Permanently integrated concrete-timber slabs may be very difficult and expensive to handle during deconstruction, weighing on the cradle-to-grave carbon balance of buildings that use them.

Post-tensioned timber can reduce overall beam depth and increase structural transparency by adding steel tension cords to timber beams or panels (see **Figures 5.13** and **5.14**).

Timber-timber composite floor panels are timber slabs with thickened timber sections that increase the panel's span capacity. The designers of Catalyst, an office building project in Spokane, Washington, conceived and developed a timber-timber composite floor panel to achieve a 30-foot span with CLT floors and shallow CLT beams integrated during panel fabrication (see **Figure 5.15**). Other manufacturers have produced mass timber

hollow core panels that combine thinner (3-ply) CLT panels for top and bottom layers, connected with internal glulam ribs. The hollow spaces are filled with insulation materials. Mass timber ribbed panel assemblies are another relatively new mass timber product; they combine CLT decks with integrated glulam ribs connected to the bottom by screws, glue, or a combination.

Hybrid Lateral Systems

Because of the stiffness of mass timber panels, hybrid approaches for lateral systems are often the most cost-effective choice.

For mid-rise structures, light-framed wood shear walls are a straightforward and cost-effective approach (as shown in **Figure 5.16**).

FIGURE 5.17: CLT POST AND BEAM STRUCTURE WITH BUCKLING RESTRAINED BRACED FRAME CORE

Carbon 12, Portland, OR; Source: Kaiser+Path

FIGURE 5.18: TIMBER BRB FRAME TEST

Source: Timberlabs

For taller buildings, concrete cores can be advantageous from a permitting and constructability perspective. Concrete cure times should be considered and construction sequencing optimized, so building the cores does not offset the time-saving advantages of timber framing.

Buckling Restrained Braced (BRB) frame cores and walls, which can be prefabricated with steel (as seen in **Figure 5.17**) or glulam (as seen in **Figure 5.18**) cross bracing, have time-saving advantages over concrete. BRB frames can be designed with bolted rather than welded connections, working with the mass timber components as a kit-of-parts

for rapid on-site assembly in any weather. An all-timber BRB frame lateral system that works in high seismic zones is under development at the University of Utah. Final testing is scheduled for spring 2023.[12]

Post-tensioned CLT shear walls combine strong, rigid wood panels with steel tendons and fuses for added ductility and seismic force dissipation (see also chapter 8's section on resiliency). The technology was developed in New Zealand and has been in use there for nearly a decade. Peavy Hall at Oregon State University is the first installation of its kind in North America (see **Figure 5.19**).

Ballistic/Blast Performance

The US military is interested in using mass timber in construction projects, with one estimate finding that military construction using CLT instead of concrete and steel could create a market of $1.9 billion annually for buildings, housing, and

12 University of Utah et al., Wood Innovations Grant, BRB Braced Frames for Seismically Resilient Mass Timber Buildings (USDA Forest Service, 2021).

FIGURE 5.19: POST-TENSIONED CLT 'ROCKING' SHEAR WALL INSTALLATION

Peavy Hall, Oregon State University; Photo Credit: Hannah O'Leary

facilities requiring low levels of blast resistance.[13] When designing military buildings, architects are often required to integrate blast- and projectile-resistant materials.

Initial blast-resistance tests conducted at Tyndall Air Force Base in Florida validated acceptable levels of blast resistance for structures built with NLT and CLT. All structures remained intact and matched modeling predictions for acceptable levels of damage.

In addition, efforts are underway to understand how mass timber structures perform when struck by projectiles. Georgia Institute of Technology (Georgia Tech) completed studies in which CLT panels made of spruce, pine, fir (SPF) and Southern Yellow Pine (SYP) were subjected to ballistic testing. The results showed that both types of conventional CLT materials' inherent penetration resistances are significantly greater than that of the dimension lumber and plywood now used for temporary military structures. Additionally, the testing showed that US military guidelines (UFC 4-023-07) for determining required wood thickness based on ballistic threat underestimated the performance of CLT. The tests resulted in new

13   WoodWorks, Cross Laminated Timber Blasts its Way into Government Construction. https://www.woodworks.org/learn/mass-timber-clt/protective-design/

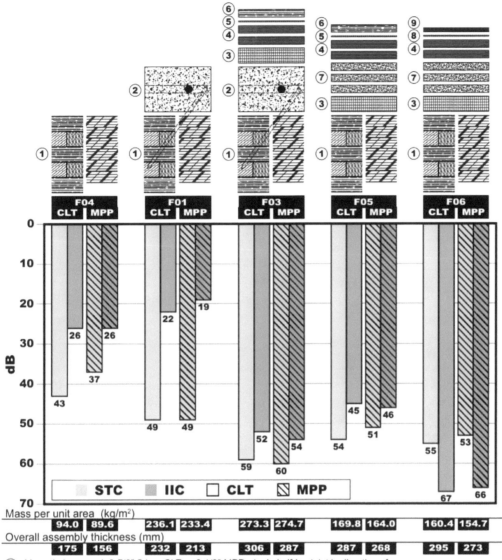

① Mass timber panel, 6-7/8" 5-lam CLT or 6-1/8" MPP, single half-lap joint in direction of span
② 2-1/4" concrete slab @ 145 pcf density, #3 rebar, 6" o.c. in span direction, 12" o.c. perpendicular to span, 8mm x 220mm shear fastener, 12" o.c. field spacing @ 45°
③ 1" acoustic underlayment, install in opposing direction to flooring
④ 5/8" OSB, 2 layers, glued in direction of span, stagger seams, adhere with construction adhesive
⑤ 1/8" acoustic underlayment
⑥ 6-1/2" x 1/2" random length engineered pine floating floor, T&G, sanded, oiled
⑦ 1/2" cement board, 3 layers, stagger seams, adhere with construction adhesive
⑧ 3/8" 8lb carpet pad
⑨ 1/2" pile nylon carpet, 97.5 oz/sq.yd face weight

FIGURE 5.20: CLT + MPP FLOOR ASSEMBLY ACOUSTIC TESTING

Source: University of Oregon, Acoustic Lab Testing (ASTM E492-2016, ASTM E90-2016) of CLT and MPP Wall and Floor Assemblies for Multifamily Residential

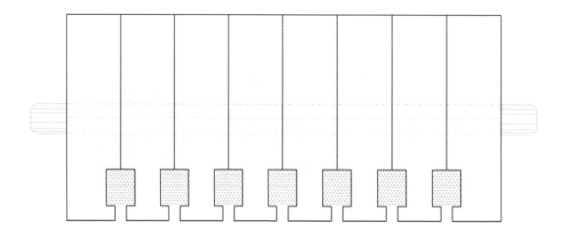

FIGURE 5.21: SIDE VIEW OF ACOUSTICALLY DESIGNED DLT PANEL

Source: StructureCraft

equations for predicting the required thickness of CLT for ballistic protection.[14]

5.5   ACOUSTIC PROPERTIES

Mass timber has advantages as an acoustic solution. The massive arrangement helps mitigate the transfer of low-frequency sound vibrations. Combining mass timber with other building materials can create relatively thin assemblies with high Sound Transmission Class (STC) and Impact Insulation Class (IIC) values.

Standard assemblies for acoustical performance in mass timber buildings have been developed, in addition to an array of proprietary solutions. WoodWorks has an online inventory of hundreds of mass timber assemblies that have been acoustically tested.[15] Additionally, some guidelines have

been developed for floor assemblies, including a mass timber floor with a raised access floor, a mass timber "dry" build-up, and numerous assemblies specific to the 2021 IBC tall mass timber construction types. In Europe, where noise and vibration transmission standards for various classes of buildings are more stringent than in North America, many panelized mass timber projects use special durable polymer dampening seals in pedestal-type floor-to-wall connections to further reduce vibration and sound transmission.

A 2019 research project[16] at TallWood Design Institute (TDI) showed promising outcomes for 5 common floor assemblies, each with a CLT and MPP iteration (see **Figure 5.20**). STC and IIC values were above 50 for all floor assemblies with acoustic underlayment and floating floors, except for IIC values on a dry assembly with tongue-and-groove engineered pine flooring. STC

---

14   Kathryn P. Sanborn, PhD, "Exploring Cross-Laminated Timber Use for Temporary Military Structures" (thesis, Georgia Institute of Technology, 2018).

15   https://www.woodworks.org/wp-content/uploads/Acoustically-Tested-Mass-Timber-Assemblies-WoodWorks.pdf

16   Kevin Van Den Wymelenberg, *Acoustic Testing of Typical Multi-Family Residential CLT and MPP Dry and Concrete-Composite Wall and Floor Assemblies.* https://tallwoodinstitute.org/acoustic-lab-testing-of-typical-multi-family-residential-clt-and-mpp-dry-and-concrete-composite-wall-and-floor-assemblies/

MATERIAL	THERMAL CONDUCTIVITY K-VALUE (W/(M K))
Sheep wool	0.04
Insulation, average quality	0.04
Sawdust	0.08
Douglas fir	0.12
Hemlock	0.12
Plywood	0.13
Southern Yellow Pine	0.15
Gypsum board	0.17
Plaster and wood lath	0.28
Concrete, medium	0.4 - 0.7
Concrete, dense	1.0 - 1.8
Steel, 1% carbon	43.00

TABLE 5.1: THERMAL CONDUCTIVITY OF BUILDING MATERIALS

Source: Engineering Toolbox, Thermal Conductivity of Common Materials and Gases (2003)

neer can review floor and wall assemblies, make performance recommendations, and provide project-specific STC and IIC values.

Some mass timber panels are designed for acoustic performance. For example, StructureCraft produces a sound-dampening DLT panel with insulation-filled grooves engineered to absorb sound waves (see **Figure 5.21**).

5.6 THERMAL PERFORMANCE

The thermal performance of a building directly influences not only its energy efficiency but also its occupants' comfort and the life span of some building components. Mass timber is an excellent material selection for thermal performance. Wood is a good insulator and is universally appealing, with exposed wood surfaces giving occupants a "warm" feeling (see chapter 7 for more on occupant comfort).

The thermal performance of a building is dependent on many factors, including climate, building shape, building orientation, architecture, and building and insulating materials. The R-values and k-values of various building materials help determine the overall thermal performance of a structure. The k-value, known as "thermal conductivity," is a measure of the rate of heat transfer through a material. The unit of measure for this rate is watts per meter kelvin (W/[m-K]); the measure is independent of the material's thickness. Materials with high thermal conductivity transfer heat more quickly and thus are generally not useful insulators. Materials with low thermal conductivity transfer heat more slowly and are more likely to be found in insulating applications. **Table 5.1** shows common building materials (and

and IIC values for bare timber assemblies and bare timber-composite assemblies fell below 50, but STC values were 49 for bare concrete-timber composite floors.

As with other code-required assemblies, permitting authorities may allow a performance-based approach for acoustic ratings. An acoustic engi-

other materials for comparison) and their thermal conductivity values.

The thermal R-value, known as "thermal resistance" (not to be confused with the structural R-value discussed in an earlier section), can be measured for an individual layer of material. It quantifies the effectiveness of that layer as an insulator, given its thickness. Thermal R-value is calculated by taking the thickness of a layer and dividing it by the thermal conductivity of the material. Solid wood has relatively low thermal conductivity and can therefore be used as an insulator. The thermal conductivity of solid wood is up to 15 times lower than concrete and over 350 times lower than steel. Mass timber buildings can be designed and built with superior thermal performance, leading to reduced energy requirements over their life span, cost savings for building owners and occupants, and reductions in the operational carbon footprint.

Air infiltration rates of exterior envelopes contribute significantly to the energy performance of a building. CLT has an exceptionally low air infiltration rate, making it a good choice for the high-performing exterior walls required for very low-energy building design.

5.7 MOISTURE

A mass timber designer will need to consider moisture concerns similar to those associated with light-frame construction and finished wood products, but they must also be aware of a few key differences. Understanding wood's behavior as an organic material is foundational to establishing best practices.

Wood has a cellular structure ideal for holding and distributing moisture within a live tree. Once harvested, wood fibers continue to be hygroscopic, readily expanding and contracting as the environmental moisture content (MC) increases or decreases. Controlling the moisture exposure of wood building products is important along the entire supply chain, from lumber processing to fabrication, delivery, construction, and occupancy. Maintaining a relatively stable MC at each stage avoids the performance and aesthetic concerns that arise from dimensional changes, cracking or checking, staining, and decay. Factors most commonly contributing to these issues are exposure to weather before or after occupancy, trapped (unventilated) moisture, and roof or plumbing leaks.

The MC of logs at harvest may exceed 100 percent (i.e., there may be more water than dry woody substance) by "oven dry base," the metric used by the lumber industry. Of the total weight of the water in a log, about 60 percent is "bound" within the anatomical structure of individual cells. The balance is "free" water in cavities between the wood cells. Industry expectations are that the types of lumber used to make mass timber will be dried to 12 percent moisture (+ or − 3 percent, i.e., 12 percent is the target; 9 to 15 percent is the acceptable range). Drying lumber to this level helps ensure dimensional stability during mass timber manufacturing and in situ, and it prevents decay. In wet climates, wood structures might absorb moisture during the construction phase, in which case a building must go through a "dry-out" phase before the wood is enclosed—or risk compromise.

A building with properly ventilated and dried wood will stabilize during the first 2 or 3 years

FIGURE 5.22: MOISTURE MONITORING CLT FLOORS WITH A HAMMER-IN PROBE

Source: Kaiser+Path; Photo Credit: Kevin Lee

of occupancy to match the ambient moisture content. MC, for example, will typically stabilize at around 6 to 8 percent for wood in interior use applications in the Pacific Northwest. The greater the MC differential within a wood member, or between the installed wood and the future occupied building, the greater the impact of shrinkage and checking. Fungus is most likely to grow if the MC reaches a range of 26 to 60 percent. Factors contributing to the variances include wood species, fungus species, temperature, and time (rate of dry out).

Ongoing research in academia and in the industry will continue to inform the best practices for protection and detailing. Although industry standards are nascent for many of the issues specific to mass timber and moisture mitigation, resources for designers are developing. RDH Building Science Inc. has published advice to designers on some aspects of detailing mass timber buildings to protect and recover from moisture exposure.[17]

A project studying water in mass timber"[18] is ongoing at TDI via grants from the US Department of Agriculture (USDA) and the Agricultural Research Service (ARS). One aspect of this project is exploring the effects of a variety of moisture exposures (ambient exposure through sustained flooding) on the performance of timber connections and providing benchmark data for engineering models. In early 2020, hundreds of connection samples were prepared and inoculated with 2 decay fungi. Some testing of water-exposed connections as well as biological degradation has been completed. Some results are available while additional results and data will be available by fall 2023.

---

17   RDH Building Science, Mass Timber Building Enclosure Best Practice Design Guide V2 (2021).
18   Arijit Sinha, *Water in Mass Timber*, Oregon State University (OSU). https://tallwoodinstitute.org/water-and-mass-timber/

Moisture Management and Monitoring

Design specifications should include expectations about weather protection for stored and in situ materials during construction. A moisture management plan should be in place before construction starts, and a clear strategy should be proposed before building costs are finalized (see also chapter 6). Monitoring moisture before and during dry out with an instrument designed to measure wood MC (see **Figure 5.22**) will determine if panels are ready to be enclosed or encapsulated with other materials.

Massive panels dry at different rates than stick framing (see chapter 6 on weather and weather protection for more information); the dry-out period should also be considered in terms of both schedule and technique. Allowing wood to slowly reach moisture equilibrium mitigates potential shrinkage and checking issues, of special concern where structural wood doubles as a finished surface.

The smooth, precise look of a freshly pressed CLT panel is more likely to be preserved if MC is stable from manufacture through installation. A CLT panel is manufactured with little to no gap between each board in a lamination. If a CLT panel becomes saturated, the added moisture can cause each laminated board to swell and push against the others, although the overall panel width and length dimensions remain stable. The more significant the drop in the MC of a panel, the larger the gaps between each board—or cracks in the case of edge-glued boards. Some European-sourced panels have edge-glued boards to eliminate shrinkage gaps at each board seam. Because CLT adhesives are stronger than wood fiber bonds, shrinkage cracks then occur within boards, rather than between them, as a panel takes on and releases moisture.

Mitigation

The most effective and low-cost way for a designer to protect a wood building from moisture is through architectural detailing. Treatments or coatings add to the cost and environmental footprint of a project, so they should be used sparingly, but they may be warranted in various exposure conditions.

Proper architectural detailing, with little to no additional cost, incorporates expansion joints to allow for shrinkage, considers protection from direct moisture contact, and allows wood in place to breathe (release moisture). These details should also protect wood from exposure and contact with materials like concrete that can transfer moisture. Designers should consider that moisture is absorbed and expelled most rapidly through the wood's end-grain, and that most shrinkage happens tangentially or radially (see **Figure 5.1**).

Wood coatings can add protection against moisture and ultraviolet (UV) radiation to the completed building or during construction exposure—or both. Mass timber manufacturers often have standard temporary coatings to protect wood during transport, storage, and installation. These products should be included in the specifications for clarity and for coordination with other specified coatings. Coatings applied to encapsulate dry wood and keep it from gaining moisture from the external environment work if the coating is not compromised. Any intended cuts or scratches in a coated element create breaches that allow moisture in, while the remaining intact coat prevents drying.

Dimensional Stability

Engineered wood elements like CLT are less susceptible to in-plane moisture- and temperature-related dimensional changes than lumber or sawn timber because adhesives and multiple fiber directions hold their overall dimensions (excepting panel thickness) stable. CLT and MPP therefore have an advantage over NLT or DLT if a building is constructed during wet weather. Potential dimensional changes during construction in wet climates should always be factored into architectural and structural detailing.

Building Shrinkage

Cut wood contracts and expands differently depending on its relationship to the growth rings and the direction the fiber runs. Radial and tangential dimensions change more significantly than those in the direction of the grain. In light-wood framing, shrinkage is calculated mostly within the top and sill plates. Vertical wall studs contribute little to potential building shrinkage.

Mass timber elements will contribute to the prevention of shrinkage, depending on the detailing and the products used. CLT will contribute to shrinkage in a platform-framed building, but this effect could be avoided with a balloon-frame approach. Because shrinkage in the direction of the grain is almost negligible, shrinkage can be largely avoided with details that use end-grain to end-grain connections. For example, both the 18-story Brock Commons at the University of British Columbia (UBC), shown in **Figure 5.23**, and the 8-story Carbon12 in Portland were designed with stacked glulam columns with steel connections in between. This design has more impact in taller buildings, where the accumula-

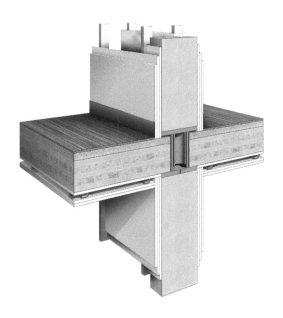

FIGURE 5.23: END-GRAIN TO END-GRAIN COLUMN CONNECTIONS MINIMIZE SHRINKAGE

Brock Commons, University of British Columbia
Source: Acton Ostry Architects

Treated wood is common for exterior wood structures such as bridges, decks, railroad ties, and telephone poles. Not all treatments are appropriate for occupied structures, as many formulas come with human health risks. Treatments come at a higher cost than coatings, but they are highly effective. Chemical changes at the cellular level may alter the composition of the wood, and in some cases, can diminish its strength. The mass timber market has few options for treated wood, owing in part to the large dimensions of mass timber components, but several testing efforts are in progress to analyze the structural performance of treated mass timber and its interactions with adhesives. Treated mass timber panels could also have insect-repellent capabilities, expanding geographic acceptance into regions with termites. With the available treatment processes, the large sizes of the panels make post-fabrication treatment impractical.

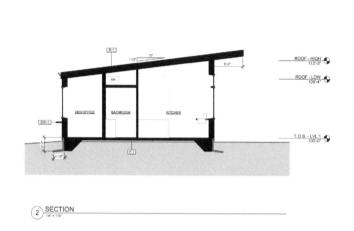

ADU FLOOR PLAN

CASE STUDY: MTG'S 3-PHASE EVALUATION SYSTEM

LOCATION: MISSOULA, MONTANA

COMPLETION DATE: FALL 2023

DEVELOPER: MASS TIMBER GROUP

ARCHITECT: MMW ARCHITECTS

STRUCTURAL ENGINEER: DCI

GENERAL CONTRACTOR: HONE BUILDERS

MASS TIMBER MANUFACTURER: VAAGEN TIMBERS

WHY ISN'T MORE mass timber used in single-family, 2- to 4-unit residential construction? Many of those reading know the benefits of mass timber, including carbon dioxide (CO_2) sequestration, sustainability, aesthetics, speed, rental/resale premiums, acoustics, and more. But ask many builders, and they'll say it's either too expensive or they don't know enough about it. Mass Timber Group (MTG) out of Missoula, Montana, wants to change that. Their solution: education, conversation, and execution.

MTG partnered with a local builder who had experience with mass timber. Yet one problem remained. Mass timber, specifically Cross-Laminated Timber (CLT), can sometimes be seen as more expensive than traditional light-frame construction when evaluated on a materials-only basis using traditional design methods. So how can an effective evaluation of mass timber be done? MTG and their mass timber team created a 3-phase Mass Timber Residential Building System to do just that.

SINGLE UNIT RENDERING

PHASE I:

Introduce, familiarize, and establish a local design/build team with whom to work. Design units for efficiency in permitting; zoning compliance; site layout; construction process, including mechanical, electrical, and plumbing (MEP) and build time; panel production; materials selection; and cost. Complete a proof-of-concept accessory dwelling unit (ADU) to show the way for other investors and developers.

PHASE II:

Modularize the designs so the number and size of units can be scaled to match the unit density at any given site, including bedroom and bathroom counts, and stackable and mirrorable units. Use the established team to scale building construction, including for 2- to 4-unit buildings.

PHASE III:

Develop a mass timber subdivision using the concepts, teams, and techniques developed in Phases I and II. Phase I is a CLT ADU design that is cost-competitive with traditional light-frame methods. At the smallest scale—and at the most expensive cost per square foot—MTG calculates a cost premium of less than 8 percent. That premium is expected to be reduced in Phase III as the size and unit count increase.

MTG's ADU is breaking ground in the summer of 2023. The entire building envelope is composed of Vaagen Timbers' CLT and glulam, sourced from sustainably managed forests using more than 85 percent restoration wood from local US Forest Service grounds. ⬤

tion of floor-to-floor shrinkage becomes a greater concern because of the greater number of floors.

5.8 PROJECT MANAGEMENT AND COORDINATION

In these early stages of the introduction of mass timber to North America, design teams need to be well educated about how to best integrate the many benefits of these products into their projects. Development teams must include architects and engineers who understand the advantages and disadvantages of these products. CLT is not simply a replacement for concrete. They have very different characteristics and design considerations.

Planning Ahead

Design-phase forward planning can result in significant improvements to construction schedules, but it requires more coordination and investment in the design process. Project managers should account for this when advising owners, determining fees, scheduling staff, and choosing consultants and software tools. More coordination time before construction starts can reduce costly field labor and project overhead costs, and it can deliver a superior product.

Design Partners

Early mechanical, electrical, and plumbing (MEP) coordination, for example, can have positive aesthetic, cost, and maintenance implications in the final building. Many traditional MEP consultants provide a diagrammatic design, intending the final layouts to be largely field coordinated. In a mass timber building, however, the structure is often substantially exposed. Thoughtfully expos-

ing utilities where necessary or desired requires working with consultants early on to consolidate utilities in carefully planned zones and to arrange for higher-quality materials in exposed areas. If penetration locations are determined before timber components are fabricated, on-site trade conflicts and installation time can be reduced. Planning for more off-site fabricated components can also improve scheduling and craftsmanship while reducing risks.

The benefits to a building owner go beyond aesthetics and construction. In the completed building, as-built reference documents will be more accurate and require fewer modifications from the original design documents. Building operations and management teams working with logical, accurate reference materials will also be more efficient and successful.

Procurement and Construction Partners

One of the unusual opportunities inherent in designing with mass timber is how it makes clear the stark advantages of an integrated design-and-build team. To produce an efficient and cost-effective mass timber design, the design team ideally works with the procurement team early in the design process to track and advise on market and supply trends as the design evolves. A building owner should be advised to use collaborative contract models that support effective prebid coordination (see also chapter 8). Working with design-build trade partners can also provide valuable continuity from early design through closeout.

Site coordination and installation approaches can impact estimated costs significantly. A general contractor who can quantify the efficiencies

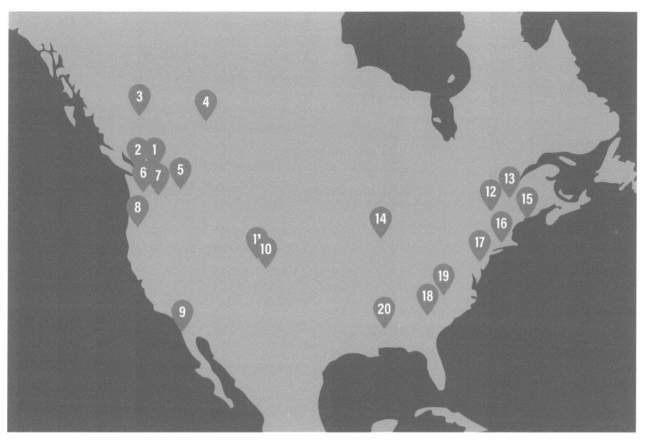

FIGURE 5.24: INDUSTRY-COLLABORATIVE WOOD RESEARCH INSTITUTIONS IN NORTH AMERICA

achieved by a modular mass timber structure will be able to advise on overall construction schedule reductions when compared with other construction techniques. Choosing a construction partner familiar with the unusual time and cost savings mass timber can offer is key to realizing those savings in early cost models or bids. Structural mass timber panel manufacturing companies often offer architectural and engineering design, modeling, project management, and construction as an integrated package. Assistance in all these functions may also be offered to clients selecting external designers and/or contractors.

Research Partners

For novel and performance-based design approaches, design teams can seek testing and research resources available through collaborative research institutions throughout North America. **Figure 5.24** and the list below identify nonprofit, building-industry supportive institutions with physical laboratory facilities and expertise in mass timber specific areas.

Northwest

1. FPInnovations (Vancouver, British Columbia)

2. University of British Columbia Timber Engineering and Applied Mechanics Laboratory (Vancouver, British Columbia)

3. University of Northern British Columbia, The Wood Innovation Research Lab (Prince George, British Columbia)

4. University of Alberta Advanced Research in Timber System (Edmonton, Alberta)

5. Washington State University Wood Materials & Engineering Laboratory (Spokane, Washington)

6. University of Washington Construction Materials Lab (Seattle, Washington)

7. APA Research Center (Tacoma, Washington)

8. Tallwood Design Institute, Oregon State University (Corvallis, Oregon) and University of Oregon (Eugene, Oregon)

Southwest

9. NEHRI Shake Table (San Diego, California)

10. Colorado School of Mines (Golden, Colorado)

11. Colorado State University (Fort Collins, Colorado)

Northeast

12. FPInnovations (Pointe-Claire, Québec)

13. Université Laval CRMR Lab (Québec, Québec)

14. Forest Products Laboratory: USDA Forest Service (Madison, Wisconsin)

15. University of Maine Advanced Structures & Composites Center (Orono, Maine)

16. UMass Amherst Wood Mechanics Lab (Amherst, Massachusetts)

17. Lehigh University (has done some testing) (Bethlehem, Pennsylvania)

Southeast

18. Clemson Wood Utilization & Design Institute (Clemson, South Carolina)

19. Virginia Tech Sustainable Biomaterials Lab (Blacksburg, Virginia)

20. Mississippi State University Department of Sustainable Bioproducts (Starkville, Mississippi)

Building Information Modeling

Building Information Modeling (BIM) is the process of creating virtual models built in 3 (and sometimes 4) dimensions, including detailed or approximated components that will make up a building. BIM models are used for coordination and collaboration across architecture, engineering, manufacturing, and construction fields. In the last decade or so, BIM programs have become standard tools for design documentation, and they have revolutionized construction coordination and "clash-detection" as well. These developments are auspiciously synchronized with the development of modular timber construction techniques. Design and construction models can often be adapted into shop drawings, facilitating communication around complex 3D-material intersections. BIM models can be highly detailed, so it is possible to have the quantities and dimensions of any building component, from conduits to fasteners to mass timber panels, determined well before it arrives on site.

Precision and Prefabrication

The precision and design control of prefabricated building components (see **Figure 5.25**) appeal to designers around the world. Prefabrication has many benefits for the construction schedule,

FIGURE 5.25: STRUCTURE DETAIL AT PREFABRICATED OFFICE BUILDING

IZM Building, CREE and Hermann Kaufmann
Source: Emily Dawson

as discussed in more detail in chapters 6 and 8. Because mass timber is inherently prefabricated, designing with it may lead to further discussions of off-site fabrication, allowing it to grow from a focus on structure into more complex systems components, full wall assemblies, or even volumetric modular spaces. A build partner familiar with these techniques will be able to quantify the benefits of working with more complex prefabricated components. A project's location and the availability of prefabrication facilities will also play a role in cost and viability.

Implications for the design team include planning for more up-front coordination and understanding connections between prefabricated elements.

Consider the extent of prefabricated components—and how they are sourced, manufactured, and procured—to estimate the amount of extra coordination required.

5.9 BUILDING CODES

Historically, common wood structural building materials and methods have been included in building codes across North America using Type IV construction. Type IV allows for the use of heavy, solid sawn timbers (6 inches and larger in vertical framing components and 8 inches and larger in horizontal components), as well as commonly available wood composites, such as glulam beams. Other construction types (I, II, III, and

V) allow for the use of wood elements in places, though additional protections may be required to increase fire resistance.

When a building material or construction method is not included in applicable building codes, any building project team desiring to use that material or method must have the building permitted using an "alternate means" or "performance" approach to demonstrate to the permitting body that the materials and methods are at least equivalent to the adopted codes for the specified use. Although common for unusual building designs of all kinds, this process can be costly, time-consuming, and difficult, and its outcome is not guaranteed. Including newly developed mass timber products and methods in building codes removes significant barriers to that product or technology's adoption in the marketplace. Although organizations in the US and Canada develop building codes at the national level—the International Code Council (ICC) and the Canadian Commission of Building and Fire Codes (CCBFC)—state/provincial and local authorities adopt these codes on different timelines, creating a patchwork effect.

In recent years, several building code changes specific to the use of wood structural components have been made at the national, state or province, and local levels.

2015 National Building Code of Canada

The 2015 National Building Code of Canada (NBC) allows wood to be used as the structural frame in buildings as tall as 6 stories for residential, office, and mixed-use occupancies. The previous version of the code allowed wood only in residential buildings, and they were limited to 4 stories. This update also recognizes mass timber

for use in podiums, considered noncombustible (NC). Two construction types are recognized in this version of the code: (1) combustible, including heavy timber, but recognized as having NC properties; and (2) NC. Updates to the NBC, developed by the CCBFC, come out every 5 years and are adopted on a province-by-province basis. Most regions in Canada have adopted the 2015 code.

2020 National Building Code of Canada

The 2020 update of the NBC was released in early 2022 and adds a new construction type: Encapsulated Mass Timber Construction (EMTC), commonly referred to as the EMTC provisions. The new code increases the maximum allowable height of mass timber structures from 6 to 12 stories. Requirements include encapsulation of structural timber with NC materials, and there are limited permissions for exposed structures.

The City of Vancouver, British Columbia, recognizes its own code authority autonomously from the province, and it has adopted the Tall Wood aspects of the 2020 NBC code. British Columbia and Alberta have allowed jurisdictions to apply for early adoption, and dozens have. Ontario has been supportive of alternative equivalent solutions for mass timber projects. Though it has not been considering early adoption, several projects over 6 stories are planned for construction in the coming year, including an 11-story project in Toronto.

2015 International Building Codes

In early 2015, the ICC adopted new codes allowing the use of CLT in buildings up to 6 stories for offices and up to 5 stories for residential. However, CLT use in taller buildings was not

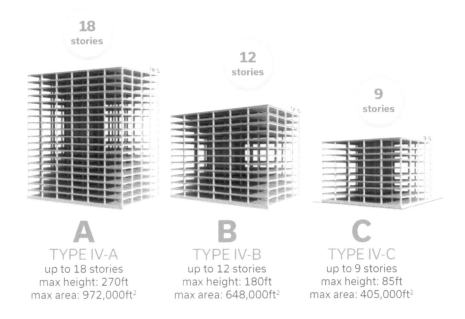

18 stories

12 stories

9 stories

A
TYPE IV-A
up to 18 stories
max height: 270ft
max area: 972,000ft²

B
TYPE IV-B
up to 12 stories
max height: 180ft
max area: 648,000ft²

C
TYPE IV-C
up to 9 stories
max height: 85ft
max area: 405,000ft²

FIGURE 5.26: TALL WOOD CONSTRUCTION TYPES ADDED TO THE 2021 IBC

Think Wood Research Brief Mass Timber 2021 Code

addressed. Because CLT is viewed as having the most competitive advantages in terms of cost and appropriateness of application in buildings that are 6 to 16 stories tall, the 2015 IBC adoption was considered only a partial improvement. IBC updates are adopted on a state-by-state basis.

2021 International Building Codes

The 2021 edition of the IBC includes major changes to Type IV construction specific to mass timber. They include provisions for the use of mass timber as a primary structural material in buildings up to 18 stories. These changes are often referred to as the "Tall Wood Provisions."

Construction Type IV was revised to IV-HT and includes 3 additional types, distinguished by fire resistance, height, and area restrictions (see **Figure 5.26**).

Type IV-HT: Maximum 6 stories, 85 feet in height, and 108,000 square feet in area. Concealed spaces are now allowed with exceptions for sprinklers, filled cavities, and protection with NC construction, such as gypsum.

Type IV-C: Maximum 9 stories, 85 feet in height, and 405,000 square feet in area, and all mass timber designed for a 2-hour fire resistance may be exposed. Concealed spaces are allowed if protected with NC construction.

Type IV-B: Maximum 12 stories, 180 feet in height, and 648,000 square feet in area. Exposed mass timber walls and ceilings are allowed with limitations, and concealed spaces are allowed if protected with NC construction.

Type IV-A: Maximum 18 stories, 270 feet in height, and 972,000 square feet in area. NC fire protection is required on all mass timber elements, and concealed spaces are allowed if protected with NC construction.

More states in the US have been adopting the Tall Wood Provisions since the 2021 IBC was released. Oregon and Washington have been leaders in the adoption of mass timber construction, proactively adopting the Tall Wood CLT Provisions in 2018. Utah adopted them in 2020, and Virginia amended the 2018 code by adding a reference to include the new types of tall mass timber construction. Maine incorporated them into the state building code in January 2021, followed by California and Georgia in July of that year. Idaho is the most recent state to approve the provisions, in 2022.

Proactive city jurisdictions have been adopting the provisions ahead of state approvals. In December 2019, Denver, Colorado, approved the new provisions for immediate use; Austin, Texas, adopted them in September 2021. In October 2021, the New York City Council approved the use of mass timber for construction of buildings of up to 85 feet tall.

Future Code Updates

The Tall Wood Provisions are a huge step for the uptake of mass timber in the US, though the extent of the encapsulation requirements is questioned as overly conservative. Because encapsulation adds cost and diminishes many of the occupant and market benefits, cost-effectiveness remains a challenge for taller wood structures. The industry regards this as an urgent area of research. Through wood innovation grants, testing to reduce the encapsulation requirements has made meaningful progress.

Following a successful fire compartment testing study performed in Sweden in 2020[19] that included technical advisory partners from around the world, the ICC 2024 Group A Code committee voted to allow 100 percent exposed ceilings in Type IV-B construction. This decision was made public in January 2022, and it will be included in the 2024 IBC.

Mass timber components are allowed in exterior wall assemblies, though only up to 40 feet (60 feet if using fire retardant-treated wood). The Tall Wood Provisions of the 2021 IBC indicate the potential to go higher with language allowing timber in exterior wall assemblies for taller buildings, but these provisions are not reconciled with limitations in other sections of the code. Testing completed in spring 2022[20] demonstrated that "it is safe to utilize CLT in an exterior wall application above 40 feet in height." The tests were performed with 3-ply CLT exposed on the interior side. The published test reports will help project teams use the material in this application before incorporation into building codes.

5.10 AUTHORITATIVE SOURCES

Table 5.2 lists various authoritative sources referenced throughout chapter 5 and where they can be found for further research. Many must be purchased. However, acquiring up-to-date versions of these guides and standards will ensure that the user has access to complete and current information.

---

19   https://www.ri.se/en/what-we-do/projects/fire-safe-implementation-of-mass-timber-in-tall-buildings
20   Timberlab et al., *Wood Innovations Grant: Cross Laminated Timber Exterior Wall Testing to NFPA 285 Test Standard* (USDA Forest Service, 2021), and https://www.fs.usda.gov/sites/default/files/TimberLab-FireSafe.pdf

STANDARD	WEBSITE
National Building Code of Canada Fire Safety Design in Buildings	http://cwc.ca/design-with-wood/building-code/
AIBC Encapsulated Mass Timber Construction up to 12 Stories	https://aibc.ca/
Mass Timber Resources, Varied	https://www.woodworks.org/design-and-tools/building-systems/mass-timberclt-code-related/
NDS for Wood Construction; NDS Supplement; Special Design Provisions for Wind; and Seismic Manual for Engineered Wood Construction	https://awc.org/codes-standards/publications/nds-2018
Nail-Laminated Timber Design and Construction Guide	https://www.thinkwood.com/products-and-systems/nail-laminated-timber
CLT Handbook-US Edition Design and Cost Optimization Checklists and Downloads	https://info.thinkwood.com/clt-handbook https://info.thinkwood.com/mass-timber-direct-2
CLT Handbook-Canadian Edition	clt.fpinnovations.ca
ANSI/APA PRG 320: Standard for Performance-Rated Cross-Laminated Timber; Glulam Product Guide; Glued-Laminated Beam Design Tables; ANSI/APA A190.1: Standard for Wood Products-Structural Glued-Laminated Timber; ANSI 405: Standard for Adhesives for Use in Structural Glued-Laminated Timber; Many more	https://www.apawood.org/resource-library
American Institute of Timber Construction: Test Methods for Structural Glued-Laminated Timber	https://www.aitc-glulam.org
CSA Standard 0177-06: Qualification Code for Manufacturers of Structural Glued-Laminated Timber	https://www.csagroup.org
International Building Code	https://www.iccsafe.org

TABLE 5.2: AUTHORITATIVE SOURCES

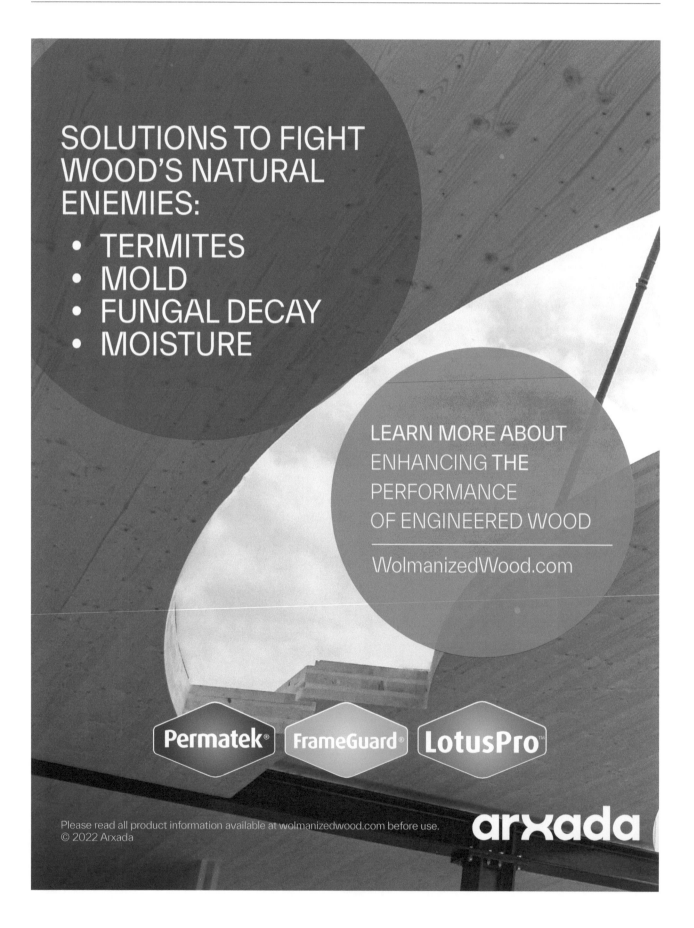

CASE STUDY: 1925 VICTORIA PARK

NAME OF PROJECT: 1925 VICTORIA PARK

OWNER: WELL GROUNDED REAL ESTATE

LOCATION: TORONTO, CANADA

COMPLETION DATE: MARCH 2024

ARCHITECT: PARTISANS

STRUCTURAL ENGINEER: ASPECT

PROJECT MANAGERS: SEROTINY AND URBAN ONE

SYSTEM PROVIDER: CREE BUILDINGS

MAJOR PARTNERS: EHSAN REZAZADEH AZAR
(TORONTO METROPOLITAN UNIVERSITY)

RENDERING OF VICTORIA PARK AVENUE
Source: Partisans

INDUSTRIAL CONSTRUCTION PROMISES efficiency through integrated delivery, yet most design, engineering, and delivery teams remain fragmented. Design-build construction that prioritizes manufacturing efficiency but relies on traditional design, procurement, and logistics processes cannot meet the holistic needs of developers, planners, underwriters, facility managers, and end users, resulting in stalled or value-engineered products.

CREE Building's hybrid-timber building system and decentralized platform allow for unusually agile implementation. Free from geographic and manufacturing constraints, development is focused on a standardized, consolidated, and integrated delivery process. Here, designers can harmonize performance, budget, and schedule from conception to production.

1925 Victoria Park is a pilot for this new type of delivery. Located in the fast-growing district of Scarborough in Toronto, the 1925 Victoria Park project is a multiunit residential complex that aims to address the growing demand for sustainable, affordable housing. Planned to start in June 2023 and be completed in March 2024, this 200,000-square-foot building includes 11-, 6-, and 5-story sections. It will provide 168 residential units. It is also intended to demonstrate the viability of a new type of sustainable development using the CREE system. Likewise, it will showcase a new system-based approach for moving modular timber-hybrid construction from a unique project mindset to a product-based system.

Logistic and element tracking remains the biggest challenge in prefab construction. In this project, instead of point-to-point (subcontractors to the site)

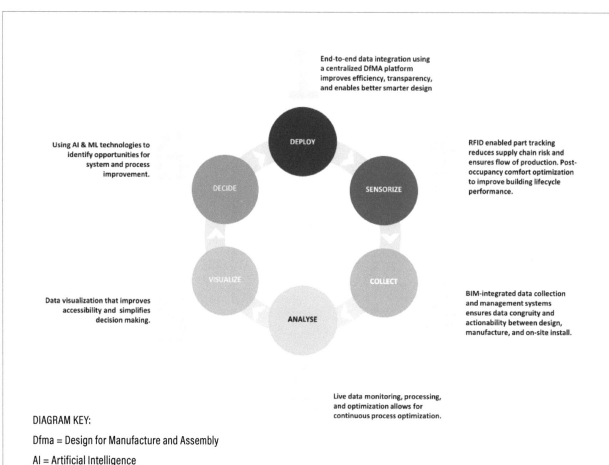

End-to-end data integration using a centralized DfMA platform improves efficiency, transparency, and enables better smarter design

RFID enabled part tracking reduces supply chain risk and ensures flow of production. Post-occupancy comfort optimization to improve building lifecycle performance.

BIM-integrated data collection and management systems ensures data congruity and actionability between design, manufacture, and on-site install.

Live data monitoring, processing, and optimization allows for continuous process optimization.

Data visualization that improves accessibility and simplifies decision making.

Using AI & ML technologies to identify opportunities for system and process improvement.

DIAGRAM KEY:

Dfma = Design for Manufacture and Assembly

AI = Artificial Intelligence

Ml = Machine Learning

(RFID and BIM are used and defined above.)

ELEMENT TRACKING WORKFLOW
Source: Serotiny

delivery, the proposed approach streamlines supply chains and logistics through a central storage and processing hub. Enabled by radio-frequency identification (RFID) tags on elements, this hub receives modular building elements from different suppliers, sorts them based on the assembly sequence, and sends them in the correct order to the project.

This way, the project can implement a lean construction strategy with effective delivery of the modular elements. This approach requires an integrated delivery information system that tracks all the elements from manufacturing to installation in real time. The system enables optimization of storage and delivery of the elements to the jobsite and can enhance the use of cranes and installation crews. Cranes can pick elements from delivery trucks and lift them to the installation position. The envisioned information system is integrated with a Building Information Modeling (BIM) platform to improve central processing and visualization of the progress of the elements' delivery and installation.

1925 Victoria Park is a pilot for the future—making sustainability affordable. Here, the product is not necessarily the building but its delivery process. ○

Photo Credit: Joe Aker, Aker Imaging

CASE STUDY: SAN JACINTO COLLEGE ANDERSON-BALL CLASSROOM BUILDING

LOCATION: PASADENA, TEXAS

COMPLETION DATE: FEBRUARY 2022

OWNER/DEVELOPER: SAN JACINTO COLLEGE

ARCHITECT: KIRKSEY ARCHITECTURE

STRUCTURAL ENGINEER: WALTER P MOORE

MECHANICAL, ELECTRICAL, AND PLUMBING: DBR

CIVIL ENGINEER: DUPLANTIS DESIGN GROUP

MASS TIMBER CONSULTANT: FAST + EPP

TECHNOLOGY: DATACOM DESIGN GROUP

LANDSCAPE: KUDELA & WEINHEIMER

MASS TIMBER MANUFACTURER: NORDIC STRUCTURES

THE NEW SAN Jacinto Anderson-Ball Classroom Building is a 122,000-square-foot mass timber structure on the district's central campus. The classroom building supports engineering, mathematics, college preparatory, and early high school learning students. The 3-story building is constructed of mass timber manufactured from black spruce trees from Canada, except for steel bracing used for lateral support, making it one of the first mass timber buildings in the greater Houston area. It is also the nation's largest mass timber academic building on a college campus.

The decision to use a mass timber structural system was primarily based on cost savings. At the time of the early design, the cost of steel was unstable and fluctuating frequently. Ongoing national discussions about steel tariffs were underway, and steel costs with trading partners around the world were rising. Wood prices had been stable for decades, and efficiencies in mass timber components and

Photo Credits: Joe Aker, Aker Imaging

fabrication made sense from an economic standpoint. The client chose mass timber as a way to neutralize the risk involved in purchasing one of the larger material components of the project.

A mass timber structural system is fairly rigid. At the onset of design, the project team focused on keeping corridors as open as possible to ensure long expanses of exposed wood. At the same time, understanding that the mechanical system would take lots of space throughout, the team agreed that limiting the exposed wood in each classroom was acceptable as long as all the building utilities could freely run within a drop-down plenum space. Beams and the framing system were designed to run parallel to the utility runs; and where piping, conduits, and ducts needed to cross wood beams, the engineering team worked through the Computer Numerical Control (CNC)-cut openings to ensure clear pathways. In addition, the lobby structure incorporated a 2-column, 2-beam system in lieu of the typical 1-column, 1-beam solution to provide greater design interest. This unusual feature allowed more wood

to be exposed and provided a space to conceal the fire sprinkler lines and electrical conduits.

Exposing as much wood as possible within the code limitations was a priority. Designers created a detailed lobby space inspired by Japanese detailing, notching double columns and beams. While the double column/double notched beam draws the visitor's eyes, the design creates a void, or dark space, for lighting system connections and fire suppression pipes—doing away with the typical distracting features.

The incorporation of a "hanging" ramp using large glulam beams that connect the new building to the older existing building creates a bit of drama in the simply designed lobby.

A further design moment occurs at the monument stair connecting the first and second floors. This feature was created using custom-made glulam timber beams anchored by a Y column at the midway landing. The designs of these community spaces emphasize the mass timber structure and put its beauty on display. ⏺

CHAPTER 6: BUILDERS

Mass timber is a disruptive technology with respect to building construction, with increased off-site fabrication and highly collaborative construction approaches. The necessity of these approaches is a result of the size and weight of the structural components, precluding significant modifications at the construction site. As such, many contractors will find the information in chapter 5 relevant as teams become more integrated, optimizing the design, schedule, and costs together in real time.

Prefabricated mass timber panels are typically made to order once the project's architectural and engineering design is complete and construction site logistics are understood and integrated. This naturally puts a high premium on integration of the design, manufacturing, and construction aspects of the project, relying on tight collaboration of all parties from the start and creating an incentive for vertical integration of companies along the supply chain.

GLOBAL PERSPECTIVE

 Building codes, construction practices, and even the structures of the building industries themselves vary greatly around the globe. The variations are perhaps too great to make a comprehensive comparison with the equally diverse situation in the United States. But two aspects related to the perceived and real barriers to building with mass timber may be worth noting: one is the availability of a qualified and well-trained workforce that the mass-timber panel industry desperately needs. The other is the mechanisms available to industries at national level for removing structural barriers, and implementing new codes, standards, rules, and guidelines.

Many European countries, though not all by far, have long run apprenticeship programs, and vocational and technical schools supported by their respective states. These rigorous programs promote a culture of meticulous craftsmanship, and enjoy the respect of industries that absorb graduates into their employee ranks with limited on-the-job training. The value of such systems is clear to anyone trying to imagine on-the-job training for a Computer Numerical Control (CNC) machinist or similar jobs that require rare and sophisticated skill sets. The shortage of highly skilled, job-ready personnel in the mass-timber industry in the US may be explained to some extent by the absence of such systems.

Another difference between the US and many other mass-timber panel producing countries is that dot-com and dot-gov are more trusting of each other, for historical and cultural reasons. Although volumes may be written about costs and benefits of governments' greater involvement in the marketplace, a much closer working relationship between industries and their respective governments might go a long way toward removing structural barriers and systematic inefficiencies. It could also create incentives, facilitate imaginative partnerships, smooth out inherent risks, and help implement codes and standards that are supportive of the mass timber industry internally and internationally. The effectiveness of such actions is, of course, a matter of the competence of the governments involved.

These observations may help create an understanding of the differences between the US business environment and that of many other

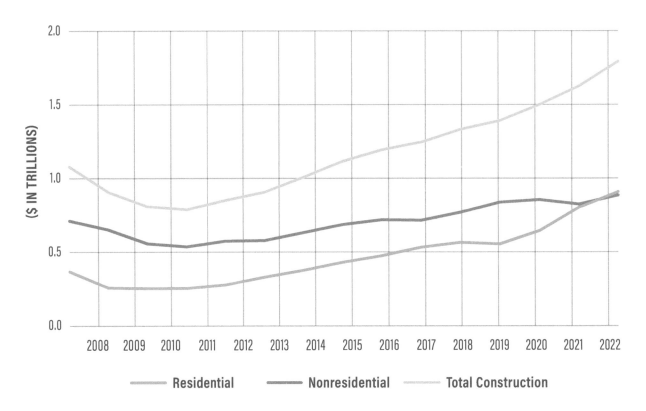

FIGURE 6.1: ANNUAL VALUE OF ALL CONSTRUCTION, 2008 TO 2021 ($ IN TRILLIONS)

Source: https://www.census.gov/construction/c30/historical_data.html

mass timber-producing countries, but it is very hard to imagine a cultural or political change along these lines transforming the US any time soon. Do not hold your breaths.

6.1 MARKET CONTEXT

Construction Value

FIGURE 6.1 shows the value of all construction in the United States, per US Census Bureau data. The data is categorized by building use as either nonresidential or residential. The annual value of all construction was $1.8 trillion in 2022, a healthy increase of about 10 percent from 2021. See section 8.1 for broader market insights related

to inflation, labor, and supply chain issues. While residential construction has typically accounted for 30 percent to 40 percent of total US construction values in the last 14 years, it jumped to nearly 50 percent during the COVID-19 pandemic, and in 2022 exceeded 50%. Most residential construction is wood-based, and around one-third of all mass timber projects are residential (see also the Market Development section in Chapter 8).

6.2 WOOD AS A CONSTRUCTION MATERIAL

Compared to steel and concrete, the other 2 primary construction materials, wood is unusually strong in both tension and compression for its weight, and it is the only innately renewable struc-

FIGURE 6.2: LIGHT FRAME WOOD BUILDING
Source: APA – The Engineered Wood Association

tural material with a significant market presence. The structural properties of timber result from trees evolving to carry substantial crown loads and to resist swaying in the wind. These properties make wood highly effective for dynamic loading and fatigue as well. As such, wood has a high potential for resilience—uncompromised recovery—as a structural material under strong gravity loads, as well as seismic and wind loads. Three types of wood construction are reviewed here: light frame, traditional heavy timber, and mass timber.

Light Frame

This type of construction, also known as "stick frame," is the most common construction method for residential buildings in North America. Light wood-frame construction can be panelized for a prefabricated construction approach, and it can be combined with mass timber in a hybrid structural system. It is also widely used in low- and mid-rise commercial buildings. For lateral resistance and spanning between "sticks," Engineered Wood Products (EWPs) such as plywood or Oriented Strand Board (OSB) sheathing are commonly used (see **Figure 6.2**).

FIGURE 6.3: POST AND BEAM BUILDING
Source: Nordic Structures

The advantages of this building system are low cost, and ease and speed of assembly. Lumber, plywood, OSB, and other wooden building materials are readily available and relatively inexpensive. Workers can move the building materials around a jobsite with relative ease compared to larger and bulkier materials such as steel beams, and they can use relatively inexpensive, lightweight tools. Lumber and structural panels arrive on the construction site in bulk, and the standard sizes are cut to fit the design at the site, meaning that the design may be adjusted until the framing is complete. All these factors contribute to the widespread use of this construction type for buildings that have lower fire-resistance requirements.

A disadvantage of light wood-frame construction is the amount of waste generated on-site, increasing the cost of in-place materials. Of all the building styles discussed here, light wood-frame carries the highest risk of fire damage.

Heavy Timber

Heavy timber is another traditional method of wood construction, often referred to as "post and beam." In this construction style, large timbers form vertical columns, and horizontal beams are connected either with wooden joinery or metal connectors (see **Figure 6.3**). A key implication of this design is that the columns bear the building's weight, meaning the walls are not load-bearing.

Because the timber columns and beams bear the weight, post and beam construction offers greater design flexibility and allows customized and open floor plans. Another advantage is quick completion of the structure. Many post and beam

FIGURE 6.4: A CLT AND GLULAM MASS TIMBER OFFICE BUILDING
First Tech Federal Credit Union, Hillsboro, Oregon; Source: Swinerton Builders

designs leave the large dimension beams and columns exposed, for many consumers find the natural warmth and elegance of exposed wood surfaces appealing. In addition, the mass and size of these timbers provides fire resistance.

Mass Timber

Mass timber (see **Figure 6.4**) refers to engineered wood members that offer a high level of fire resistance because of their size. (See chapter 1 for definitions of the many types of components that fall into this category.) Up to this point, most mass timber buildings in North America have been low- to mid-rise. However, US building code changes enacted by the International Code Council (ICC) have been incorporated into the 2021 International Building Code (IBC) to include buildings up to 18 stories (270 feet). Canada has also developed the Tall Wood Provisions. For more details, and for information on regional adoptions of these codes, see chapter 5. The benefits and challenges of mass timber construction are explored in detail in the remainder of this chapter.

6.3 PRECONSTRUCTION

When mass timber started making headway as a building material in North America, few building contractors were experienced in expanding what had been the post and beam, heavy timber paradigm. New mass timber technologies necessitated a fresh approach.

Educating building contractors about the best practices for planning and bidding a mass timber building is an identified industry need. A 2017 report[1] by the British Columbia Construction Association (BCCA), for example, identified barriers to innovation as they relate to using mass timber in buildings. Many barriers were identified, including these:

- lack of transparency in the procurement process

- issues over responsibility and allocation of risk

- lack of clear leadership to ensure that construction is properly planned using a design-led approach

- procurement models that inadvertently promote an adversarial relationship among parties

- building contractors who may not be familiar with best practices for managing and mitigating such risks as they pertain to mass timber, including contracted provisions for weather protection, lifting and storing materials, and fire protection

Each of these barriers is related to a paradigm shift in construction that enforces integration of the design, manufacturing, and construction processes. Integration challenges traditional procurement processes and standard allocation of risks and responsibility. A panel manufacturer might include project management, design, and construction in their scope of work, for instance. These integrated approaches offering solutions akin to a turnkey package may create conflicts with parties bidding for individual parts.

Because of the urgent need to train construction teams in the US, WoodWorks has published resources to help guide contractors on the particularities of bidding, planning, and constructing with mass timber.[2] With partners nationwide, WoodWorks also offers workshops on mass timber project management and training in installation.

To bid and plan mass timber projects successfully, build team members should familiarize themselves with key considerations, such as project optimization during design and procurement, digital tools like Building Information Modeling (BIM) and Computer Numerical Control (CNC) technology, and the use of prefabricated components.

Optimize during Design

A custom mass timber package can save significant field costs, but only if the design and procurement/build teams work together as early as possible in the design process. Traditional procurement processes are a barrier to early collaboration among designers, builders, and manufacturers. A property owner considering a mass timber building should choose a procurement process that supports the close collaboration required for the best value outcome (also see chapter 8). In some cases, the realization of the advantages of integrated "building production" processes led to the vertical integration of traditionally separate functions within one company. An alternative is an alliance of partners with know-how and a history of collaboration.

---

1   British Columbia Construction Association, *Procuring Innovation in Construction: A Review of Models, Processes, and Practices* (2017), https://www.naturallywood.com/wp-content/uploads/procuring-innovation-in-construction_report_bcca.pdf

2   WoodWorks, *Mass Timber Construction Manual* (October 2021).

CASE STUDY: HOLDEN'S REPRODUCIBLE SINGLE-FAMILY HOMES

CASE STUDY: MINKA ADU + SFR

LOCATION: KANSAS CITY, KANSAS

OWNER/DEVELOPER: HOLDEN CO.

ARCHITECTURAL DESIGN: HOLDEN CO.

STRUCTURAL ENGINEER: ACORN PROJECTS

MASS TIMBER MANUFACTURER: VAAGEN TIMBERS

HOLDEN CO. WANTS to bring about an evolution in housing, holding that current construction methods are antiquated, lack efficiency, and fail to consider the ecological effects. When Holden considered alternative materials, it chose mass timber as the core element of its four designs. COVE, DOMO, SAIL, and MINKA feature glulam beams and posts, along with Cross-Laminated Timber

(CLT) walls, floors, and ceiling panels. In keeping with Holden's commitment to use renewable materials, the designs also feature wood fiber insulation.

Mass timber provides the following benefits:

· Prefabricated panels mean more precision, a faster build, and less on-site labor.

· Mass timber and other renewable materials make the finished product more sustainable and friendly to the environment, especially through carbon sequestration and zero waste.

· Using biophilic design principles, exposed wood is not only beautiful; it also benefits people's health and well-being.

Holden aims to bring forth a product that streamlines the entire construction process, improves the human condition, and creates the ability to build

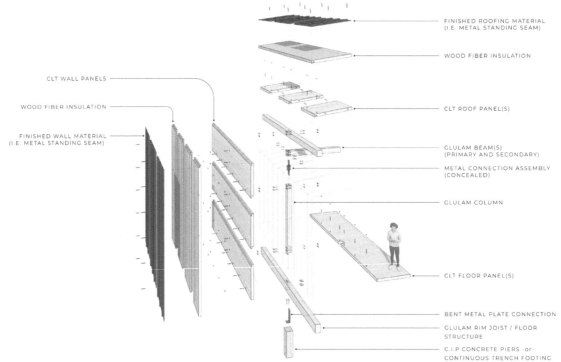

FINISHED ROOFING MATERIAL (I.E. METAL STANDING SEAM)

WOOD FIBER INSULATION

CLT ROOF PANEL(S)

GLULAM BEAM(S) (PRIMARY AND SECONDARY)

METAL CONNECTION ASSEMBLY (CONCEALED)

GLULAM COLUMN

CLT FLOOR PANEL(S)

BENT METAL PLATE CONNECTION

GLULAM RIM JOIST / FLOOR STRUCTURE

C.I.P CONCRETE PIERS -or- CONTINUOUS TRENCH FOOTING

CLT WALL PANELS

WOOD FIBER INSULATION

FINISHED WALL MATERIAL (I.E. METAL STANDING SEAM)

anywhere. Holden is working with Vaagen Timbers, a mass timber pioneer, to bring its innovative design, MINKA, to an urban patchwork in Kansas City.

MINKA, which means "house of the people," is equal parts geometric expression and tectonic evolution, for it reevaluates and reinterprets the construction process. MINKA is an all-encompassing look at what it takes to build a reproducible single-family home with mass timber. This project is expected to break ground in the spring of 2023. ⬤

Forest Service
U.S. DEPARTMENT OF AGRICULTURE

Expanding Mass Timber Market Opportunities

Talk to us about getting your mass timber project from the drawing board to market. Our Wood Innovations team manages grants and provides technical expertise to assist in realizing the full potential of the growing demand for mass timber construction. Our Forest Products Lab provides wood product research. The USDA Forest Service is here for you.

USDA Forest Service Wood Innovations Program and Forest Products Lab

• Innovation Grants support design and engineering, development of U.S.-sourced timber, and U.S. manufacturing of mass timber and other wood products

• Research on Building and Fire Science, Sustainability and Life Cycle Assessments

Contact Us
fs.usda.gov
fpl.fs.fed.us

🔵 @forestservice
🔵 @USForestService
🔵 @fsWoodLab

Photo Credits (from top to bottom)
Vaagen Timbers
Albina Yard: Jeremy Bittermann courtesy LEVER Architecture
CLT Fire Testing: USFS
Building construction: LEVER Architecture
After harvest: Vaagen Timbers

Each manufacturer has specific efficiencies and limitations that should be worked into the design and logistics plans. Optimizing the design and erection process balances the premium costs of early planning, higher-unit-cost materials, and prefabrication. Early communication among the design, manufacturing, and construction teams can also lead to efficiencies offered by available component sizes, prefabrication, and high-precision CNC finishing. If layout and detail optimization begin later in the process, such as during bidding, significant redesign may be required to achieve an on-budget package. Performing design work during the construction phase creates cost and schedule risks; one of the biggest cost advantages of the mass timber construction approach is a dramatic reduction of these risks.

A successful cost model is necessary to begin construction, but the benefits of early coordination go far beyond that. Efficient field coordination is where schedule benefits are realized, and a savvy contractor will amplify the structural coordination benefits into other trades as well. A high level of coordination during design, for example, was an essential part of the construction-phase success of Carbon12, the 8-story mass timber building in Portland, Oregon. The project team chose a design-build approach, allowing significant time for mechanical, electrical, plumbing, and fire (MEPF) system coordination with the Cross-Laminated Timber (CLT) package. Along with optimizing the structure, the MEPF penetrations were also reduced by careful consideration from an installation-sequencing standpoint. A sequencing plan ensured trades were not in conflict during installation, leading to the subcontractors "working together like a well-oiled machine."[3]

This high level of coordination and early involvement of integrated design, fabrication, and construction teams are often offered as part of a package by seasoned mass timber panel companies in Europe, Australia, and New Zealand, and/or by contracting companies specializing in mass timber panel construction.

For best practices for early coordination, Wood-Works has created mass timber cost and design optimization checklists to assist project teams.[4]

Quantifying Cost Savings

There are many reasons that mass timber buildings can be less costly than other construction types. Cost estimating, however, is traditionally based on a wealth of data from past projects, and few contractors in North America have a portfolio of mass timber data to draw from yet. Early estimates that are not holistically coordinated with the design, procurement, and logistics teams will be less accurate.

One of the most quantifiable ways to estimate the difference, and one that will have many ripple effects on cost for the building owner, is through the schedule. Mass timber construction is quicker, uses lighter equipment, and has less on-site labor than a comparable building of steel or concrete. Thus, fewer resources are required for a shorter period.

---

3   www.buildingCarbon12.com
4   https://www.woodworks.org/wp-content/uploads/wood_solution_paper-Mass-Timber-Design-Cost-Optimization-Checklists.pdf

Identical buildings are rarely constructed using different structural materials, so apples-to-apples cost comparisons are also rare. Cost comparisons between structural materials may be made, but they are based on plans and estimates, not on actual construction costs. Developers often want to test different structural materials for the same project and then do a comparative cost analysis. In this process, when high-unit-cost items are flagged for replacement with lower-cost materials, mass timber is often eliminated. Looking holistically at estimated schedule impacts is crucial when comparing mass timber with other building materials. Just as important is considering materials reductions throughout the building, such as reduced foundation and excavation costs, and the elimination of drywall, framing, and painting of exposed wood surfaces.

Procurement

The advantages of contractor involvement in project planning include adding valuable insight into material availability. The number of mass timber manufacturers in North America is increasing every year, but available capacity can still vary greatly depending on regional project demands. This supply-and-demand pressure will continue to shift as the market matures, more facilities come online, and mass timber building designs become more common. Establishing a rough timeline with a manufacturer well in advance of breaking ground will ensure a project meets delivery expectations and avoids the high cost of storing massive elements between fabrication and construction. One often-overlooked aspect driving lead time is the custom detailing work the manufacturer needs to do during production. Selecting and engaging with a manufacturer early on can help ensure that the planning team has plenty of time to coordinate and approve shop drawings.

While engineered mass timber components are custom products, they are composed of wood fiber that is subject to the fluctuations of a commodity market. Wood fiber prices can change from week to week, playing a part in estimating and timing orders.

BIM and CNC

Mass timber, BIM, and CNC (see chapter 5 for more information) are coming of age together, a synergy that is contributing to the exponential uptake of mass timber technologies. The planning and coordination required for reducing on-site construction time through prefabrication is well supported by a collaborative virtual building model that feeds information directly to the manufacturing equipment. BIM's potential to streamline coordination through design, manufacturing, and construction is developing rapidly.

Integrated procurement models are also becoming more common. Procurement barriers discussed in other chapters can limit early coordination for nonintegrated teams, but BIM is also a relatively new technology, and all parties involved are still becoming accustomed to an integrated modeling process. A traditional building contract can also benefit from BIM at all stages.

The most common and effective way to use BIM for mass timber coordination is for the architectural, structural, and MEPF designers to create intersecting three-dimensional (3D) models. These 3D models can also be shared with the mass timber manufacturer to create shop drawings for fabrication. Leading mass timber companies and specialized construction companies working with mass timber panels also use BIM for coordinating construction and optimizing sequencing of construction and building finishing jobs.

Using BIM to coordinate a mass timber project can be as straightforward as the timber manufacturer using computer-aided design (CAD) files from designers to model components for the CNC machine that will cut each panel to precise specifications. The process often reaches higher levels of sophistication and can involve each member of the design and build team, depending on the skills of the team and the objectives of the project. Possibilities include detailing down to the level of fasteners, using the model for materials takeoffs and ordering, clash detection (a digital analysis of potential field conflicts) for all building systems, and modeling for prefabrication of each building component. This up-front coordination avoids major adjustments of massive components on the construction site, when adding even small cuts to address unforeseen conflicts with other systems can be laborious and costly. The on-site construction activity should be treated, in these cases, more like the assembly of a kit-of-parts. The confluence of BIM and mass timber is leading to increasing conversations about the potential of fabricating more—and more complex—components off-site.

6.4 PREFABRICATION

Successful projects that maximize prefabrication are pushing the building industry to reconsider project delivery. The Modular Building Institute estimates that modular construction projects reduce construction schedules by 30 to 50 percent.[5] Modularizing an entire structural system has

benefits for on-site safety, schedule efficiencies, and precision, appealing broadly to installers, building owners, and designers. In this way, mass timber has become a catalyst for prefabrication in North America, following diverse and successful European precedents.

The potential for off-site fabrication is huge, but facilities are limited in North America. The most common approach is component-based, where large, complex, precise elements are manufactured off-site and set in place, reducing off- and on-site buffer storage needs, installation time, and overall schedules. Flat-pack wall systems and volumetric strategies are designed to install multiple interacting materials, utilities, and finishes in a climate-controlled interior environment. The benefits include a higher level of quality control and very fast on-site erection times. Whatever the approach, local jurisdictional inspection requirements, transportation limitations, and shipping and handling expenses should be considered. These added costs should be weighed against the potential efficiencies of the design, fabrication, construction, and at times, potential aesthetic impact.

Large-scale timber components typically arrive on site in stacks organized for rapid erection of walls and floors. Because a crane is necessary to move these large components into place, the design and build teams can take advantage of the investment and look for opportunities to fabricate time-consuming building elements into larger components, such as facades or mechanical systems. This is especially true for sites where transportation and labor costs are high or lay-down

---

5   https://www.modular.org/what-is-modular-construction/

FIGURE 6.5: PRECISION COMPONENTS QUICKLY ASSEMBLED ON A CONSTRAINED SITE

Project One, San Francisco, California, Gurnet Point Construction, DCI Engineers, Freres Lumber Co.

and staging space is minimal, such as remote locations or constrained urban sites.

Prefabrication and a design-build partnership were key to the significant schedule savings realized at the 4-story residential building Project One (see **Figure 6.5**). Located on a site in San Francisco with no lay-down area, the building's original structural framing schedule was estimated at 3 months. Using precision-fabricated Mass Plywood Panel (MPP) components for the floors and roof, and panelized light framed walls and moment frames, the structure was completed on budget in just 24 working days. [6] The design-build

team worked closely with the MPP manufacturer on design coordination and delivery, and the owner deemed the approach a huge success.

When MEPF penetrations are precisely located, as with a coordinated BIM process, many components can be fabricated off-site and installed directly in-place. Improved planning results in fewer trade conflicts on-site, whether or not additional off-site construction is part of those trades' strategies. Maximizing prefabrication can also lead to a rapid sequencing of other trades' critical path components that is able to keep up with—

6   Information from Freres Lumber Co. Inc.

FIGURE 6.6: PREFABRICATED FACADE PANELS FOLLOW CLOSELY BEHIND STRUCTURAL FRAMING

Brock Commons, University of British Columbia; Source: Ralph Austin at Seagate Structures

and take advantage of—the speed of mass timber structural erection.

Brock Commons, an 18-story student residence hall at the University of British Columbia (UBC) in Vancouver, was erected at 2 floors per week, following the concrete foundation and cores. The CLT and glulam levels were closely followed by a panelized timber facade (see **Figure 6.6**), providing immediate weather protection and savings in on-site scaffolding, time, labor, and risk. In fall 2017, only 66 days from when the first panels arrived on-site, the building was structurally topped out and enclosed.

A modular building approach naturally leads to less time on-site, cutting down on construction-related disruptions such as increased traffic, lane closures, and noise. Smaller crews require fewer parking spaces, and reduced or eliminated field modifications make for a quiet site. Large structural components delivered in predetermined sequences can be off-loaded relatively quickly and immediately set in place, with fewer overall deliveries. In Europe, where urban site constraints frequently have high impacts on construction approaches, mass timber has been found to reduce structural site deliveries by as much as 80 percent. Plus, less lay-down space is needed when installation coincides with just-in-time delivery.

FIGURE 6.7: ASSEMBLING PREFABRICATED COMPONENTS IN A FACTORY SETTING

Source: Katerra; Photo Credit: Kristopher Grunert

Relocation of Labor

Increased prefabrication of building components has excellent implications for the workforce. In a study of 100 mass timber buildings in the United Kingdom, Waugh Thistleton Architects found a 50 to 70 percent reduction in site staff for structural framing. In Oregon, the 38,000-square-foot Carbon12 required only 4 carpenters for the 10-week duration of structural erection for all 8 stories. When more labor takes place at a manufacturing facility (see **Figure 6.7**), on-site construction crews become smaller (see **Figure 6.8**).

Safety

In a factory setting, the hazards experienced on a construction site are dramatically reduced. Worker safety is improved, and the likelihood of

FIGURE 6.8: A SMALL FRAMING CREW GUIDES PANEL PLACEMENT

Source: The Canyons; Photo Credit: Marcus Kauffman, Oregon Department of Forestry

accidents decreases by about half. According to research from University of Utah, "By moving to prefabrication, the construction industry and its workers can experience a much safer environment by a factor of 2."[7]

Climate Control

In some climates, harsh conditions are not only challenging for human health but also limit the hours available for construction. A framing crew working in a hot climate, for example, will arrive on-site as early in the day as possible to avoid noon sun exposure, possibly conflicting with local noise ordinances. Prolonged exposure to extreme conditions, as on an unshaded or freezing jobsite, stresses human health and increases safety risks. Controlled temperatures, air quality, noise, and light levels can be provided in an interior environment. Such conditions are healthier and safer for long-term work, and they open jobs to more candidates.

Commute

Construction workers who commute to a jobsite are at the mercy of the project location and its distance from their home and community. Some remote jobsites require temporary accommodations, and laborers travel home only for weekends. Long and always-changing commutes are challenging for families and workers, and they must sacrifice family time, sleep, or other healthy habits.

Ergonomics

For repetitive tasks, a factory can provide more ergonomically designed support. A work surface, for example, can be set at a comfortable height for tasks that might require kneeling on-site.

Diversity

Because of the factors cited above, factory environments make jobs more accessible to women, people with health concerns or disabilities, and older workers. Diversity within a company has many proven benefits, including increased productivity, creativity, engagement, and profit, and reduced turnover. The benefits ripple beyond projects and companies into healthier, more sustainable communities.

Skills and Training

In a factory producing complex building components, greater opportunities exist for a wide range of skill sets. A mass timber manufacturing facility will have positions that require little training, as well as positions that require high-level skills with more earning potential. Unskilled workers are more easily supervised and represent less risk in a controlled facility than on a construction site. Skilled labor might range from craft and finish work to operating computer-aided equipment (like a CNC machine) to coordinating BIM processes with external design teams. "[T]he prefabrication architecture laborer is much more skilled than any mass-production laborer in previous generations, moving to more intellectual, computer, or even management tasks."[8] Such a range of job opportunities supports diverse communities—especially beneficial in rural communities with limited job options.

---

7   Ryan E. Smith, *Prefab Architecture* (2010), 86.
8   Ryan E. Smith, *Prefab Architecture* (2010), 87.

FIGURE 1: SHOWCASING THE TIMBER AT STREET LEVEL AND AT THE TERRACES ABOVE ENSURES
THAT EVERYONE CAN EXPERIENCE THE INVITING, BEAUTIFUL, AND NATURAL MATERIAL.
Source: Andrew Keithly Photography

CASE STUDY: 1030 MUSIC ROW

NAME OF PROJECT: 1030 MUSIC ROW

OWNER: PANATTONI DEVELOPMENT COMPANY

LOCATION: NASHVILLE, TENNESSEE

COMPLETION DATE: SPRING 2022

ARCHITECT: ANECDOTE, FORMERLY KNOWN AS TUCK-HINTON ARCHITECTURAL + DESIGN

GENERAL CONTRACTOR: TURNER CONSTRUCTION

STRUCTURAL ENGINEER (SUPERSTRUCTURE): STRUCTURECRAFT

STRUCTURAL ENGINEER (CONCRETE): EMC

MASS TIMBER DESIGN/BUILDER: STRUCTURECRAFT

1030 MUSIC ROW is one of the first mass timber projects in Tennessee, and it showcases the building material's versatility and sustainability. During the height of the pandemic, 1030 Music Row was designed and built for the creative office market in Nashville's Music Row. It now offers its occupants a creative and collaborative biophilic space.

The 5-story mass timber office building has a 5-story parking garage. Its 20-foot-by-30-foot glulam beam and column grid support Dowel-Laminated Timber (DLT) panels with 3-inch concrete; the lateral bracing system is a structural steel core. The elevator shaft was built with a fully exposed, 2-hour rated, Cross-Laminated Timber (CLT) wall panel.

FIGURE 2: THE STEEL CORE ACTS AS THE LATERAL BRACING SYSTEM, SAVING SIGNIFICANT CONSTRUCTION TIME COMPARED TO A TRADITIONAL CONCRETE OR CMU CORE.
Source: Big Acorn Studios

FIGURE 3: INHERENTLY, 2-BY-8 DLT HAS A 38 SOUND TRANSMISSION CLASS (STC) RATING. BUT WITH THE ADDITION OF A ¾-INCH ACOUSTI-MAT AND 3-INCH TOPPING SLAB, THE STC CAN EXCEED 50. THAT HELPS MITIGATE NOISE FROM ABOVE AND FORMS A CREATIVE SPACE FOR SINGERS AND SONGWRITERS.
Source: Andrew Keithly Photography

Mass timber—as part of biophilic design—increases people's overall psychological, physical, and cognitive well-being. Special attention was given to the intersection of wood and concrete beginning at Level 1, allowing the timber building to float over the base. The wood creates warm, comfortable, and visually appealing interior and exterior spaces.

1030 Music Row's facade is designed with a unitized curtain wall to improve overall envelope integrity, and the glass skin shows off the warm timber interiors. All the glass was tinted to reduce glare and help with solar heat gain while still contributing to the well-being of the occupants and supplying as much natural light as possible. Energy costs—including lighting, heating, and cooling—are reduced, and all floors have access to open-air terraces.

A key structural aspect of 1030 Music Row is its core system. Instead of using traditional concrete or concrete masonry unit (CMU) shear walls, the building uses a structural steel core with bracing to resist the lateral loads. Crews installed the steel frame concurrent with the timber, allowing construction to be completed much faster and with a smaller construction crew than when using traditional methods.

The warmth and clean aesthetics of the wood make finishes within the space unnecessary, reducing overall cost to the space's user and reducing future material waste. After the building's life span is complete, the mass timber can be recycled as something else because it's bolted together rather than welded. There is no need to demolish it and put it in a landfill.

Total embodied carbon with mass timber construction is less than that of a structure made of concrete or steel. Additionally, when wood is grown, it absorbs up to 2 tons of carbon dioxide (CO_2) from the atmosphere, creating up to 1 ton of its own dry mass. Mass timber is typically constructed off-site, reducing emissions on-site by about 20 percent. It also uses 30 times less water to produce than reinforced concrete. 🔘

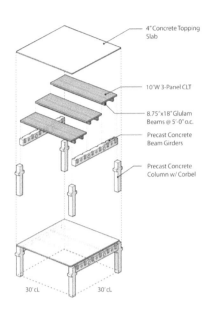

4" Concrete Topping Slab

10'W 3-Panel CLT

8.75"x18" Glulam Beams @ 5'-0" o.c.

Precast Concrete Beam Girders

Precast Concrete Column w/ Corbel

30'cL   30'cL

ABOVE AND RIGHT — FIGURE 6.9: COMPOSITE TIMBER AND PRECAST CONCRETE STRUCTURE

Adidas North American Headquarters, Portland, Oregon
Source: Lever Architecture and Turner Construction

6.5 PRECISION AND CONNECTIONS

Custom-engineered timber components are very precise, with tolerances in the range of $\frac{1}{16}$ inch. They must be fully coordinated in advance to ensure no field modifications are necessary. Interfaces between mass timber components and other building materials should be identified and proper tolerances allowed for in the design details. Designers should identify where greater levels of precision are most crucial, and contractors can advise on where constructability issues may arise.

Installation conflicts can be reduced or eliminated through close advance coordination of fabrication. Constructability analyses for tolerances are especially important at frequently repeated intersections. A thorough analysis can result in

huge risk reductions by avoiding the multiplying effect of repetitive field modifications. Recurring details are also an important opportunity to optimize the sequencing of the build to find schedule and cost savings.

Attention to tolerances at common material interfaces like timber/concrete and timber/steel is crucial to project success. Options for achieving required fire-resistance ratings where material

FIGURE 6.10: CLT WALL AND ROOF
PANELS WITH STEEL FRAMING

Lincoln City Police Department, Oregon
Source: Swinerton Builders

FIGURE 6.11: CLT FLOOR DECKS WITH STEEL FRAMING

Brentwood Public Library, Brentwood, California
Source: Holmes Structures
Photo Credit: Blake Marvin Photography

tolerances may create gaps at floors, walls, shafts, and other structural connections should also be evaluated for aesthetics, cost, and constructability.

Concrete

Cast-in-place concrete can incur inconsistencies up to 1 inch in multiple planes. Because foundations are typically cast-in-place, the transition between concrete and other framing materials is a connection point that will occur on almost every mass timber project. Concrete shear walls likewise may have variances from floor to floor, or across a face. A general contractor should impress upon the concrete team to take special care in areas requiring more precision and to flag details that may require more precision than industry-standard installation practices.

Precast concrete is more precise than cast-in-place concrete. This prefabricated solution is worth

considering for exposed components with a high level of finish quality (see **Figure 6.9**).

Steel

Structural steel columns, beams, and braced frames have tolerances greater than engineered wood, typically about ¼ inch to ⅜ inch and, depending on the length of the steel, up to ¾ inch[9] (see **Figures 6.10** and **6.11**).

The design and fabrication method of exposed or concealed steel connectors, especially details that occur frequently, can significantly impact a project's schedule. Rolled steel connections will require more tolerance, and it may be wise to plan for shims or other field modifications as needed. As with larger structural components, greater length brings more potential for variation. Highly accurate cast-steel connections may have a higher up-front cost, but they may contribute to sched-

9   American Institute of Steel Construction.

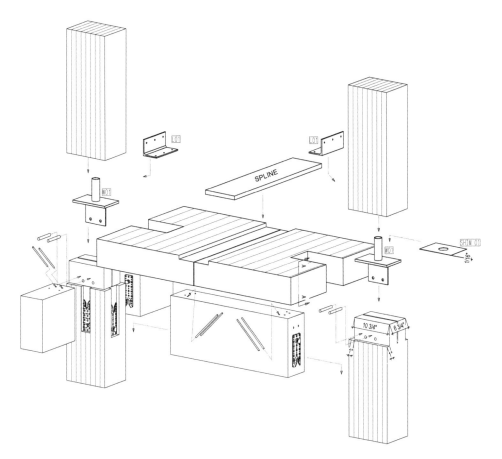

TOP — FIGURE 6.12: KIT-OF-PARTS ASSEMBLY DIAGRAM
FOR TIMBER COLUMN, BEAM, AND CLT FLOOR ATTACHMENTS

Carbon12, Portland, Oregon; Source: Kaiser+Path

BOTTOM — FIGURE 6.13: OFF-THE-SHELF BEAM CONNECTIONS
AND CUSTOM COLUMN CONNECTIONS

Carbon12, Portland, Oregon; Source: Kaiser+Path

FIGURE 6.14: TIMBER CONSTRUCTION ON CONSTRAINED URBAN SITES

(LEFT) *Sideyard, Portland, Oregon; Contractor: Andersen Construction*
Source: Catena Engineers; Photo Credit: Skylab Architecture

(RIGHT) *District Office, Portland, Oregon; Source: Andersen Construction*

ule savings by reducing field conflicts and retrofits (see **Figures 6.12** and **6.13**).

6.6   ON-SITE MATERIALS MANAGEMENT

Perhaps the most important lesson from the first mass timber projects developed in North America is that on-site materials management is crucial for efficient construction. The following topics outline the advantages and challenges of handling mass timber components on a jobsite.

Just-in-Time Delivery

In situations where on-site storage is limited, mass timber panels can be delivered on flatbed trucks using just-in-time delivery. Such a system takes considerable planning and coordination with both the trucking company and the mass timber manufacturer; many mass timber companies use their own trucking for that reason. A side benefit is that loading in construction sequences may take more time than conventional trucking companies are willing to tolerate without extra charges. Another benefit is the ability to care for the integrity of weatherproof packing, which may need some attention and adjustments during transportation in inclement weather.

The just-in-time approach can be complicated by greater distances between the building site and the mass timber manufacturer; regional restrictions on oversized loads; and routes with clearance constraints, challenging terrain, or constrained urban sites (see **Figure 6.14**). Unusually shaped panels are more challenging to balance for transport, potentially increasing the number of trucks required or complicating sequencing. The transport team can advise on route strategies and restrictions, and any added costs associated with oversized loads.

The challenges of materials management within a given space at a building site aren't specific to mass timber. However, each prefabricated mass timber element has a precise installed location,

FIGURE 6.15: STAGING AND HANDLING
Source: Nordic Structures

creating additional site coordination issues. When panels are loaded for shipping at the manufacturer, they can be arranged with a consideration of the order in which they will be off-loaded. This approach allows for smooth installation sequencing without on-site storage.

But efficient and safe loading of the materials on the trucks will often take precedence over the installation sequence. Shipping loads will also be informed by weight distribution, as well as by panel size and shape. Understanding the loading and shipping approach before the materials arrive on-site reduces delivery conflicts. A building design with many similarly sized panels will be more straightforward to coordinate than one with many unusual shapes. In the latter case, some laydown space should be set aside for resequencing (see **Figure 6.15**).

Coordinating a huge volume of mass timber materials has storage, schedule, and liability implications at both the manufacturing facility and the construction site. A 2018 case study published by the DLR Group[10] recommends that the construction team dedicate an engineer to manage a project's mass timber fabrication and delivery schedule.

Support Equipment

It is important to determine the amount and type of support equipment needed at the site to ensure efficient operation. Some case studies describe using forklifts or similar equipment to move mass timber (an option only in 1- or 2-story buildings) versus using a crane. If small equipment is to be used, the vehicles must be large enough to carry heavy timbers and panels. For example, a 5-ply, 10-foot-by-60-foot panel made from Douglas fir

10   DLR Group, *Tall with Timber: A Seattle Mass Timber Tower Case Study* (November 2018), https://issuu.com/dlrgroup/docs/seattle_mass_timber_tower_book_issu.

FIGURE 6.16: CRANE LIFTING WITH SLINGS
District Office, Portland, Oregon
Source: Andersen Construction; Photo Credit: Pete Eckert

FIGURE 6.17: PICK POINT LIFTING DEVICE
Source: https://mtcsolutions.com/ (formerly My-Ti-Con)

weighs over 5 tons. If panels arrive in containers, which is common for materials supplied from overseas, the equipment on-site must be robust enough to remove and lift the heavy panels and timbers. Additionally, enough space is needed to safely maneuver around the site.

Most project managers will opt to use cranes, allowing for panels or timbers to be "flown" from a truck or site storage into the designated place in the building, as in **Figure 6.16**. A key aspect of this process is the placement, number, and strength of the "pick points," or lifting devices.

Figure 6.17 illustrates a typical lifting device called a Yoke 1T, which has been designed and tested for use in mass timber construction. The device is screwed into a mass timber panel using ½-inch screws, and it is designed to safely lift panels of up to 7,000 pounds. Other lifting devices designed for lighter or heavier panels are available. A key to efficient construction is placing the lifting device on the panel in a way that allows it to balance plumb and level, easing installation. The pick points also enhance safety by serving as a place for construction workers to "tie in" after the panel/timber is in place.

Some mass timber suppliers cut small penetrations that engage with lifting slings or crane fixtures. These strategically positioned penetrations are plugged at the construction site. Others offer quick-mount/quick-release fixtures to reduce lifting cycle time. Some of these are designed to reduce the size and visibility of the permanent mark on the panel.

Waste Management

Because mass timber is prefabricated, little to no field cutting of the material is required at the jobsite, resulting in very little wood waste. Builders report that this contributes to enhanced safety because the site stays clean, and storage and removal of waste don't require managers' attention.

Panels often come wrapped in plastic for protection during transport and on-site storage. While lightweight, this plastic makes up the bulk of on-site waste volume associated with mass timber, and it is destined for the landfill. If the protection can be made reusable or multifunctional, this waste stream could be reduced or eliminated.

Metric Units of Measurement

Although the capacity of North American mass timber manufacturers is ramping up, some building projects are using mass timber produced in Europe, where the measurement units are metric, rather than using the imperial system used in the US. Several builders who have dealt with this issue reported that they (and their carpenters) were initially worried about the differing units of measurement. Crews were supplied with tape measures showing both imperial and metric measurements. That approach created confusion. The solution reported by all builders was to use tape measures calibrated only in metric units, to which the crews quickly adapted.

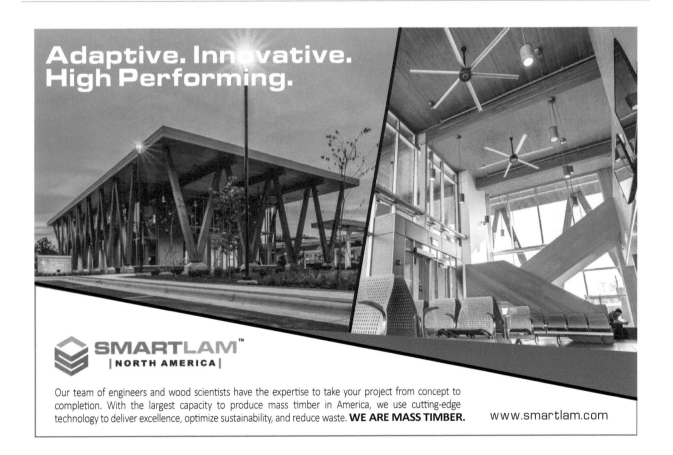

Source: Jeremy Bittermann

CASE STUDY: BUILDING IN THE RAIN

NAME OF PROJECT: THE CANYONS

STORY CREDIT: BRAD CARMICHAEL, EMILY DAWSON, AND JEFF SPEERT

LOCATION: PORTLAND, OREGON

COMPLETION DATE: FALL 2020

OWNER/DEVELOPER: KAISER GROUP INC. AND HOOSIERS HOLDINGS

ARCHITECT: PATH ARCHITECTURE INC.

ENVELOPE CONSULTANT: 4EA BUILDING SCIENCE

CONTRACTOR: R&H CONSTRUCTION

MASS TIMBER MANUFACTURER: STRUCTURLAM MASS TIMBER CORPORATION

IT IS WELL understood that wood readily absorbs water, but how much water is acceptable for a mass timber structure to be exposed to during construction? Moisture data from in-service Cross-Laminated Timber (CLT) is limited, so when the Canyons team at Kaiser+Path realized they would be building during the rainiest months of 2019–2020, they saw an opportunity.

The architects tested four 14,000-square-foot structural CLT floor decks from October through April; 1 floor was installed every 2 weeks, topping out in December. The joints between panels were taped from above, though water commonly bypassed this protection and reached lower floors. Standing water was common on the decks before the installation of the roofing, though removal efforts were ongo-

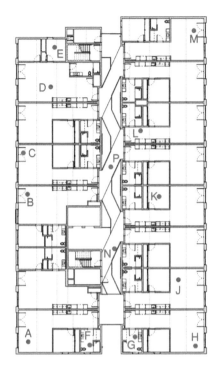

FIGURE 1: FLOOR PLAN WITH TEST LOCATIONS
Source: Kaiser+Path

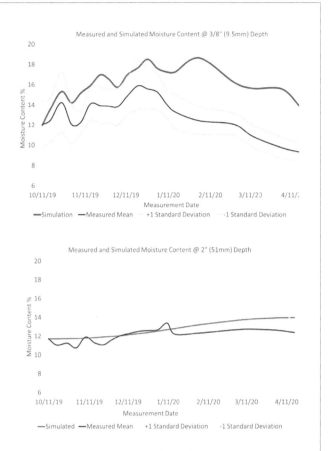

FIGURES 2 (TOP) AND 3 (BOTTOM): SIMULATED MOISTURE CONTENT (RED LINE) COMPARED WITH MEASURED MEAN AND MARGIN OF ERROR AT ⅜-INCH (9.5 MM) DEPTH AND 2-INCH (51 MM) DEPTH.
Source: 4EA Building Science

ing between rain events. A total of 1,540 individual moisture readings were taken, sampled on an almost weekly basis at 2 depths in 56 locations, ending when the final Gyp-Crete topping slab was poured. The locations **(Figure 1)** tested a variety of exposure conditions, including proximity to slab/panel edge, spline connection, windows, and directional exposure. To compare the measured moisture content over time and to determine trends, a simulated hygrothermal model using actual weather data was created to represent the CLT panels and was calibrated to include overhang protection from the floor above.

The team found that in-place CLT panels dried out more quickly than simulated values would predict, as was validated by the model. The measured moisture content over time at the 2-inch **(Figure 3)** depth was more responsive to weather chang-

es than the simulation, and it more closely tracked the corresponding peaks and valleys of the ⅜-inch **(Figure 2)** depth. This indicates a higher rate of hygric redistribution within the panels. The measured results show a time lag of about 2 to 3 weeks for moisture to fluctuate at the 2-inch depth but also showed that the highest moisture contents were at lower overall percentages at that depth.

Not surprisingly, the addition of roofing material, scaffolding wrap, and dry-in procedures were the most significant methods for preventing increases in panel moisture content.

Source : Marshall Steeves

The findings show that, when reasonably protected from direct rain and standing water, mass timber moisture content can remain within an acceptable range for several weeks to months, even during winter in the marine climate of the Pacific Northwest. In addition, moisture content readings were consistently lower than 16 percent at the 2-inch depth, remaining within suitable levels for encapsulation and flooring installation.

And, despite the significant rainfall and exposure, R&H Construction's execution of the moisture protection plan kept the rainwater free from contaminants—with virtually no staining on the exposed, uncoated timber ceilings. The Canyons has now been occupied for over 2 years, looking great and performing beautifully. ◔

Source: Emily Dawson

FIGURE 6.18: TIMBER FRAME AND STEEL CORE PROGRESSING IN COLD, SNOWY WEATHER

Carbon12, Portland, Oregon; Source: Kaiser+Path

6.7 WEATHER PROTECTION AND MOISTURE MANAGEMENT

Mass timber has inherent advantages and challenges associated with weather. Concrete has curing limitations around temperature and precipitation, and steel requires certain conditions for proper welding, but mass timber components can be installed regardless of weather conditions. This has excellent implications for reducing weather delay contingencies when timelines overlap challenging weather months.

For example, the framing for Carbon12 took place between December 2016 and February 2017, one of the wettest and coldest winters in Oregon's recent history (see **Figure 6.18**). While most construction sites in town were closed for several days at a time through the season, Carbon12 was delayed for only one day, when key members of the 4-person framing crew were unable to travel due to road conditions.

Once in place, wood components require some protection against exposure to wet weather to prevent moisture uptake. Short of coordinating construction around a dry season (only occasionally a viable option), a moisture management plan will help the team manage site practices and invest in protection measures that best fit the project. This plan should be distributed and discussed with all trades on-site during wet weather. Top concerns include staining, swelling, shrinkage, and decay, all of which can be avoided by following a well-considered protection and mitigation plan.

FIGURE 6.19: DISTRICT OFFICE IMPLEMENTED A MOISTURE MANAGEMENT PLAN

District Office, Portland, Oregon
Source: Andersen Construction

Industry standard practices for moisture management in mass timber buildings are developing. In 2020, RDH Building Science Inc. published advice on moisture risk management for mass timber builders.[11] Experienced builders, meanwhile, are developing best practices. While constructing both the George W. Peavy Forest Science Center and the district office (see **Figure 6.19**) during Oregon's wet months, Andersen Construction created a 4-part moisture management plan for wood structures: sealers, stain prevention, moisture control, and dry out. Each is elaborated upon below. (For more on managing moisture throughout design and construction, see chapter 5.)

Sealers

Shop-applied sealers can protect against moisture intrusion during construction and may come standard—or as an option—with some mass timber products. All component surfaces may benefit from different types of sealers, whether applied before delivery or on-site. Application capabilities will vary by facility and should be fully understood if sealers are to be relied upon for weather protection.

The top surface of a floor panel is more susceptible to standing water, while the bottom face is

---

11   Graham Finch, RDH Building Science Inc., *Moisture Management for Mass Timber Buildings* (2020).

more likely to be left exposed as a finished surface and to need protection from staining. Moisture uptake is quickest where timber components are most vulnerable, at the end-grain. That is also where components are typically joined together, creating hidden spaces with less air circulation for dry out. Often, the manufacturer will apply a temporary wax coating to edges where end-grain is exposed for protection during transport and installation.

Stain Prevention

Water readily transports pigments from debris—such as rust from metal-work shavings or other untreated metals, or from a spilled beverage—resulting in stained surfaces. Because multilevel buildings often have repetitive floor layouts, stacked penetrations and panel seams can create pathways for water to move from floor to floor. Managing construction activity on a mass timber structure intended for finish exposure is crucial, therefore, for preventing stains. Many tradespeople are unaccustomed to working around finished surfaces, so communication is an important part of a stain prevention plan. Superficial stains can be cleaned or sanded, but proper stain prevention will avoid the risk of permanent marks, as well as reduce cleanup time and expense.

Moisture Control

Two basic concepts are paramount to controlling moisture in structural wood. First, wood should be protected from prolonged exposure to water. Second, if wood becomes wet, it must be allowed to release moisture via proper ventilation.

As soon as mass timber components leave a climate-controlled fabrication facility, they are subject to shifting moisture content (MC), depending on the environment to which they are exposed. Mass timber manufacturers are responsible for protection during transport, commonly accomplished by durable plastic wrap, as shown in **Figure 6.20**. Once the timber is delivered to a project site, the contractor is then responsible for protection, whether stored or in place.

Strategies for protection may be holistic (like tenting the entire structure) or local (such as using tape at panel seams and penetrations).

In Nordic countries, mass timber construction is often conducted under large-scale tents doubling as overhead crane supports. Variations appropriate to the scale of construction are available. This approach is controversial because of the added cost, and it is the subject of a robust industrywide discussion in the context of the related costs and benefits.

Fully tenting a structure eliminates the need for many of the practices described in this section, but it is often prohibitively expensive, and most projects will need to implement a multipronged approach. Standing water should be minimized and removed as quickly as possible. The construction team should also prepare for dewatering activities by having adequate equipment and personnel on-site following rain events, as well as a planned approach for continuous wet weather.

Dry Out

In addition to protection, the basic principles of any approach must allow for wood to release excess moisture at an appropriate rate until the structure has reached equilibrium with ambient environmental moisture during occupancy (see

FIGURE 6.20: CLT PANELS PROTECTED WITH WRAP FOR TRANSPORT AND ON-SITE STORAGE

Hillsboro Community Center, Hillsboro, Oregon
Source: Swinerton Builders; Photo Credit: BREWSPHOTO LLC

also chapter 5). Moderate drying conditions and slower, longer drying times help prevent surface checks.

Industry standard best practices for acceptable MC in mass timber have not been firmly established. However, in the Pacific Northwest, where wet winters significantly impact construction sites, teams have found that mass timber components above about 14 percent MC should not be enclosed or encapsulated but given a controlled opportunity to release moisture.

Mass timber naturally dries out more slowly than light framing because of its larger dimensions. Because of the greater volume, more potential exists for MC differentials within a single panel or member. The greater the differential in moisture, the greater the potential for tension, compression, and movement—created by swelling and shrinking—as the wood takes on water or dries out. These stresses in the wood can lead to cracking and checking that, while typically structurally insignificant, can be aesthetically undesirable.

ONE OF THE MAIN DESIGN OBJECTIVES WAS TO SHOWCASE OREGON'S HISTORY, CULTURE, AND FOREST PRODUCTS.
Photo Credit: Matt Parker/UO Track and Field

CASE STUDY: HAYWARD FIELD

LOCATION: EUGENE, OREGON

COMPLETION DATE: 2020

OWNER/DEVELOPER: UNIVERSITY OF OREGON

ARCHITECT: SRG PARTNERSHIP

BUILDER: HOFFMAN CONSTRUCTION COMPANY

CIVIL ENGINEER: MAZZETTI

STRUCTURAL ENGINEER: MKA

MASS TIMBER MANUFACTURER: WESTERN ARCHRIB

ARCHITECTURAL COATING MANUFACTURER: SANSIN CORPORATION

ENGINEERED WOOD MANUFACTURER

Western Archrib teamed up with leaders in the fields of architectural design, structural engineer-ing, and waterborne coatings to ensure that the iconic wooden features at the reimagined Hay-ward Field at the University of Oregon in Eugene are able to go the distance.

The project's donors include Phil Knight of Nike, who competed in track and field events at the origi-nal Hayward Field while he attended the university. The 12,650-seat stadium was designed by SRG Partnership and constructed by Hoffman Construc-tion. Hayward Field was the setting for the 2020 US Olympic Team Trials and the 2022 World Athletics Championships. The venue is slated to host the Wanda Diamond League Final in 2023.

SHOWCASING MASS TIMBER

One of the design objectives was to showcase Oregon's history, culture, and industry, so 462

OVER 462 DOUGLAS FIR GLULAM STRUCTURAL WOOD
PIECES WERE USED TO CREATE 77 UNIQUE CURVES,
EACH CONTAINING SIX PIECES OF BENT WOOD.
Photo Credit: Matt Parker/UO Track and Field

THE REIMAGINED HAYWARD FIELD AT THE UNIVERSITY OF
OREGON IN EUGENE IS A "THEATER" FOR TRACK AND FIELD
EVENTS, INCLUDING THE 2020 U.S. OLYMPIC TEAM TRIALS AND
THE 2022 WORLD ATHLETICS CHAMPIONSHIPS. THE VENUE IS
SLATED TO HOST THE WANDA DIAMOND LEAGUE FINAL IN 2023.
Photo Credit: Matt Parker/UO Track and Field

glulam pieces made of Douglas fir were used to create 77 unusual curves. Each curve contains 6 glulam pieces. The design created an iconic look for the roof canopy and paid homage to the forests of the Pacific Northwest.

Engineering the wood on such a grand scale and developing a coating system to protect it from the elements were the keys to the project's success. All of the elements in the glulam curves matched the owner's specific requirements, from the chosen lumber to the coating system. Sansin's 3-coat system in a custom Golden Wheat color was selected for its durability, beauty, and environmental profile.

PROTECTING THE WOOD

The glulam was prefinished in the Western Archrib shop before shipment, using a coat of Sansin's KP12-UVW (engineered wood undercoat) and a coat of Precision Coat ENS (exterior breathable topcoat). That ensured proper preparation of the wood and adequate product coverage (mil thickness), and it protected the members while in transit and during construction. Prefinishing before the wood was

field-acclimatized also helped reduce newly opened surfaces as the wood settled. A final coat of ENS was applied at the track-and-field site to spot finish any open surfaces before the final coats were applied, as specified by a detailed quality control plan.

A MASSIVE MASS TIMBER UNDERTAKING

All of the glulam pieces were run through Western Archrib's Computer Numerical Control (CNC) machinery and Fabrication Quality Check program, ensuring they matched the drawings. The curved pieces were over 100 laminations deep, and the straight pieces were 59 laminations deep. The structural steel was placed before the glulam pieces were installed. The 6 glulam pieces in each curved frame had to be installed per grid line, and there were no repeat or common pieces. In other words, each piece had only one spot in which it could be placed. The creation of one of the world's most amazing outdoor stadiums took teamwork from all design partners and suppliers. ◖

Photo Credit: Jeppe Rasmussen

CASE STUDY: SOPHIE RADICH SCHOOL

NAME OF PROJECT: SOPHIE RADICH SCHOOL

OWNER: LILLESTRØM KOMMUNE

LOCATION: LILLESTRØM, NORWAY

COMPLETION DATE: 2022

CONTRACTOR: KRUSE SMITH

ARCHITECT: ARKITEMA

STRUCTURAL ENGINEER: RAMBØLL

A LEADING NORWEGIAN project developer and contractor used Woodsense wireless moisture sensors in the Sophie Radich School as a way of preventing damage and gaining knowledge and experience for future projects.

MOISTURE CHALLENGES WITH MASS TIMBER

Kruse Smith agreed to use mass timber to build the 12,000-square-meter school for the municipality of Lillestrøm. The school was erected without any scaffolding, as is the norm in Norway. Although contractors were not worried about constructing the building without a complete site cover, the professional contractors and building owners knew they had to be proactive about moisture management.

The main contractor found some areas of the building more worrisome than others. Keeping an eye on the quality of the subcontractors' work demanded a lot of resources. The building owners, meanwhile, also questioned design choices, thinking moisture could be a problem in some areas.

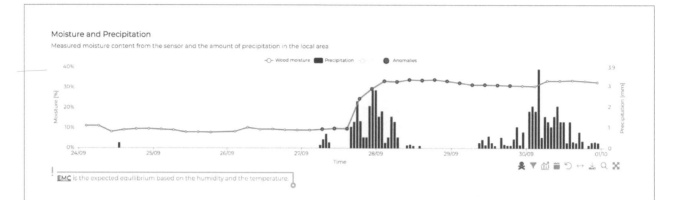

Moisture and Precipitation
Measured moisture content from the sensor and the amount of precipitation in the local area

EMC is the expected equilibrium based on the humidity and the temperature.

Photo Credit: Jeppe Rasmussen

The contractor had a choice: spend a lot of time doing moisture checks with a handheld meter, or use an automated solution.

NEW CONSTRUCTION METHODS, NEW TECHNOLOGY

Kruse Smith decided to use wireless sensors from Woodsense to measure wood moisture content, humidity, and temperature over the course of 10 years and transmit the data to interested parties.

"We have placed the sensors in exposed areas where we knew there was an increased risk of moisture based on the physique of the building and that condensation can also form in the construction," said Raymond Finstad, project engineer at Kruse Smith.

The sensors were placed against the edges of the roof to ensure roofing was done correctly; under windows on roofs; and on various facades to monitor the moisture differences in facades facing north, south, east, and west.

SENSOR DETECTED FAULT WITH ROOFING

A sensor in the roof monitored for holes in the roof felt. That sensor found a mistake and notified the developer.

"The damage that occurred was on the roof, where we had chosen to place a sensor. Water entered the construction due to the roofer not having completed the covering, which resulted in the moisture rising to more than 30 percent, and we consequently got an alarm from the sensor," Finstad said.

"Had we not had the sensor placed, we would not have found the moisture," Finstad said, adding that, without the senor, the repairs would have been more extensive.

"We have received positive feedback from the developers on the placement of the sensors in the construction because we can see that we have a better control of the moisture throughout the construction," he said. ●

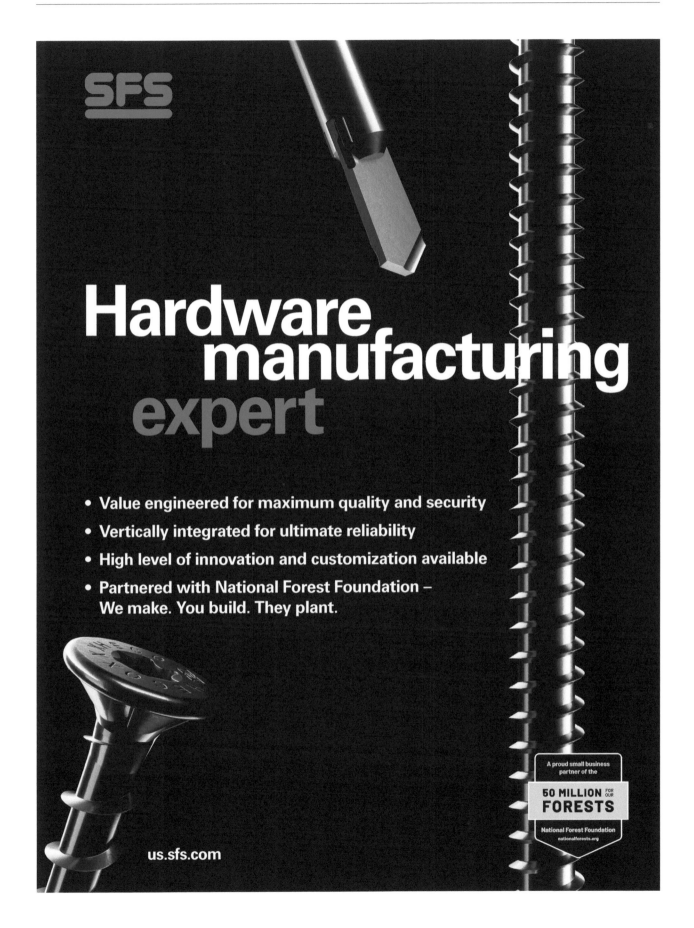

CHAPTER 7: OCCUPANTS

Mass timber buildings can boost the health, well-being, comfort, productivity, and prosocial behaviors of their residents. Human health, comfort, and behavior are closely related, but they are divided into 3 sections in this chapter. The first section, on health, looks at our acute biological responses to indoor environments; the second, on comfort, reviews the universal characteristics of those spaces and of human preferences; and the third, on behavior, considers how indoor environments influence how we interact with one another.

7.1 HEALTH

The focus on the health benefits of wood in the built environment is based on a well-established body of research showing that exposure to nature has health benefits such as lower blood pressure, lower heart rate, increased ability to focus, increased concentration, and increased creativity.

Biophilia

The powerful influence of nature in all aspects of indoor environments is known as biophilia, the innate human love for natural forms.[1] The idea of enhancing human health through building design has been described as the application of biophilia in the built environment; our bodies, as biological organisms, are supported by biophilic spaces.

Biophilic buildings connect occupants to nature by featuring natural materials, shapes, and patterns; orienting a building to take advantage of daily and seasonal light patterns; and providing views and access to the outdoors and nature.

According to a growing body of studies,[2] nature-oriented design improves health by lowering stress and blood pressure; improves mental functions, stamina, and focus; improves moods and learning rates; and decreases violent and criminal activity.

Stress Reduction

A 2011 study[3] connected the use of wood to the support of human health in the built environment. The study documented a lowered sympathetic nervous system response when occupants could see more wood surfaces in a mock office environment. Stress, as measured by heart rate and skin conductivity, was lowest for the participants in the office with the wood design. If the use of wood is extended to an entire building, the study suggests that mass timber is well-positioned to enhance the health of a building's occupants.

Another study by Japanese researchers[4] monitored subjects' physiological responses to different ratios of wood surfaces in an environment. They discovered that a moderate ratio (45 percent coverage) was subjectively "comfortable" because it lowered blood

---

1 "Biophilia" is a term that was coined by biologist Edward O. Wilson, a professor emeritus and researcher at Harvard. He defined it as the urge to affiliate with other forms of life in nature.

2 Some of the most comprehensive data gathered around the benefits of biophilic building design on human health is captured in a document by Terrapin Bright Green, *The Economics of Biophilia: Why Designing with Nature in Mind Makes Financial Sense* (2014).

3 FPInnovations, *Wood and Human Health* (2011).

4 Yuko Tsunetsugu, Yoshifumi Miyazaki, and Hiroshi Sato, "Physiological Effects in Humans Induced by the Visual Stimulation of Room Interiors with Different Wood Quantities," *Journal of Wood Science* no. 53 (2007): 11–16.

pressures and pulse rates. A large ratio of wood surfaces (90 percent) "caused significant and large decreases" in the blood pressures of test subjects.

This topic is drawing increased cross-disciplinary interest. Similar projects are being conducted at the University of Helsinki in Finland, in the University of Primorska in Slovenia, and likely by other academic and private research groups.

Recovery and Healing

Another emerging area of occupant health is evidence-based design, involving the analysis of the design of a building to assess how it impacts human health. Architects specializing in the design of health-care buildings are using wood to enhance patient recovery and health, and to optimize the well-being of staff and visitors. One study of human response to health-care facilities found that using cedar panels in hospital rooms reduced stress as measured by cortisol levels.[5]

Biophilic design in health-care environments is linked to shorter hospital stays, faster recovery rates, fewer negative comments, and reduced medication use.[6]

Infection Control

The year 2020 brought an increased awareness of how the air and the surfaces around us contribute to our safety or exposure to contagion. While our understanding of how the coronavirus is transmitted has evolved, concerns about surface transmission led to interesting findings on how wood performs.

---

5   FPInnovations, *Wood as a Restorative Material in Health-care Environments* (2015).

6   Terrapin Bright Green, *The Economics of Biophilia: Why Designing with Nature in Mind Makes Financial Sense*, (2014).

A Finnish study showed that "the contagiousness of coronaviruses decreases much more rapidly on a wooden surface than on other materials, such as plastics."[7] Wood is an effective antibacterial surface, especially when compared to materials like glass or plastic. Another Finnish study found that pine and spruce surfaces effectively prevent the growth of pathogenic bacteria common in hospitals, such as the kind that causes staph infections.[8]

The Institute for Health in the Built Environment (IHBE) at the University of Oregon is engaged in ongoing research that observes how wood's natural properties could make it difficult for pathogens to survive on it or to be transferred from person to person. Wood has a porous surface that can both sequester moisture and desiccate it. Wood also contains aromatic organic compounds called terpenes, found in many plants, that appear to have antiviral effects. These IHBE studies are investigating the effects of wood species, coatings, humidity, and simulated flooding events on the surface and air microbiome in exposed wood buildings. Other IHBE studies have shown wood's promise for promoting healthy bacteria and supporting diverse indoor biomes that contribute to human health.

These studies have the potential to significantly increase the use of wood in health-care environments.

Resiliency

Building codes ensure that occupants are as safe as possible from catastrophic events, such as earthquakes, fires, and high winds. Wood performs very well relative to building code standards, and it goes even further by contributing to highly resilient designs. Resilient buildings can recover quickly after disasters. Buildings that can be safely occupied following a disaster are invaluable to recovering communities, a fact made painfully clear every time a large-scale disaster displaces a large number of people for a long period.

7.2 COMFORT

Indoor environmental quality (IEQ) is a measurement of how a building affects its occupants' comfort and health. The Environmental Protection Agency (EPA) found that US residents spend about 90 percent of their time indoors .[9] Canadians and Europeans fare about the same, at 94 percent and 90 percent respectively. The EPA suggests that people should spend more time outside because a growing body of scientific evidence links interactions with nature to greater levels of health and happiness. It also suggests that interior spaces should incorporate natural elements as much as possible to boost health.

IEQ in relation to occupant comfort is multidimensional, including thermal comfort, indoor air quality (IAQ), acoustics, visual comfort, and safety. In the simplest terms, when people feel comfortable in a built environment, they also tend to be healthier and more productive. As outlined below, mass timber buildings can enhance occupants' comfort in several ways.

---

7   Antti Haapala, University of Eastern Finland.

8   Tiina Vainio-Kaila, "Antibacterial Properties of Scots Pine and Norway Spruce" (doctoral thesis, Technical Research Centre of Finland, 2017).

9   https://www.epa.gov/air-research/indoor-air-quality-exposure-and-characterization-research

FIGURE 7.1: FLOOR-TO-STRUCTURE WINDOWS BRING DAYLIGHT DEEPER INTO THE BUILDING

First Tech Federal Credit Union, Hillsboro, OR
Source: Swinerton Mass Timber

Visual Comfort

Key factors in the visual comfort of building occupants are visual access to nature and the amount of daylight allowed in. Research shows a link between access to daylight and improvements in mood, productivity, and sleep patterns. Views can dramatically affect mood and productivity as well. A building designed to maximize daylight access for occupants will be oriented to take advantage of daily and seasonal sunlight patterns. It will also limit floor plate depth, so occupants spend most of their time near the perimeter of the building where daylight is most prevalent.

Mass timber supports good design practices, with thin floor plates for higher ceilings and 2-way spans that can eliminate perimeter beams. Both qualities allow for more and taller windows to allow daylight farther into buildings.

Indoor Air Quality

Many factors that contribute to healthy IAQ are beyond the scope of this report, including ventilation rates, filtration systems, outdoor air quality, and occupant behavior. We focus here on providing information about how using exposed wood in interior spaces can support high IAQ characteristics, as part of a complete healthy building system.

Wood is considered hypoallergenic, meaning it is very unlikely to cause allergic reactions, and its smooth surfaces are easy to keep clean and free of particles. The terpene-based aromatics that contribute to these properties are also responsible for the pleasant, relaxing aroma we all associate with cut wood. Mass timber panels manufactured with adhesives use resins that result in virtually no formaldehyde off-gassing. Many mass timber products are "Red List-free"[10] and approved for use in certified Living Buildings.

---

10   The Red List contains 19 classes of chemicals prevalent in the building industry, which the International Living Future Institute (ILFI) has designated as worst in class.

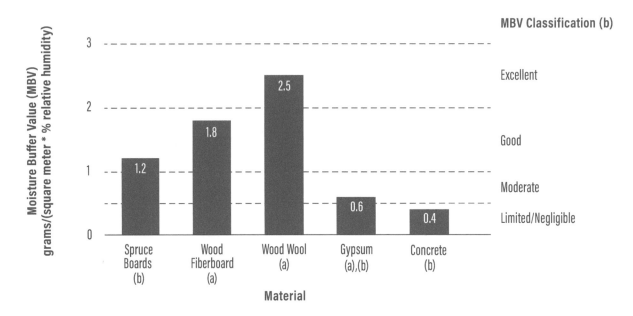

FIGURE 7.2: MOISTURE-BUFFERING VALUES OF COMMON BUILDING MATERIALS

(a) Bruce King et al., "A New Carbon Architecture, referencing Holcroft, N.A. 2016, Natural Fibre Insulation Materials for Retrofit Applications" (PhD thesis, University of Bath, UK).

(b) Rode, Peuhkuri, Time, Svennberg, and Ojanen, Moisture Buffer Value of Building Materials (2006).

Relative humidity (RH) is the amount of moisture in the air expressed as a percentage of potential moisture in the air at the same temperature in the environment. The optimum range for human health is 40 to 60 percent RH, coinciding with the least optimal range for human health-challenging organisms like bacteria, viruses, fungi, and mites. Just as materials with high thermal mass, such as stone or concrete, absorb heat on a sunny day and release it in the cool of night, so, too, can different materials help to moderate humidity levels.

Because wood is hygroscopic, it assists in moderating humidity levels by absorbing moisture during periods of high humidity and releasing moisture during periods of low humidity. The ability of any given material to perform this function is measured by its Moisture Buffering Value (MBV). Values over 1 (g/[m²%RH]) are good, and materials with values over 2 are excellent. As illustrated by Figure 7.2, wood products perform very well—2 to 5 times better than other tested common indoor materials, including gypsum board and concrete.

Acoustics

Acoustics from an occupant's perspective can be classified in 2 ways: structure-borne and ambient. Buildings with design features that control for both can significantly enhance occupant satisfaction. Adding mass to an assembly is an important aspect of acoustic mitigation. The sound-dampening qualities of solid wood have long been recognized, and mass timber performs well in managing structure-borne sound.

Ambient sound experience can be managed with sound-absorbing materials to control reverberation of noise in a space. Architectural finishes, furnishings, and even occupants themselves can absorb sound. Wood is a porous material that contributes well to the absorption strategy. It also has an interesting impact on an occupant's perception of noise. A 2019 study[11] at the University of Oregon investigated how wood affects ambient sound comfort by collecting building occupants' biometric data, including galvanic skin responses, heart rates, and emotional responses using facial recognition software. The researchers compared masonry and mass timber in office environments and found that the exposed wood in mass timber buildings may provide an "acoustic forgiveness factor" for occupants who are exposed to distracting stimuli. That means that the same sounds that irritate a person in a masonry building may not have the same negative effect on someone in a space with significant biophilic features—in this case, wood.

Thermal Comfort

Wood-framed buildings perform well thermally because wood is a natural insulator, giving designers increased flexibility when detailing insulation to meet energy efficiency codes. It makes *actual* thermal comfort a feature of a well-designed wood building. Wood also contributes to a *perceived* sense of thermal comfort, broadening acceptable temperature ranges, and saving on operational carbon emissions and energy costs.

A study performed by the Energy Studies in Buildings Laboratory (ESBL) at the University of Oregon provides evidence that exposed wood supports the thermal and visual comfort of a building's occupants. The study found that "visually 'pleasant' or 'warm' surroundings can improve perceived thermal comfort, even when the space may call for cooling."

11 Olivia Bain et al., *Auditory Visual Perception: Acoustic Distractions in Mass Timber versus Concrete Office Spaces* (2019).

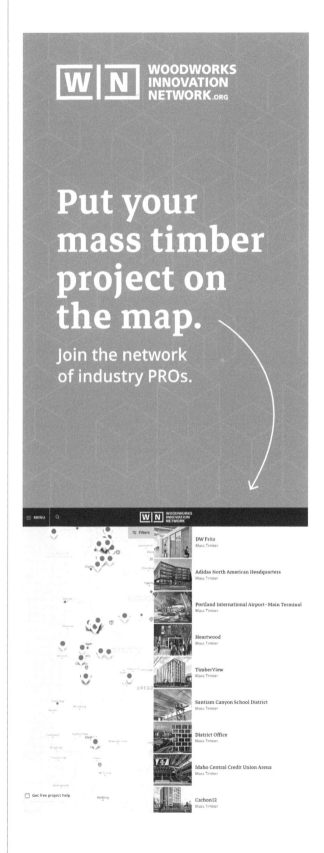

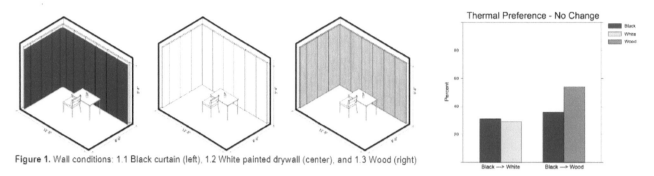

Figure 1. Wall conditions: 1.1 Black curtain (left), 1.2 White painted drywall (center), and 1.3 Wood (right)

FIGURE 7.3: STUDY FINDINGS ON THERMAL COMFORT
Visual effects of wood on thermal perception of interior environments
Denise Blankenberger, Kevin Van Den Wymelenberg, Jason Stenson, University of Oregon, Eugene, OR, 2019

Researchers investigated the perception of thermal comfort in the presence of wood versus white-painted drywall in a climate-controlled chamber. After a 40-minute acclimation period in which the materials were covered with black curtains, the drywall or wood surfaces were exposed. At intervals, the test subjects answered survey questions related to comfort and perception. In the wood room, with no other variables altered, participants were 25 percent more likely to desire no change in the thermal environment or, in other words, to be comfortable. An even stronger response was measured with a word association test. Participants related word pairs, "reveal[ing] that people found the wood walls to have more favorable qualities all-around than the white." The researchers found that "wood was considered more 'natural' than white walls or the control. Wood was also significantly more 'liked' than 'disliked' as compared to the white walls. Wood was also found to be significantly more 'expensive,' 'pleasant,' 'sturdy,' 'unique,' 'interesting,' 'new,' and 'clean' than the white."

7.3 BEHAVIOR

When people are healthy and comfortable, they are much more likely to exhibit behaviors that benefit them and the people around them.

Economic Benefits

Terrapin Bright Green's *The Economics of Biophilia* states: "The main causes for deficient productivity include absenteeism, loss of focus, negative mood, and poor health. The built environment, though not always the cause of these stressors, when well-designed, can be a reliever of these undesirable symptoms." The author adds that "10 percent of employee absences can be attributed to architecture with no connection to nature." Many employers understand the financial and social effects of a healthy workplace on employee productivity and will seek spaces that best meet those needs.

Benefits are also present in retail environments. "Retail customers judge businesses surrounded by nature and natural features to be worthy of prices up to 25 percent higher than businesses with no access to nature." An environment where customers feel both relaxed and stimulated will be more conducive to spending, contributing to the success of a business. The ESBL study cited above in the section on thermal comfort also found that test participants perceived wood surfaces as being "expensive" and "pleasant," which has implications for customer behavior.

Building maintenance is an expense, and occupant behavior can have a direct impact on maintenance costs. Occupants who enjoy a space and feel respectful toward a building will be less likely to be careless or destructive.

Social Benefits

The same effects that the presence of trees and green spaces have on lowering violent and criminal behaviors in communities can be seen inside buildings as well, reducing vandalism and other aggressive behaviors.

One example pertinent to mass timber is the William Perkin Church of England High School, completed in 2014. It is constructed with exposed Cross-Laminated Timber (CLT) walls and floors as an economic strategy to meet a tight 12-month construction schedule. The new building replaced an outgrown and dilapidated predecessor, and it serves a student body with noted behavior issues. The administration was concerned about how the new building would be treated, as vandalism may be as tempting—or even more tempting—on the new, exposed wood walls than in the previous building, and even more challenging to remove. Before the new building opened, they planned for and encouraged a behavior strategy of quiet voices in the halls using graphics, words, and quotes reminding students to be peaceful and wise. To the administration's delight, the students were

FIGURE 7.4: EXPOSED WOOD ENCOURAGES
CALM, RESPECTFUL BEHAVIORS

William Perkin Church of England School
Source: Emily Dawson

remarkably calm and respectful in the new space. Behavior issues and subsequent disciplinary actions decreased significantly. Students reported that the space made them feel valued.

A report investigating the use of wood structures and finishes in schools in British Columbia similarly found that wood surfaces are less likely to be vandalized than other surfaces.[12]

Though more research has been done on office environments and hospitals focusing on productivity or infection, researchers of biophilic effects agree that the potential for schoolchildren to benefit from the healing effects of natural materials is very promising.

12 https://www.naturallywood.com/wp-content/uploads/wood-use-in-bc-schools_report_stantec-fastepp.pdf

---

CASE STUDY: LOCAL SOLUTIONS FOR A SUSTAINABLE WORLD

OWNER: CPS LIVE LTD.

ARCHITECT, THE SOUL: AXOMIMARLIK ARCHITECTURE

ARCHITECT, MOYONI HOMES: OMT ARCHITECTS

CONTRACTOR: VOLKS.HOUSE

MASS TIMBER: ANTE-HOLZ (IMPORTED FROM GERMANY)

STRUCTURAL ENGINEER: KONBAU

OMT Architects and Volks.House aim to contribute to a sustainable future through their projects and vision. They value local traditions and connect with existing communities while researching local construction methods and resources to develop innovative design solutions. The implementation of sustainable materials, such as timber, is combined with flexible spatial layouts to support long-lived and adaptable buildings.

OMT Architects and Volks.House are engaged in a variety of mass timber residential projects in East Africa, including Moyoni homes and Soul.

MOYONI HOMES: FUMBA TOWN, ZANZIBAR

Lively Community

Positioned around a lavish green courtyard, Moyoni homes form a lively community in the heart of Fumba Town, Zanzibar. The courtyard is aligned with private gardens, offering a vast green space that community members can develop.

Moyoni homes are designed for multigenerational use. Their timber structural framework can be adapted to the needs and demands of individual occupants. The bedroom layout is eas-

ily transformed from a loft to 2 bedrooms. Even 3 bedrooms are possible. Ground, upper, and corner orientations further diversify the apartment options.

Simple and Sustainable

Building on the experience of using timber frames for single-story houses in Fumba Town, the project team designed and built Moyoni homes as multistory timber houses, the first in Africa. Their walls are constructed of prefabricated timber frame elements, and the floors are composite mass timber concrete to improve fire and acoustical performance. The exterior stairs that provide access to the apartments on the upper floor are

MOYONI HOMES

SOUL

cross-ventilated, and they are constructed of conventional concrete and masonry to meet local fire safety requirements. The houses are equipped with solar water heaters and electric cookers to further reduce their carbon footprint. The prefabricated timber elements contribute to a shorter construction time when compared to conventional buildings.

SOUL: PAJE, ZANZIBAR

The Soul

The Soul is a fully serviced, residential-leisure facility in the midst of Zanzibar's beautiful and exotic eastern coast. Surrounded by lush greenery and ocean breezes, it provides relaxation for globe-trotters, island-hoppers, or paradise seekers. Volks.House is contracted to build 6 apartment buildings.

The 3½-story buildings are designed as sustainable hybrid timber structures with concrete foundations and staircases. The prefabricated timber frame walls are made from high-quality, environmentally friendly materials. The controlled conditions of the factory allow for great precision.

For the Soul project, Volks.House is implementing—for the first time in Africa—Cross-Laminated Timber (CLT) for the ceiling slabs. CLT offers the strength and structural simplicity needed for cost-effective buildings, as well as a lighter environmental footprint than concrete or steel. Various timber technologies allow for an optimized performance with low construction time.

Resort

The Soul resort will eventually consist of 11 terraced 3½-story buildings, each with about 20 apartments, for a total of 240 full-service holiday apartments. All units will have built-in kitchens with appliances, including stoves and ovens; built-in wardrobes; and air conditioners in the living rooms and bedrooms. Additional furniture packages are available. ⬡

RENDERING
Source: Mithun

CASE STUDY: BUILDING BETTER SCHOOLS

PROJECT TEAM AND CONTRIBUTING AUTHORS: MITHUN, BAYLEY CONSTRUCTION, PCS STRUCTURAL SOLUTIONS, METRIX ENGINEERS, MASS TIMBER SERVICES, OVERCAST INNOVATIONS

Recent studies have found that humans have an innate need to connect with the natural world, a crucially important relationship in the built environments where children learn. A Mithun R+D study, *Building Better Schools*, explores an optimized approach to mass timber that maximizes biophilic benefits in K–12 schools. The result is an easily adaptable, systems-based kit of parts that is cost-competitive and improves learning environments.

THE HUMAN FACTOR: BIOPHILIA

We spend about 90 percent of our time indoors, so it's important to get the indoor climate right. A growing body of research associates biophilic spaces with student health and cognitive benefits. Sumitomo Forestry Research measured various health responses to wood. One experiment studied the effects of wood on the brain, finding that wood produces higher alpha wave activity, indicating higher levels of relaxation. During mentally demanding tasks, participants exposed to wood had more beta wave activity, pointing to higher levels of focus. In a recent Baltimore study of students in grades 6–12, classrooms with biophilic strategies that included natural patterns, views of nature, and diffuse lighting produced higher heart rate variability, indicating less stress and higher resiliency.

A KIT OF PARTS THAT PROMOTES FLEXIBILITY

In addition to biophilic strategies, well-designed modern schools take adaptability into account, providing agile learning spaces that can accommodate a variety

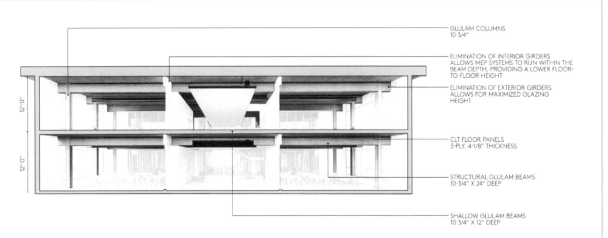

GLULAM COLUMNS
10-3/4"

ELIMINATION OF INTERIOR GIRDERS
ALLOWS MEP SYSTEMS TO RUN WITHIN THE
BEAM DEPTH, PROVIDING A LOWER FLOOR-
TO-FLOOR HEIGHT

ELIMINATION OF EXTERIOR GIRDERS
ALLOWS FOR MAXIMIZED GLAZING
HEIGHT

CLT FLOOR PANELS
3-PLY, 4-1/8" THICKNESS

STRUCTURAL GLULAM BEAMS
10-3/4" X 24" DEEP

SHALLOW GLULAM BEAMS
10-3/4" X 12" DEEP

SECTION DIAGRAM
Source: Mithun

of learning models and teaching pedagogies over time. As a prefabricated, systemized product, mass timber can achieve this flexibility, and it performs most efficiently when conceptualized as a kit of parts. By using a structural grid and sectional framework that balances efficient fiber volumes with the need for agile spaces, the kit of parts can be realized. It comprises a series of glulam beams and columns on a 10- to 12-foot by 24-foot grid and an optimal 3-ply Cross-Laminated Timber (CLT) panel. By eliminating girders, building systems can run within the beam depth, providing a lower floor-to-floor height and increased access to daylight at the perimeter.

CARBON-CUTTING STRATEGIES

Designing with mass timber can help school districts achieve their goals of reducing harmful emissions. Mass timber stores carbon over the life of the building, offsetting emissions of other building materials. Life-cycle assessments of the *Building Better Schools* method show that a mass timber school can offset all emissions incurred in material manufacturing and production, reducing Global Warming Potential (GWP) by up to 200 percent when compared to a steel-frame bench-

mark. Using mass timber can also have secondary benefits, including reducing finishes or foundation sizing. In this case, mass timber reduced finishes by approximately 65 percent by area, compared to a conventional steel or concrete school.

A COST-COMPETITIVE SOLUTION

Mass timber is proving to be cost-competitive with more conventional methods, especially when considering the construction advantages. Off-site mass timber prefabrication allows for smaller crew sizes, fewer truck deliveries, and greater on-site safety. In the factory, temperatures and air quality can be controlled, and noise can be contained, reducing the impact of construction on nearby communities. These benefits, combined with the reduced embodied carbon and improved well-being of students and staff, may outweigh any premium seen in up-front costs of building with mass timber.

This research demonstrates that, by working within the design parameters of mass timber to minimize wood fiber, a 3-ply CLT solution can compete with more conventional structural systems; minimize carbon; and provide the most benefits to districts, students, and teachers. ●

Mass Timber Innovations

From CLT, GLT, and LVL, to MPP and more

USNR is a comprehensive supplier of equipment and technology for many innovative mass timber products like Mass Plywood Panels (MPP) to large-scale CLT production, including finger-jointing, material handling, grade sorting, lay-up, and panel pressing.

USNR systems are expertly integrated to achieve an efficient and automated operation. Ask about our controlled migration program that takes you from manual CLT panel lay-up to a fully-automated panel assembly system. It's a cost-effective entry point to the global CLT market.

Our patented CLT press has a modular design that allows for infinite expansion along the length. It can grow with your operation, enabling you to meet the needs of the market today. *Contact us to learn more about our equipment and technology for mass timber.*

CHAPTER 8: OWNERS AND DEVELOPERS

Many designers and building owners are drawn to mass timber for its environmental credentials because sustainably harvested wood fits naturally into a circular carbon economy. It is likely that the carbon impact of any investment will soon factor into its market value, and the development of forest carbon markets has the potential to inform timber use in real estate investments. Many believe that consumers who support sustainable forestry practices and policies will push the market toward the maximum carbon storage potential of forest products. Additionally, resilient, high-value buildings support communities facing natural disasters by providing immediate, or quickly available, safe shelter.

But to meet such ambitious goals, an array of other concurrent advantages must be realized. At this stage in the evolution of mass timber, building owners are true pioneers in adopting a relatively new technology while exploring evolving financing and procurement systems. Although the data developers typically rely on for pro forma validation is still nascent for mass timber real estate investments, many educational resources, case studies, and anecdotes illuminate the reasons the market is seeing such strong growth.

8.1 MARKET DEVELOPMENT

Increased decarbonization and digitalization are both promising economic forecasts for prefabricated, bio-based construction materials like mass timber. For the last few years, the COVID-19 pandemic has driven reports on the construction economy worldwide, and the disruption continues most significantly in materials cost inflation and labor shortages. The conflict in Ukraine has added pressure to global inflation and construction materials supply chains. Following a global 2022 inflation rate of 12.5 percent, and alongside interest rate and energy cost increases, these trends are expected to continue in the coming year.[1]

US Mass Timber Projects

For mass timber in the US, 2022 was another year of growth and progress. The number of projects either under construction or completed has increased by about 30 percent in both 2021 and 2022, despite a volatile construction market. And despite an overall decline in architectural project billings,[2] the number of proposed projects has also increased by 30 percent, up from 20 percent last year.

Because light framing is competitive for many low-rise buildings, and mass timber is consistently cited as competitive with concrete under 20 stories, a "sweet spot" has emerged for mass timber between 4 stories and 18 stories, depending on the market in question. With increasing urban density, the largest growth in the new building market is projected to be in the mid-rise range, about 3 stories to 8 stories. Because of this, mass timber is poised to be a competitive option for most foreseeable increases in building stock in the US. WoodWorks reports that tall timber projects (over 6 stories of wood) are now breaking ground across the country every quarter year. Around 33 percent of the mass timber projects actively in de-

---

1 Rider Levett Bucknall, *International Report, Construction Market Intelligence*, (Fourth Quarter 2022)
2 Rider Levett Bucknall, *North America Quarterly Construction Cost Report*, (Fourth Quarter 2022).

sign (as of January 2022) are multifamily projects. For tall wood, the multifamily share of projects in design is 65 percent—the bulk of which are 7 to 12 stories.

The following figures and tables illustrate the development of the mass timber industry in the US and provide insights into the popularity of primary materials, the regional popularity of mass timber, occupancy types, building sizes, the total square footage, and number of projects by construction start date. The data was provided by WoodWorks, a nonprofit group that offers free one-on-one project assistance for nonresidential and multifamily wood buildings. Technical experts offer support from design through construction on issues such as allowable heights, suitable areas for different construction types, structural design, lateral systems, and fire- or acoustical-rated assemblies. WoodWorks has provided input on

most of the mass timber structures designed and/or built in North America in recent years. It also tracks details related to mass timber projects.

Figure 8.1 illustrates the increasing number of mass timber building projects, broken out by type of timber technology. On a project count basis, most annual growth has been in the use of Cross-Laminated Timber (CLT).

Figure 8.2 uses the same information, but rather than counting buildings, it illustrates the total constructed square footage. In 2022, mass timber projects totaled 8.8 million square feet, a 49 percent increase from 5.9 million square feet in 2021. The average project size was 65,000 square feet, with CLT accounting for nearly 80 percent of the total square footage and 65 percent of the building projects that broke ground in 2022.

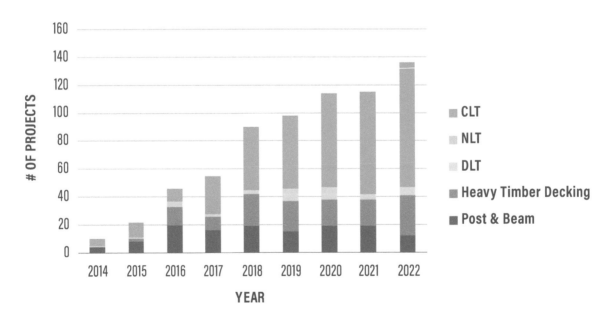

FIGURE 8.1: UNITED STATES PROJECTS BY PRIMARY MASS TIMBER MATERIAL

Data provided by WoodWorks

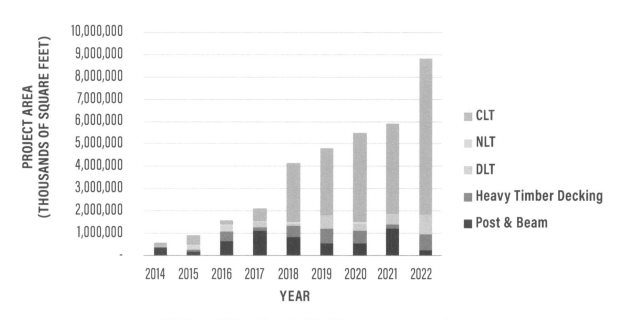

FIGURE 8.2: UNITED STATES BUILDING SQUARE FOOTAGE BY PRIMARY MASS TIMBER MATERIAL

Data provided by WoodWorks

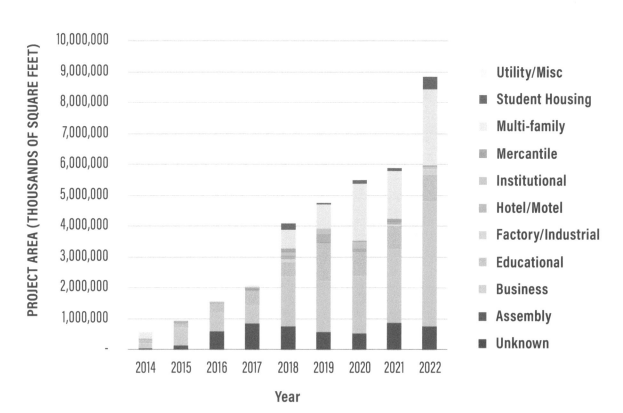

FIGURE 8.3: UNITED STATES MASS TIMBER BUILDING SQUARE FOOTAGE BY OCCUPANCY

Data provided by WoodWorks

STAGE			
STATE	CONSTRUCTION STARTED / BUILT	IN DESIGN	GRAND TOTAL
AK		2	2
AL	11	8	19
AR	8	7	15
AZ	2	4	6
CA	100	147	247
CO	28	30	58
CT	11	4	15
DC	7	15	22
DE	1		1
FL	28	46	74
GA	19	25	44
HI	2	1	3
IA	6	3	9
ID	10	6	16
IL	16	19	35
IN	4	5	9
KS	2	4	6
KY	5	6	11
LA	2	9	11
MA	27	70	97
MD	7	13	20
ME	8	15	23
MI	2	33	35
MN	12	8	20
MO	10	8	18
MS	2	4	6
MT	15	13	28
NC	42	29	71
ND		1	1
NE	4	13	17
NH	2	5	7
NJ	5	5	10
NM	2	2	4
NV		6	6
NY	23	39	62
OH	9	15	24
OK	4	2	6
OR	88	34	122
PA	8	12	20
RI	5	1	6
SC	21	12	33
SD	2	1	3
TN	10	21	31
TX	50	84	134
UT	11	14	25
VA	10	24	34
VT	3	9	12
WA	94	55	149
WI	24	19	43
WV	2	1	3
WY	3		3
Grand Total	767	910	1,677

TABLE 8.1: US MASS TIMBER PROJECTS BY STATE
Data provided by WoodWorks

Figure 8.3 shows total built square footage by building occupancy type. Business occupancies have been consistently dominant, representing 46 percent of the total built square footage in 2022, a 6 percent increase from last year. Residential uses represent the next most significant occupancy category, with multi-family and student housing making up a combined 33 percent of all mass timber square footage built last year.

Table 8.1 shows the number of mass timber projects in the US by state. California, Colorado, Massachusetts, Oregon, Texas, and Washington all added 20 or more projects since last year's report. Four states more than doubled the number of planned or completed projects: Indiana, New Mexico, Nevada, and Tennessee.

Figures 8.4 and **8.5** combine the data depicted in the previous charts to show the total square footage and total number of projects in the US by occupancy type.

8.2 RATIONALE AND MOTIVATION

In a 2014 survey[3] of tall wood building owners worldwide, their most cited motivations were market leadership and innovation, the environmental benefits associated with wood, and construction schedule savings. Owners must balance those rationales with their responsibility to seek the best return on their investment and the need to deliver a building within the allotted time frame, while ensuring the safety of construction workers and building occupants. As expertise grows in the Architecture, Engineering, and Construction (AEC) community and more mass timber projects

---

3   Perkins&Will, *Survey of International Tall Wood Buildings* (2014).

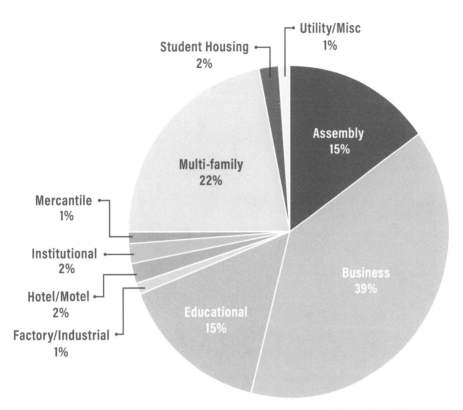

FIGURE 8.4: US TOTAL MASS TIMBER BUILDING
SQUARE FOOTAGE BY OCCUPANCY TYPE

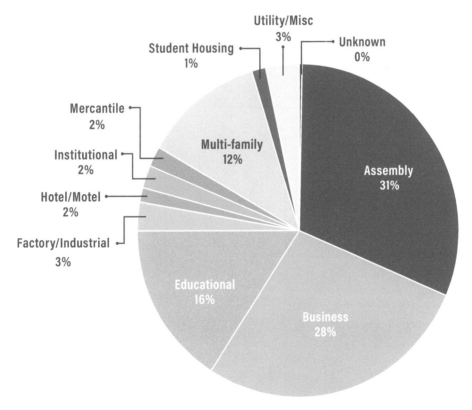

FIGURE 8.5: US TOTAL NUMBER OF MASS TIMBER
BUILDINGS BY OCCUPANCY TYPE

Source: Sierra Institute for Community and Environment

CASE STUDY: MOSAIC HOUSING

LOCATION: GREENVILLE, CALIFORNIA

DEVELOPER: SIERRA INSTITUTE FOR COMMUNITY AND ENVIRONMENT

ARCHITECT: ATELIERJONES

MASS TIMBER CONSULTANT: MASS TIMBER STRATEGY

ENGINEER: HARRIOTT VALENTINE ENGINEERS

CONTRACTOR: LIGHTS CREEK CONSTRUCTION

MASS TIMBER MANUFACTURER: DR JOHNSON

PLUMAS COUNTY IS no stranger to the devastating effects of increased wildfire activity. Over the past 20 years, 63 percent of the county has burned. In August 2021, the devastating Dixie Fire swept through Indian Valley, decimating the towns of Greenville and Indian Falls, along with Canyondam and the Warner Valley community to the north. More than 1,300 structures were lost and nearly a million acres were burned across the Northern Sierra and Southern Cascades, making Dixie the second-largest wildfire in California history.

REBUILDING COMMUNITIES TO BETTER WITHSTAND FIRES

The Sierra Institute, a nonprofit in Indian Valley focused on community and environmental health, partnered with Steve Marshall of Mass Timber Strategy and renowned Seattle-based architects atelierjones, to envision a new way of building homes in the region using Cross-Laminated Timber (CLT). The result of this partnership is Mosaic Housing. CLT is known for its fire resistance and

Source: atelierjones

structural robustness—ideal for a region that faces both wildfire and seismic activity. It is being used to rebuild the community safely and sustainably. In the US, CLT has mainly been used for large-scale urban buildings, less often in areas where the wood is grown. Mosaic Housing is a rebuild effort that orients CLT as a strategy for rebuilding in areas vulnerable to wildfire.

DILIGENT FORESTRY MEETS THOUGHTFUL ARCHITECTURE

To address immediate community needs, the partners worked with the Sierra Institute to design 3 CLT housing options: 1-bedroom, 2-bedroom, and 3-bedroom. These homes, available to community members for postfire rebuilds, are Passive House-inspired. They use design principles that emphasize minimal energy consumption and a low carbon footprint to create energy-efficient homes that can better withstand increasingly common

periods of extreme heat or intense snow and avoid expensive utility bills. To decrease construction time, modular "wet cores" containing the bathroom and kitchen are prefabricated off-site by Method Homes, shipped to Northern California from the Seattle area, and nested into place with a crane in a matter of minutes. The use of prefabricated components, including CLT panels, decreases construction time and can increase housing stock more quickly. In addition, the homes' fire-resistant mineral wool insulation and noncombustible metal siding can better withstand an extreme fire.

Construction began on 3 homes in Greenville, California, during fall of 2022 with expected completion in early 2023, less than 15 months after the Dixie Fire was brought under control. As the Sierra Institute prepares for the next building season, more homes and additional models are being planned to help more community members rebuild with mass timber. ⦿

FIGURE 8.6: LARGE CORPORATE BUILDING OWNERS ARE TURNING TO MASS TIMBER

Source: Microsoft, Holmes structures;
Photo Credit: Blake Marvin Photography

go to market, successes are helping to allay the perceived risks.

Mass timber market data is limited by the relatively small number of buildings and the short amount of time these buildings have been on the market. However, mass timber buildings have been shown to perform well in terms of lease-up rates, tenant retention, sales, and market premiums. This performance is likely related to the topics discussed in chapter 7, including the biophilic and human health benefits of being near natural materials.

Environmental and carbon sequestration credentials likely will be attractive to a growing market of environmentally conscious tenants and buyers, particularly in the home and corporate markets (see **Figure 8.6**). These buildings may also have a place in the carbon markets discussed in chapter 9.

Incentives

Incentives for sustainable and low-carbon buildings vary by jurisdiction and project type. Mass timber construction may have associated financing or zoning incentives (such as increased floor area ratio [FAR]) for reducing embodied carbon or other innovative technologies.

Rigorous whole-building or structural Life Cycle Analysis (LCA) studies are becoming more numerous as the mass timber industry matures. Collectively, these studies indicate that wood products do significantly contribute to lower embodied-carbon construction. To cite 2 examples, a study of Katerra's Catalyst Building[4] in Spokane, Washington, determined that the building's wood product carbon stores nearly offset the up-front carbon required to construct it. Another completed office building, Platte Fifteen in Denver, Colorado, gained a 70 to 76 percent savings in Global Warming Potential (GWP) by choosing a

---

4   Carbon Leadership Forum (CLF) and Center for International Trade in Forest Products (CINTRAFOR), *Life Cycle Assessment of Katerra's Cross Laminated Timber (CLT) Catalyst Building* (2020).

mass timber structural system when compared to primarily steel or concrete systems. And it did so for a negligible (2 percent) cost premium.[5] Over 99 percent of the GWP in that system was contributed by the reinforced concrete topping slab.

Maximize Allowable Building Area

A timber building, on average, weighs only 20 percent as much as a steel or concrete structure. On sites with challenging soil conditions and bearing pressure limitations, a lighter building could be built larger or taller than a heavier one. The lighter weight can be particularly advantageous in regions with high seismic activity. In areas where foundations that can support a heavier building are prohibitively expensive, a lighter building may be the difference that makes a project viable.

Another opportunity for increasing overall building area is with additional floors because of reduced floor-to-floor heights. Mass timber floor sections can be designed more thinly than other options and have inherent fire resistance, requiring no added fireproofing layers at certain building heights.

Leasing and Tenant Retention

Increased demand for biophilic buildings is driving down the leasing period for exposed mass timber buildings (**Figure 8.7**). Securing tenants early allows the building to more quickly reach stabilization, when the building is at full occupancy and generating regular income. Once the building is stabilized, permanent financing can be obtained at a fixed interest rate, or the building can be sold. The earlier the building is fully leased, the better the return on the investment.

FIGURE 8.7: RADIATOR BUILDING
Source: Andrew Pogue Photography

Studies have not yet been done to aggregate data on the market success of mass timber real estate, but as it matures, the anecdotal evidence is increasingly positive. The Platte Fifteen LCA study cited in the "Incentives" section also reflected the economic success of the project; the building was 85 percent leased only 1 month after completion, and its lease rates were higher than any comparable building in the area.

The Portland metro area in Oregon has the highest concentration of mass timber building projects in the US, and local developers are reporting significant leasing advantages for offices:

- Beam Development opened its district office in 2020, and it was 66 percent leased

5   https://assets2.katerra.com/wp-content/uploads/2020/02/25111837/Katerra-LCA-Final-Report-2020-update.pdf

FIGURE 8.8: ONE NORTH DEVELOPMENT
Source: Kaiser+Path

at project completion, doubling comparison expectations of 20 to 30 percent. By January 2022, the building was 73 percent leased. 811 Stark opened in 2015 with 100 percent of its office space leased, and its retail space leased shortly thereafter. The building has remained completely leased since opening.[6]

- The PAE Living Building, developed by PAE and Edlen & Co., opened in fall 2021 with 88 percent of its office space and 25 percent of its retail space leased.[7]

- Killian Pacific's growing mass timber portfolio includes Nova and The Hudson. Both opened in 2016 and stabilized in 2 months and 5 months, respectively. Two years later, Convene was completed and stabilized at opening. Skylight was also completed in 2018, quickly leased to 84 percent, and stabilized in 14 months.[8]

- One North, a collaborative development by Karuna Properties II LLC and Kaiser Group Inc. (see **Figure 8.8**) was completed in 2014, with key anchor tenants committed before

---

6   Interview with a representative of Beam Development.
7   Interview with a representative of PAE and Edlen & Co.
8   Interview with a representative of Killian Pacific.

groundbreaking. Even with unprecedented lease rates for the east side of Portland and very little parking, the buildings were fully leased 6 months faster than the pro forma had assumed.[9]

In addition to faster lease-up rates, mass timber buildings can demand premium rental income. Exposed wood ceilings are a premium finish when compared with painted drywall or concrete. Floor-to-ceiling dimensions can be greater because of the strength and spanning capacity of the panels, and the beauty of exposing the structural deck. These factors contribute to higher lease rates for little to no added construction costs, translating to a higher sales price for the building in the long term.

Construction Risk Reduction

The modularity, precision, and beauty of large, engineered timber components has refreshed conversations about the benefits of off-site construction for other building systems. When a modular structural system like CLT is assembled in half the time of a traditional structure with lower risk and a higher level of craftsmanship, designers and builders start to look for ways to shift the fabrication of other components into more controlled environments.

Site-built construction is often challenged by weather, traffic, noise ordinances, labor shortages, and any number of physical site constraints, as shown in **Figure 8.9**. Customized prefabrication can alleviate these issues, depending on the project and the extent to which the design and build teams can plan and coordinate it. The resulting buildings are more precise than site-built structures because of the increased quality control afforded by climate-controlled factory environments.

Chapters 5 and 6 go into depth on the advantages of off-site fabrication, and the design processes and collaboration necessary to achieve success. In short, taking more time to collaborate in the design phase pays off in construction-phase speed and predictability. The precision of custom components and a highly organized modular structural package contribute to expedited construction with fewer field modifications, change orders, and delays. Other associated benefits include fewer potential weather delays and lower costs associated with traffic disturbances.

Considering that a building's superstructure is usually about 20 to 25 percent of the total construction cost, investing in a highly predictable assembled structure may significantly reduce risk. Mechanical, electrical, plumbing, and fire (MEPF) systems account for another 30 to 35 percent of a building's cost, or about 15 percent for core-and-shell projects. These systems may also be fabricated off-site for schedule savings. If well-coordinated with the structure, the associated change risk also drops.

Carrying Costs

The construction cost savings of a modular approach such as CLT is multiplied when financing impacts are also considered. Comparative information about the construction duration of different structural options can have a significant impact when applied to carrying costs such as loan interest payments, property taxes, and other fees. Every week of reduced carrying costs translates

9   Interview with a representative of Kaiser + Path.

FIGURE 8.9: SIDEYARD

Source: Project: Sideyard; Photo Credit: Skylab Architecture

into tangible savings that should be included in comparative cost models.

8.3   TALL TIMBER

While mid-rise construction will continue to be the most common new building stock for all construction types, buildings over 20 stories create an impact from both a market and an environmental resource standpoint. Using mass timber in buildings above the current US code limit of 18 stories shows increasing potential. The tallest mass timber buildings in the world use CLT and glulam as the primary structural materials, and concrete for cores and/or additional mass:

- 18 stories, 174 feet (53 meters): Brock Commons, University of British Columbia, Vancouver, BC (2017)

- 24 stories, 276 feet (84 meters): HoHo Vienna, Woschitz Group, Vienna, Austria (2019)

- 18 stories, 279 feet (85 meters): Mjøstårnet, AB Invest, Brumunddal, Norway (2019)

- 25 stories, 284 feet (87 meters): Ascent, New Land Enterprises, Milwaukee, Wisconsin (2021)

Additionally, a growing number of studies and proposals are validating the effectiveness of timber structures up to 35, 40—even 80 stories.[10,11,12,13]

Allowable timber building heights increased in the 2021 International Building Code (IBC) to 9, 12, and 18 stories, with varying amounts of exposed wood allowed. The next round of updates, to be formalized in 2024, increases the allowance of exposed wood surfaces (see chapter 5 for more information). Well-designed wood buildings that are taller or include more exposed wood than codes allow can be proven viable and safe. Depending on the jurisdiction, such designs may be permissible through an alternate means-and-methods, performance-based permitting approach.

The Council on Tall Buildings and Urban Habitat (CTBUH) is developing resources for project teams pursuing tall mass timber buildings, supported by grant funding from the US Forest Service. The group worked to establish the inclusion of timber projects within the CTBUH height criteria and published *Timber Rising*, a compilation of the best research and resources for tall timber projects.

8.4   EXECUTING AN INNOVATIVE PROJECT

Although mass timber uptake in North America continues at an exceptional rate, it is still an emerging technology in most markets. Finding an experienced team is one effective way to mitigate risks associated with innovative approaches, but strong goals and leadership on the ownership side are just as crucial. This section identifies key issues that building owners and developers face when using mass timber.

Choosing a Team

Investors in mass timber buildings can benefit from the early recognition that a high level of integration between the design and build teams is a necessity, not an option. Some high points are listed below, but the relevant sections in chapters 5 (design) and 6 (build) provide more detail on integrated approaches.

The British Columbia Construction Association (BCCA) sponsored a study of innovative technologies and strategies in building construction procurement.[14] It found that qualities of successful projects include the following:

- a highly effective and collaborative project team that puts the interests of the project first

- multiproject engagements of consultants and contractors to foster collaboration, learning, and team cohesion

10   https://www.woodworkingnetwork.com/news/woodworking-industry-news/worlds-tallest-timber-residential-building-planned

11   https://www.gensler.com/blog/developing-worlds-tallest-net-zero-timber-building-sidewalk

12   https://perkinswill.com/project/canadas-earth-tower/

13   https://perkinswill.com/project/river-beech-tower/

14   British Columbia Construction Association (BCCA), *Procuring Innovation in Construction: A Review of Models, Processes, and Practices* (2016).

- greater collaboration, leading to more successful outcomes and higher-level team performance

- starting the procurement process as early as possible to allow collaboration to start and creative ideas to blossom

- allowing the project team input on when research and development, tours, and project documentation activities can best occur to maintain an efficient and safe site

- Construction Management at Risk (CMAR) or Single-Purpose Entity (SPE) for Integrated Project Delivery (IPD) contracts (such as multiparty agreements) that encourage collaboration may be best suited for innovative projects that are not well-defined in scope.

- requiring evidence of the qualifications of individuals as part of the evaluation; the names of key project team members, including important trade companies, need to be written into contract documents to ensure their expertise is being applied to the project and that the project is not passed on to others in the company

- the owner ensuring that it has the capacity to carry out project leadership and oversight effectively, potentially through an external project manager (operations and maintenance personnel should also be involved)

- encouraging businesses of all sizes to participate because small- to medium-size enterprises are sometimes the most innovative

- reducing barriers to participation by simplifying the procurement process as much as possible, e.g., admitting bidders who may not have directly relevant project experience but have transferable expertise with a similar

project type; focus is on the quality of the references rather than quantity

In summary, highly collaborative, nimble teams of people who are eager to innovate and willing to solve problems are more likely to achieve success with new approaches.

Design-Phase Forward Planning

Mass timber is a catalyst for unusual design-phase forward planning that can have significant impacts on construction schedules. An experienced team will plan for adequate coordination time before construction starts, to reduce costly field labor and project overhead. The advantages to investing in early coordination include the following:

- Precision placement of mechanical, electrical, and plumbing (MEP) penetrations results in fewer trade conflicts on-site and allows for off-site fabrication of components for rapid sequencing.

- A custom mass timber package is predictable to install and precise to a ⅛-inch tolerance. If the package is fully coordinated, it should require no field modifications.

- Change orders associated with the structure and MEP trades are minimized by up-front coordination.

Understanding the schedule savings and the reduction of on-site risk is crucial for producing an accurate cost model. According to Swinerton, a commercial construction company with experience in mass timber, "A large-scale mass timber project can be up to 2 percent higher in direct costs, but a minimum of 20 percent lower in project overhead costs. The net result is cost neutrality and higher value."[15]

By investing more time in the design phase to facilitate more efficient manufacturing and fabrication, project managers can reduce construction time and increase construction predictability. This may have implications for how the project is financed, increasing up-front soft costs but decreasing hard costs and interest payments.

Cost Certainty

The marketplace for mass timber products is increasingly competitive as the number of manufacturers grows, both in North America and abroad. Although the learning curve for mass timber construction is relatively easy to overcome, inexperienced builders will have difficulty estimating the savings associated with using mass timber and learning to be a part of an up-front planning process. The number of manufacturers, designers, and builders who understand how to deliver efficient, cost-effective mass timber buildings is growing because the value of completed buildings is being proven in the marketplace.

As the industry evolves, evidence is growing that, although the materials cost for a mass timber building may be higher than for concrete or steel, mass timber construction remains competitive because of labor savings, less costly foundations, reduced project and financing timelines, and more quickly realized revenue from a completed building.

When there is a comparative cost increase associated with using mass timber over other structural systems, the premium should be balanced by adjusting the pro forma to include increased market value, illuminating payback periods. The development team for The Canyons, a 6-story apartment building completed in late 2020 in Portland, Oregon, compared a CLT structure to light framing and painted drywall. They discovered that the payback period for the premium structure was just over 3 years, and they proceeded with the mass timber option. Ensuring premium market differentiation with a short payback period justified the relatively small capital cost increase.

Procurement Processes

Standard procurement processes can be a barrier to maximizing the cost benefits of mass timber, as discussed at length in chapters 5 and 6.

A traditional Design-Bid-Build (DBB) procurement process is common and, as such, preferred by many investors. For the purposes of this section, the issues are like those of the Construction Manager/General Contractor (CM/GC) process:

- Design a building to a given program, budget, and the local jurisdiction's requirements.

- Request bids from building contractors who seek the best value from a variety of installers and manufacturers.

- Select a contractor (or subcontractors) to construct the building based on the apparent best value.

An effective mass timber design, however, requires extensive coordination with a procurement and installation team before putting the project out

---

15   Erica Spiritos and Chris Evans, Swinerton Builders, "Mass Timber Construction Management: Economics & Risk Mitigation" (presentation, Mass Timber Conference, 2019).

for bid. Efficiencies in materials layout and site logistics can be accurately incorporated into early cost estimates only if an experienced team is consulted. A mass timber building can be designed with average assumptions about efficient fiber use, fire ratings, cost, and availability. This approach, however, carries risks because of possible delays and costs associated with the unanticipated need for redesign further along in the process, including design fees, permit revisions, constructability issues, and materials availability. The earlier a procurement and installation team is brought on board, the more refined and cost-effective the design and construction process will be.

One option in a traditional DBB contract model is to partner with a manufacturer during the design phase, using a separate contract or a letter of intent to select that manufacturer during bidding. This can be done as an agreement with the owner or with the CM/GC. The advantages of this approach include design optimization, detailed pricing feedback during design, and early assurances of product delivery dates. The risks include lack of precedent, resulting in limited availability of fabrication teams who are unaccustomed to design team integration. But remaining flexible until a project is ready to order can have advantages in a changing market. Until manufacturing supply catches up with the increasing demand for mass timber products, the lead time for detailing on the manufacturer's end can be a deciding factor.

Building owners may also choose a different, more inherently collaborative procurement model to avoid these issues and support an integrated design process. Design-Build, where the contractor and the design team are chosen and contracted together, or IPD, where all parties are financially incentivized for project success, naturally support early and efficient coordination. Having a design optimized early on will help ensure that fabrication timelines will be met if market demand is high. An experienced procurement team will be able to navigate these challenges.

The necessary prefabrication of massive panel elements creates an incentive for panel manufacturers to integrate along the traditional building project supply/value chain and to offer an integrated solution package rather than fabricated elements alone. As a result, many companies incorporate internal design, project management, and construction teams—or they ally with experienced companies. When possible, it makes sense for investors to consider such an integrated package and to make sure there are good reasons for seeking alternatives.

Insurance

Insurance coverage for building owners is classified by susceptibility to damage by fire as determined by past incidence rates. Without a breadth of experience or data on mass timber buildings, the insurance industry perceives all wood buildings similarly. A lack of data, to insurance underwriters, indicates high risk. To date, mass timber structures have been grouped with light frame structures, despite markedly different performance regarding fire, seismic, and water damage. As a result, premiums are just as high as combustible construction types, though timber structures are more analogous to noncombustible types. According to a Perkins&Will study,[16] mass timber has yet to be fully recognized by the

---

16 Perkins&Will, *Mass Timber Influencers: Understanding Mass Timber Perceptions among Key Industry Influencers* (October 2018).

insurance industry as comparable to a concrete-and-steel structure. Efforts are underway in the insurance industry to recognize mass timber as a distinct structural building category. In a 2021 paper exploring these issues, WoodWorks stated that a new classification code is a possibility.[17] Other benefits that could reduce perceived risks include the resiliency (or the ability to swiftly recover from catastrophic events) of some mass timber designs.

Further development of moisture protection and construction schedule reference data would likely also support lower builder's risk insurance premiums. Understanding how moisture control methods are implemented and monitored could reassure providers about the level of risk involved in the construction of timber buildings in wet climates. The risk may not be as high as presumed. A 2022 study[18] found that a building constructed during a wet winter in the Pacific Northwest "dried out more quickly than simulated values would predict." The significant risk advantages of dramatically reduced construction times for modular structural approaches should also be a factor.

As developers turn to more sustainable portfolios, insurance offerings will naturally become more competitive. Some North American insurance companies have recognized the growing market and the opportunity to align with sustainable practices. Perhaps not surprisingly, European-based companies are more comfortable with the construction type, as they've had more time to build mass timber structures into their portfolios and observe how they perform. Swiss-based

insurance company Zurich North America recognizes the increasingly popular segment of the construction market[19] and has increased builder's risk capacity in the mass timber sector.

Public Perception of Mass Timber

According to a 2015 public survey[20] by Perkins&Will, the public perceives the following factors to be the greatest barriers to wider adoption of mass timber:

- the flammability of wood

- wood's strength compared to concrete and steel

- deforestation concerns

The same study found that these barriers diminish as the public gains knowledge about and experience with mass timber buildings. Nevertheless, these perceptions are often obstacles that building developers must address.

Sources of Reliable Information

WoodWorks and other organizations have provided extensive support to mass timber building projects. Resources in the form of handbooks, standards, networks, conferences, published best practices, case studies, and more are growing exponentially with the expansion of the market.

8.5 MAINTENANCE AND BUILDING MANAGEMENT

Operational ease and savings are more achievable with a highly collaborative design phase, resulting

17   WoodWorks, *Insurance for Mass Timber Construction: Assessing Risk and Providing Answers* (2021).
18   Carmichael, Dawson, and Speert, *Mass Timber Moisture Monitoring and Simulation: A Marine Climate Case Study* (2022).
19   https://www.zurichna.com/knowledge/articles/2021/10/mass-timber-is-taking-root-in-commercial-construction
20   Shawna Hammon, "Tall Wood Survey," *Perkins&Will Research Journal* 8, no. 01 (2016).

in fewer changes during the construction phase. Although timber has material-specific upkeep, such as coatings, the natural beauty of wood offers some surprising benefits.

Utilities

Exposed wood is often a primary reason to use timber as a structural material. This decision should be paired with a deliberate approach to locating utilities, whether visible or concealed within chases and soffits. Mass timber buildings require more planning in the design phase, often leading to predetermined slab and wall penetrations for ductwork, conduits, and piping. This provides an opportunity to design utility systems with ingenuity and precision, and it ensures that systems are installed according to plan. Having reliable as-built documents can lead to more efficient routine maintenance, and when systems issues arise, to more timely action.

Durability

Coatings such as sealers or paints may be added to structural timber to protect it from ultraviolet light and weather, to add aesthetic appeal, or to make cleaning easier. Coatings on any surface require some upkeep and reapplication. Maintenance timelines vary by product, application method, and exposure; the more the wood is protected from weather, the longer the coatings will last.

Wood naturally changes color over time, with the hue depending on exposure and species. In Europe, it is more common to let exterior wood naturally age with weather and sunlight, creating a beautiful, varied texture on a building's facade. In the US, it is more common to seek a controlled,

even look. The preference is cultural, as wood that is given sufficient protection through good architectural detailing will take a long time to degrade, even without protective coatings.

Because wood is porous, many building owners are concerned about occupant damage such as staining, impact damage, or vandalism. But owners of wood buildings have reported higher levels of occupant care with wood surfaces and reduced occurrences of vandalism. (See chapter 7's section on occupant behavior for more information.) Staining can often be easily sanded away. The susceptibility of wood surfaces to visible damage from minor impacts depends on the species. Some variation and patina will occur over time, and again, it is a matter of preference whether the change is considered negative or positive.

8.6 RESILIENCY AND END-OF-LIFE VALUE

A building that consists of high-quality modular components that can be easily reappropriated for new uses will have an inherently higher value at the end of its life than a building slated to go entirely to the landfill. Design for Disassembly (DfD) is a growing area of knowledge for designers and builders, and one a building owner may be inclined to pursue as a point of interest for future buyers.

Though it is far too early to generate data on the deconstruction advantages of the recent wave of mass timber construction, the potential for reuse is likely to be an asset as these buildings age. Most other primary structural systems are difficult and costly to salvage, and total demolition is often the only viable solution from a cost standpoint. When salvage is possible, material is not usually reused as a complete element but as recycled material in newly formed components. But, like large steel members, salvaged and reused mass timber elements could have viable market use with much less reconfiguration.

There are a few important issues to resolve before mass timber panel buildings reach their end of life in substantial numbers:[21]

- Current practice promotes long, self-tapping screw connectors that are strong and easy to install. However, they are difficult to remove without damaging the panel perimeter.

- Current practice favors concrete finishing of hybrid mass timber panels in certain classes of public and industrial buildings. It is also used in residential buildings for vibration and impact sound mitigation. These integrated floors may pose difficulties to orderly disassembly and may preclude reuse.

- Mass timber panels are custom-produced for specific products. No current market exists for blank panels unassigned to specific projects. It is reasonable to presume, therefore, that finding a market for panels prefabricated for a decommissioned project could be difficult, especially for those that are integrated with multiple other materials and trades, including windows, doors, conduit openings, and connector nests.

These concerns are all possible to address through a DfD process that promotes circular use of decommissioned elements. DfD is achieved through mindful design and detailing. Investors can lead the way by emphasizing the importance of designing pathways for cost-effective deconstruction and reuse of recovered elements. An architectural design team following DfD principles may consider the potential for reusing entire subassemblies to reduce the substantial costs of refabrication and related waste. The cascading use of recovered elements should be planned during the initial design of the building, well ahead of deconstruction.

A building that has been designed for disassembly will also be easier to retrofit or repair after a disaster.

Resiliency

Resiliency is a term used to describe a building's ability to recover from a disaster such as an earthquake, fire, hurricane, or flood. Mass timber has several resiliency advantages over steel, concrete, and light frame structures.

Mass timber is both strong and flexible, and therefore, it is well-suited to resisting large forces and returning to its original shape. It is also very fire-resistant because of the thickness of each member. Unlike steel and concrete, failures or compromises in wood structural members are visible, so they require no special forensic equipment or destructive means for analysis, such as radar or core drilling. Being able to quickly verify the safety of a building after an event hastens reoccupancy.

Provided a design makes retrofitting damaged elements possible (see the earlier section on end-of-life value), mass timber components that show signs of compromise can be more easily replaced.

---

21   Lech Muszyński et al., *Conceptualizing the End of Life for Mass Timber Panel Buildings towards Circularity: Mapping the Gaps in Knowledge* (2021).

FIGURE 8.10: CLT ROCKING SHEAR WALL

Wall has steel fuses for dissipating seismic forces. Broken fuses are easily replaced.
Source: Project: Oregon State University Peavy Hall Replacement; Photo Credit: Andersen Construction

FIGURE 8.11: ROCKING SHEAR WALL FUSE

Source: Project: Oregon State University Peavy Hall Replacement; Photo Credit: Hannah O'Leary

Instead of an entire building being condemned, areas requiring repair can be isolated and retrofitted.

An innovative, earthquake-resistant "rocking" shear wall design has been installed in the new George W. Peavy Forest Science Center building on the Oregon State University campus, the first example of such construction in North America (see **Figure 8.10**). The design allows the wall to shift and return to place during a seismic event, with the added flexibility of steel tension rods that run the height of the wall and energy-dissipating steel "fuses" (**Figure 8.11**) that connect panels. The easily replaceable fuses are designed to break under high force, rather than allowing the destructive forces to transfer to the structure. They can be easily accessed and are low-cost to replace, if necessary. Seismic damage is confined to these components.

SIR MATTHEW BEGBIE ELEMENTARY SCHOOL UNDER CONSTRUCTION

CASE STUDY: MASS TIMBER IN BRITISH COLUMBIA

BRITISH COLUMBIA (BC) launched a Mass Timber Action Plan (*https://www2.gov.bc.ca/assets/gov/business/construction-industry/bc_mass-timber_action_plan_2022.pdf*) in spring 2022 that focused on building demand for mass timber to help shift the province's forestry sector—a cornerstone of BC's economy—from high volume to high value. It aims to reduce the province's construction carbon footprint and provide new opportunities for jobs, growth, and innovation in every corner.

LEARNING BY DOING

To help more people understand the benefits of mass timber, BC is offering incentives for mass timber construction in the private and public sectors. It has committed over $8 million to private-sector projects. Since 2021, the Mass Timber Demonstration Program has funded 12 projects that showcase technical innovation, building types, and regional representation. The results of a third intake are to be announced. More information is available at *https://www.masstimberbc.ca/*.

A recent change in the government's capital buildings program requires that all new provincially funded buildings use mass timber where appropriate. All ministries are to work together to adopt mass timber as a material of choice. To date, 17 public-sector buildings have been constructed using mass timber, including schools, student housing, education and training facilities, and the Royal

BC Museum's collections and research building. Further project details are available at *https://www. naturallywood.com/*

These diverse projects will help develop skills in using virtual design or three-dimensional (3D) modeling to support off-site prefabrication; create deeper understanding of Life Cycle Analysis (LCA), greenhouse gas (GHG) mitigation, and related carbon accounting analysis; and demonstrate the performance and commercial success of BC-based mass timber technologies.

Thus, the projects will inform the business case for mass timber use and the learning curve of the construction industry.

CHANGING THE SYSTEM

BC's regulatory system is changing to meet the needs of the mass timber sector. In 2020, for example, BC invited all local governments to adopt code provisions enabling 7-story to 12-story encapsulated mass timber construction. Twenty-two communities approved it ahead of the national code process.

BC-funded researchers at Simon Fraser University (SFU) are identifying potential barriers to building with mass timber at the local government level. SFU will engage elected officials and local government staff to disseminate its findings. BC will continue to work closely with the industry and researchers to identify and overcome regulatory barriers and make technical resources more widely available.

RESEARCH AS A BUILDING BLOCK

Since 2020, BC has invested over $3 million in 55 research projects that support mass timber inno-

vation and create a credible body of knowledge. The industry and the public can access scientifically supported information about mass timber.

These projects include improving the ability to estimate the environmental impacts of buildings during the design phase; making a more robust business case for mass timber; creating more accurate costing tools; and advancing prefabrication manufacturing technology.

BC co-funded a test in Ottawa, Ontario, for example, that demonstrated that mass timber performs well under fire conditions. Other research projects support a free costing tool that compares mass timber to other construction methods, and zoning and design guidelines at the local government level.

INFLUENCING THE FUTURE WORKFORCE

The province works with 25 public postsecondary institutions and industry partners to increase mass timber skills training through trades programs.

The British Columbia Institute of Technology has established new programs, for example, including a microcredential program and an associate's certificate in mass timber construction.

Through these programs, British Columbians will realize the rewards of construction innovation, greener jobs and development, and more economic value for every tree harvested. ◖

TALLEST MASS TIMBER BUILDING ON THE WEST COAST RISES TO THE OCCASION

NAME OF PROJECT/LOCATION: 1510 WEBSTER

OWNER: OWOW

LOCATION: OAKLAND, CALIFORNIA

COMPLETION DATE: MARCH 2025

MAJOR CONTRIBUTORS: OWOW DEVELOPMENT, OWOW DESIGN, OWOW CONSTRUCTION, DCI ENGINEERS, AND FRERES ENGINEERED WOOD

WOOD IS LITERALLY on the rise with the tallest mass timber building on the West Coast being built in Oakland, California. Oakland-based oWOW, a real estate company with vertically integrated development, design, construction, and property management in-house, is reimagining the construction process to provide luxury housing for the "missing middle" in this 19-story multifamily project.

To accomplish its goal, oWOW experimented with various types of mass timber, concrete, and steel on an earlier 5-story project in Oakland. It sought the most efficient, environmentally friendly, cost-effective building materials and processes to create sustainable urban living. As a result, oWOW has developed an unusual mass timber construction system to build high-quality housing in less time and at a lower cost than its competitors, and it selected Freres Engineered Wood's Mass Ply Panels for the structural floors of the 19-story high-rise at 1510 Webster.

The company discovered that it could assemble two floors per week—twice as fast as traditional steel and concrete-based construction—significantly reducing time to market as well as costs. Andrew Ball, oWOW president, said this will be the tallest structure in the world made with mass ply products.

oWow found that building with sustainable, engineered lumber or heavy mass timber is less wasteful, faster, and more cost-effective than concrete and steel. The panels, which are 40 feet by 10 feet and 5 inches thick, can be set in 15 minutes. That means a 6,000 square-foot floor and ceiling can be installed in four hours.

oWOW's design uses a single concrete core with Mass Plywood Panels (MPPs) built around it. The core houses the stairs and elevators while providing shear loading for seismic support. "After doing independent structural testing in accordance with ASTM 119 standards that proved MPP to be more than two times stronger than CLT (Cross-Laminated Timber), we were able to make several improvements to an innovative, point-supported column connection to the floor panel," Ball said. The beams were eliminated, saving 21 inches floor-to-floor; the floor thickness was reduced by 1 inch, and the total number of columns was reduced by 630. In addition, oWOW is optimizing efficiency throughout all their building systems, including with rooftop solar energy to supplement power to an all-electric building.

RENDERING OF OWOW'S 19-STORY AFFORDABLE HOUSING PROJECT. FRERES ENGINEERED WOOD'S MASS PLY PANELS WERE SELECTED FOR THEIR EFFICIENT, SUSTAINABLE, EASY-TO-INSTALL, AND COST-EFFECTIVE ATTRIBUTES.

Source: oWOW

"We also love that MPP is made in America," Ball said. "Previous to discovering Freres' MPP, we were having to ship in Austrian Spruce CLT. With recent supply chain issues and Freres being in Oregon, we have matched the quality of the Austrian product with MPP and are saving significantly in transportation costs."

This new building will provide 236 1- and 2-bedroom units affordable to people making 80 to 120 percent of the area's median income without any public subsidies, Ball said. ⬤

OSU Cascades- Edward J. Ray Hall
Dean Guernsey

Side Curve
Weyerhaeuser

Tsawwassen Shores
Harp Specialty Lumber

PDX Next
Brewington Photography

CHAPTER 9: CARBON CONSIDERATIONS AND MASS TIMBER

One of mass timber's significant strengths is its carbon/climate story. The potential for all members of the building sector, working in concert, to reduce the embodied energy/carbon content of the built environment through mass timber and other means is substantial. Our built environment could function as a carbon storehouse rather than a source of emissions. That is a powerful vision.

The urgent need for reductions in global greenhouse emissions, as identified in the Paris Agreement, has added impetus to our transition to nonfossil energy sources. Construction techniques and codes have improved dramatically, contributing to a decline in operational fossil energy use in new buildings. The transition away from fossil fuels now underway further reduces the operational carbon footprints of buildings. The use of mass timber provides the opportunity to address the embodied fossil carbon and energy footprint of the built environment, from single-family housing to high-rises.

This chapter provides overviews of the 3 Ss: (1) the role of forests as carbon *sinks*, by sequestering carbon out of the atmosphere; (2) the function of wood products for short- and long-term *storage* of carbon in building components; and (3) the *substitution* benefit of using low- or negative-fossil carbon products in place of high-fossil ones. A vital prerequisite is that the wood should come from sustainably managed forests. The challenge is to create a system that provides synergistic rewards for capturing as much benefit as possible from the 3 Ss.

Crucial questions are being asked by members of the building sector and their clients about other values or services of forests because carbon is one of the many benefits forests provide. Biodiversity, watershed function—both quantity and quality—recreation, aesthetics, and carbon storage are often referred to as ecosystem services. We provide contextual discussion about whether all these values are compatible with producing wood products and creating cities that are carbon sinks rather than sources.

9.1 FOREST CARBON: SEQUESTRATION

The Nature Conservancy (TNC) led a global analysis of the potential for natural carbon storage in 2017;[1] it published a similar one focused on the US in 2018.[2] These studies found that the potential contribution of nature-based sequestration is substantial, approximately one-third of the solution toward achieving net-zero carbon. The studies also found that forests provide the greatest percentage of that benefit within the array of natural storage opportunities. This natural role of forests can be managed to enhance the sequestration function and create products that will substitute for carbon-intensive materials and store carbon for the life of the building and beyond.

Forests are crucial to the Earth's natural carbon capture and storage system. During photosynthesis, trees take in carbon dioxide, sunlight, and wa-

---

1   Bronson W. Griscom et al., "Natural Climate Solutions," *Proceedings of the National Academy of Sciences* 114, no. 144 (2017), accessed December 18, 2022, https://www.pnas.org/doi/10.1073/pnas.1710465114.
2   Joseph E. Fargione et al., "Natural Climate Solutions for the United States," *Science Advances* 4, no. 11 (2018), accessed December 18, 2022, https://www.science.org/doi/pdf/10.1126/sciadv.aat1869.

ter to create simple carbohydrates, or sugars, that can be used to either nourish the trees' existing cells or create new cells (growth). When used for growth, carbon is stored in woody material. When sugars are consumed for nourishment, the trees release carbon dioxide back into the atmosphere. In the continental US alone, forests store more than 14 billion metric tons of carbon (see **Table 9.1**).

If unaltered by human activity, the complete life cycle of a tree is carbon neutral. This cycle can take tens to thousands of years to complete, depending on local climatic conditions, the tree species, and the disturbance regimes. (Disturbance regime equals the mix of fire, storms, insects, disease, etc. that shapes the evolution of a forest.) Some species—such as quaking aspen, loblolly pine, and lodgepole pine—are relatively short-lived (only 80 to 140 years). Others—such as ponderosa pine, Douglas-fir, tulip-poplar, Western larch, longleaf pine, cedars, and oaks—can live many centuries. These time spans are the potential life spans; however, just as most humans do not live to their full potential age of 120 years, most trees do not achieve their potential life span.

Natural forests are often a mix of species with varying life spans and adaptations, but they also can be monocultures. Natural disturbances and competition among trees kill some and truncate the lives of others. Some ecosystems' natural disturbance cycles are only years to a few decades apart, and others have cycles lasting centuries. Death comes in many forms: fire, insect epidemics, disease, droughts, hurricanes, ice storms, windstorms, competition among trees, and more. Many of these disturbances interact, creating synergies. A windstorm, for example, can blow down hundreds or thousands of acres of trees that then provide food for bark beetles or other insects

that breed and expand their populations enough to attack live trees. These events can set the stage for high fuel loads that can feed a severe wildfire. In forests set aside for national parks, wilderness, and other designations, these disturbance cycles are sometimes allowed to proceed.

A landowner who aims to produce timber or capture carbon will try to minimize the effects of these unplanned mortality events through planned disturbances, such as prescribed burns and harvests.

The natural, or unmanaged, tree and forest cycles have three phases: carbon capture, carbon storage, and carbon release. The cycles for an individual tree and the overall forest may not be synchronous, depending on the disturbance regime. In the first phase, a tree grows and uses most of the carbon dioxide it absorbs as building blocks. In the second phase, the tree is mature and no longer uses as much carbon for growth. Instead, the tree consumes a larger portion of its sugars to maintain its systems, so it is not as efficient at capturing and storing carbon. In the third phase, the tree releases more carbon than it captures as it declines in vigor and parts begin to decay or die. It then dies of old age, disease, insect attack, or fire, eventually releasing most of its remaining carbon back into the atmosphere. The entire process may take decades or centuries, depending on the disturbance regime and the tree species. A small portion of the carbon will remain in the soil, if undisturbed.

In a natural forest, some trees decline or die, and others regenerate, grow, and replace them, absorbing and sequestering more carbon in the process. In a forest with a long disturbance cycle, the dead trees might retain large amounts of carbon as they slowly decay, or they might release it

STATE	NATIONAL FOREST	OTHER FEDERAL	PRIVATE	STATE & LOCAL	TOTAL
AL	21	9	492	19	541
AR	65	18	318	18	419
AZ	70	12	53	7	142
CA	494	79	352	51	976
CO	184	46	53	7	290
CT	0	0	44	18	62
DE	0	0	9	3	12
FL	22	23	191	70	306
GA	32	21	473	23	549
IA	0	3	49	7	59
ID	318	14	48	24	404
IL	8	2	96	11	118
IN	6	5	106	11	129
KS	0	2	40	1	42
KY	28	12	284	8	333
LA	20	13	262	21	316
MA	0	2	69	33	104
MD	0	2	64	22	88
ME	2	4	299	28	333
MI	65	7	254	83	409
MN	38	4	124	83	249
MO	32	7	251	19	309
MS	39	15	408	13	476
MT	270	25	62	14	371
NC	45	25	414	31	516
ND	11	1	7	1	20
NE	0	1	18	1	21
NH	23	2	97	14	136
NJ	0	3	27	26	56
NM	84	12	63	9	169
NV	21	38	2	0	61
NY	1	4	388	157	549
OH	9	2	185	27	223
OK	9	9	120	7	144
OR	539	159	257	52	1,007
PA	19	5	344	144	512
RI	0	0	8	4	12
SC	20	14	255	19	307
SD	0	0	8	1	10
TN	25	23	313	32	394
TX	21	13	421	13	468
UT	71	46	23	11	151
VA	56	19	387	22	484
VT	14	2	105	15	136
WA	349	111	250	131	841
WI	32	5	226	57	319
WV	43	7	327	13	391
WY	81	30	12	3	126
Total	**3,189**	**856**	**8,659**	**1,383**	**14,087**

TABLE 9.1: TONS OF CARBON IN FORESTS BY STATE BY OWNERSHIP TYPE (METRIC TONS IN MILLIONS)

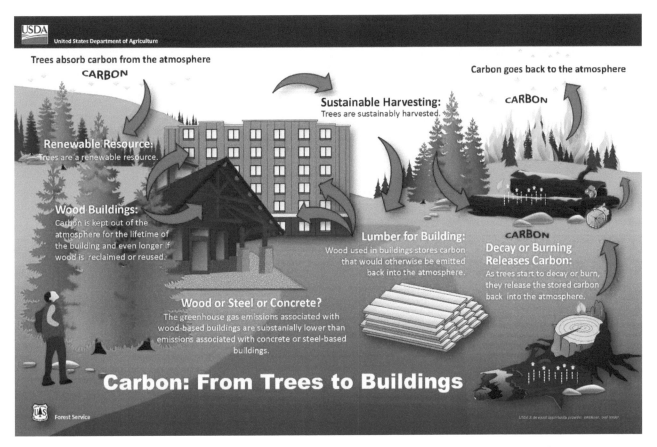

FIGURE 9.1: FOREST PRODUCTS' CARBON STORAGE

relatively quickly if the species is more susceptible to rot fungi. In a forest with more frequent disturbances, a much smaller amount of carbon is stored in dead wood, litter, and duff.

When forests are actively managed, the first phase of carbon capture can be extended through thinnings[3] that help maintain the rapid growth and carbon capture of the first phase. Thinnings also avoid potential mortality from intertree competition, and those thinned trees become products. The thinning extends the overlap of the rapid growth phase with the storage phase, for the remaining trees are larger but still growing. Management can

thus store more usable carbon and produce more wood from the same number of acres.

After the harvest, the forests can be regenerated by planting seedlings or relying on seeds from trees left in the area, with vigorous young trees starting a new cycle. Wood from the harvested trees enters the industrial cycle in the form of products that store carbon, such as building structures, furniture, insulation, packaging, paper, and energy (see **Figure 9.1**).

The carbon sequestration impact of a forest and the carbon storage in wood products are contin-

---

3   Robert O. Curtis, "Extended Rotations and Culmination Age of Coast Douglas-Fir: Old Studies Speak to Current Issues" (research paper PNW-RP-485, US Department of Agriculture, Forest Service, Pacific Northwest Research Station, Portland, Oregon, 1995).

gent on sustainable management. Forest certifications like the Forest Stewardship Council (FSC), Sustainable Forestry Initiative (SFI), and American Tree Farm System (ATFS) for private land, and laws and regulations for public land, help consumers source sustainable materials. (See chapter 2.) Ongoing research and appropriate incentives help shape the evolution of forest practices and set the stage for building design and construction teams to incorporate the use of wood into their Life Cycle Analyses (LCA).

Triple Bottom Line

The shift to forestry practices that achieve a balanced triple bottom line of economic, environmental, and social goals is underway at each point in the wood products supply chain, but consensus has not yet been reached among all perspectives. Mass timber products have captured the public imagination in ways not seen since Smokey Bear, pushing a wave of multidisciplinary conversations around carbon stewardship. One of the efforts to facilitate understanding is The Forests Dialogue[4] (TFD), hosted by the Yale School of the Environment. One of their initiatives, Climate Positive Forest Products (CPFP), is hosted in conjunction with the World Resources Institute and the Climate Smart Forest Economy Program (CSFEP). Representatives from around the world meet to share information about developing a collective understanding of the potential to significantly reduce greenhouse gas (GHG) emissions. Participants were provided with background papers synthesizing the most recent published research before they met in 2021 and 2022.[5] These papers refer to recently published studies from Europe, North America, and around

the world and address wood supply and the carbon benefits of wood versus concrete and steel through LCA. They substantiate the carbon benefits of wood, as well as sustainably managed forests' ability to supply the wood needed for expanded use of mass timber. This kind of dialogue and understanding is essential if the potential for mass timber to decrease embodied carbon emissions is to be achieved worldwide.

In recent years, carbon offset markets have paid landowners for the additional carbon value they create through management practices that enhance forests' ability to sequester more carbon.

Land Use

One of the biggest concerns in using forest-sourced products is the fear of deforestation or forest degradation. Deforestation is defined as the conversion of land from growing forests to some other use. Therefore, clear-cutting a forest is not considered deforestation as long as a new forest is established. Forest degradation can occur when logging practices cause biodiversity loss or reduce the ecological resilience of an ecosystem. Designers should consider the sources of the fiber they specify, and they can turn to forest certifications as one way to support sustainable forest practices (see chapter 2).

The biggest cause of deforestation is the conversion of forests to agriculture and development. When land worldwide is not valued as forests, it tends to get turned into something else. Thus, the idea—counterintuitive at first, but economically logical—that the use of forest products may con-

---

4   https://theforestsdialogue.org/initiative/climate-positive-forest-products-cpfp
5   Edie S. Hall and Barbara K. Reck, "Current State of Mass Timber and Wood Product Value Chains in Europe" (2022), https://theforestsdialogue.org/sites/default/files/tfd_cpfp_finland_backgroundpaper_2022.pdf.

tribute to an increase in lands used for forestry. North America and Western Europe have some of the highest per capita wood use in the world, but they also have net-positive forest growth. That's because the demand for and value of wood products create economic incentives to maintain or expand forests.

The offset payment for storing more carbon can increase the incentive to maintain or expand forested lands. The publications led by TNC show that expanding the amount of forest land is the largest natural carbon storage practice among the many options. Having an economic incentive, i.e., being paid for carbon storage and for timber products at the end of a rotation, is an essential driver of this practice.

Forestry Practices

An increased demand for forest products appears to also drive more sustainable forestry practices. According to the Carbon Leadership Forum (CLF), "Transitioning construction of low to mid-rise commercial and nonresidential structures to cross-laminated timber (CLT)/heavy timber construction could have a positive impact on the environment. It could also develop a new market for the smaller diameter and lower quality logs derived from forest thinning and forest health operations, thereby providing an incentive to undertake forest management activities designed to improve forest health and resiliency. Finally, the development of a cross-laminated timber industry would provide substantial economic benefits and employment opportunities for rural timber-dependent communities."[6]

Climate Smart Forestry

Forest certification systems, as discussed in chapter 2, address many issues other than carbon storage and the role of forests in climate change. In recent years, the term Climate Smart Forestry (CSF) has emerged. North Carolina State University's website says that CSF enables "forests and society to transform, adapt to, and mitigate climate-induced changes."[7] It helps forests adapt to a changing climate as well as mitigates climate change. How is this done? By managing for the resilience that protects the carbon stored in the forest and supports its ability to store more. It varies by forest type, ecological setting, and disturbance regimes. Some talk about "carbon defense" management practices. That may mean favoring better-adapted species and/or reducing forest density so the remaining trees are better adapted to drought, wildfire, and insects.

CSFEP[8] is supported by a coalition of national and international organizations that stress the 3 Ss and are working to integrate them. Their goal is to make them synergistic. Thus, the use of wood creates an economic incentive to grow forests in a way that stores more carbon and produces more wood per acre than conventional practices. The organizations also emphasize the management of forests for biodiversity and other environmental services, such as water and recreation.

Some groups advocate for what they call "proforestation" as a climate change mitigation strategy. They say mature and old-growth forests should be left alone so they can store more carbon. Deferring harvest may allow for more carbon capture compared to harvesting and regrowing a

---

6   https://carbonleadershipforum.org/cross-laminated-timber-optimization/
7   Accessed December 18, 2022, https://content.ces.ncsu.edu/what-is-climate-smart-forestry-a-brief-overview.
8   Accessed December 18, 2022, https://www.csfep.org/our-work.

new forest. These groups argue that keeping these forests and the carbon they have sequestered intact is more valuable than sustainable harvesting.

Proforestation does not yet consider the trade-offs for storage and substitution discussed below, or the disturbance regime of a forest ecosystem. Mature and older forests/trees, especially in a drought-stressed environment, are more susceptible to insect attacks and diseases. Forests in several states in the western US have become sources of carbon (rather than sinks) as a result of insect epidemics, wildfires, or a combination of the two. The Society of American Foresters recently released a white paper[9] addressing the concept.

Carbon Markets

Carbon offset markets have allowed forest owners to adopt certain management practices that will increase the amount of carbon they capture and store, and get paid for it. These markets, either voluntary or compliance markets, have different requirements for monitoring and verification. The prices paid for the carbon also differ. Some climate activists have expressed concerns about the potential for carbon leakage and the possibility that companies may use the markets as an excuse to avoid reducing their emissions from fossil fuels. The United Nations Climate Change Conference (COP26) adopted Article 6 to provide transparent methods developed by the Task Force on Scaling Voluntary Carbon Markets to minimize these risks.[10]

The American Forest Foundation and TNC initiated the Family Forest Carbon Program, which helps small landowners access carbon offset markets if they apply a practice that stores more carbon. At the end of their contract, they will also have more wood to sell. The program offers shorter-term contracts of 10 to 20 years (rather than 100 years), making it more attractive for small holdings.

Providing landowners with an additional revenue stream besides wood products allows them to conduct better carbon management and achieve better wood production. The synergy between these kinds of practices can expand the availability of wood and sequester more carbon.

We have not seen a situation where a building developer has been paid for avoiding emissions by using wood instead of steel or concrete, but the potential is there.

9.2 WOOD PRODUCTS: CARBON STORAGE

Many designers and building owners are drawn to mass timber for its environmental credentials and the intuitive benefits of storing carbon. A rapidly developing area of research seeks to answer their questions about how to quantify and maximize the benefits of this choice. Architecture 2030, a non-profit organization whose climate goals have been adopted by the American Institute of Architects (AIA) in the form of the AIA 2030 Challenge, has identified a time frame of less than 10 years to reach net-zero emissions in the building industry to curb catastrophic climate change.[11] So getting it right is crucial. The engineered properties of mass timber

---

9 Accessed December 18, 2022, https://www.eforester.org/Main/SAF_News/2022/SAF-Develops-Resource-on-Proforestation.aspx.

10 Accessed December 18, 2022, https://www.iif.com/Portals/1/Files/TSVCM_Phase_2_Report.pdf.

11 *Architecture Magazine*, The Carbon Issue, January 2020, guest edited by Architecture 2030.

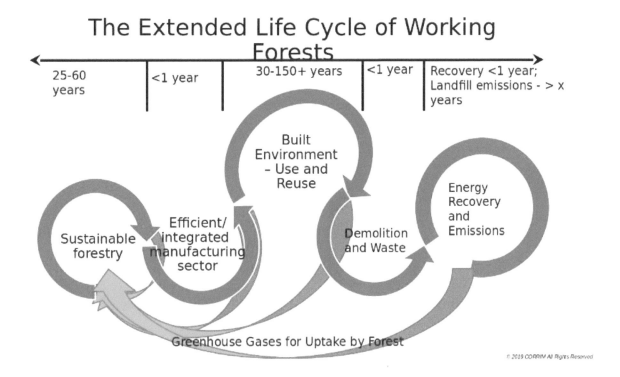

The Extended Life Cycle of Working Forests

| 25-60 years | <1 year | 30-150+ years | <1 year | Recovery <1 year; Landfill emissions - > x years |

Built Environment – Use and Reuse

Sustainable forestry

Efficient/integrated manufacturing sector

Demolition and Waste

Energy Recovery and Emissions

Greenhouse Gases for Uptake by Forest

© 2019 CORRIM All Rights Reserved

FIGURE 9.2: EXTENDED LIFE CYCLES OF WORKING FORESTS

Source: Reprinted with permission, Elaine Oneil, Consortium for Research on Renewable Industrial Materials (CORRIM), www.corrim.org

products help meet that goal and have opened up a whole new suite of uses for wood products.

Tools and Techniques

This section, and the next section on substitution, outline the tools and techniques for selecting and measuring the carbon impacts of mass timber in building projects. We also discuss how choosing to use mass timber, along with other wood products, especially at scale as the market sector grows, also benefits land-use and forestry practices. We separated carbon storage from substitution to clearly differentiate their separate but complementary benefits.

Biogenic Carbon

The ScienceDirect website says, "Biogenic carbon refers to carbon that is sequestered from the atmosphere during biomass growth and may be released back to the atmosphere later due to combustion of the biomass or decomposition."[12] One cubic meter of wood stores approximately one ton of carbon dioxide equivalent. This differentiates biogenic carbon from fossil fuel carbon that is released from geologic storage.

Wood, as a building material, provides long-term biogenic carbon storage. As illustrated in **Figure 9.2**, carbon storage in long-lived wood products can extend the biogenic carbon cycle. Constructing buildings with wood products increases the

12 https://www.sciencedirect.com/topics/engineering/biogenic-carbon

CASE STUDY: TIMBERHP AND CARBON-NEGATIVE INSULATION

TIMBERHP BY GO LAB is set to manufacture a comprehensive line of wood fiber insulation products for the first time in North America, redefining assumptions about high-performance building and the role of construction in addressing the climate crisis.

Wood fiber loose-fill, press-fit batt, and continuous board insulations work well as affordable drop-in replacements for existing insulations and as complete, above-grade systems for residential construction and light commercial buildings.

Made from wood chips left over from lumber production and from the low-grade, woody biomass produced by sustainable forest thinning operations, these products are free of toxins and abrasive fibers and provide carbon-negative insulation.

Wood fiber insulation provides the following benefits:

MOISTURE MANAGEMENT

High vapor permeability (40 to 70 perms/inch) allows drying in both the inside and outside of buildings; it also absorbs, redistributes, and releases moisture—all without losing insulating properties. This ability to manage moisture delivers high structural resilience, reduces the conditions that lead to rot, provides for more comfortable indoor humidity levels, and generates healthier indoor air quality.

TEMPERATURE BALANCE

Stable, long-term R-values are created while reducing airflow through assemblies. Density combined with low thermal conductivity and high heat capacity balance temperature swings in conditioned spaces, reducing heating and cooling loads.

HEALTHY INDOOR HABITATS

Wood fiber insulation reduces threats associated with high levels of indoor humidity and trapped moisture, such as mold and mildew growth, that can cause respiratory issues and intensify allergies. Best-in-class acoustics make wood fiber insulation the ideal stand-alone and assembly solution for reducing airborne and impact noise.

PRODUCTION PROCESS, PRODUCT SPECIFICATIONS, AND INSTALLATION METHODS

TimberFill

Wood chips are steamed and mechanically refined, then treated with a small amount of boric acid in the wet phase of production for fire protection as well as mold and pest protection. The fiber is then dried to lock in the treatment and packaged. Using standard pneumatic insulation blowers, TimberFill can be dense packed in cavities or installed as an attic blanket.

Product Merits
- R-3.8/inch
- Achieve desired R-value with less volume compared to other blown-in options
- Shape and size of fibers reduce issues with settling, preventing voids and air pockets
- Pure, consistent feedstock: no toxins; free of printing ink and other foreign contaminants
- Class A fire performance (ASTM E84)

TimberBatt

The treated TimberFill fiber is blended with polyamide binding fiber and melted in an oven to cre-

TIMBERFILL, TIMBERBATT, TIMBERBOARD
Source: TimberHP

ate a flexible batt. TimberBatt works equally well for thermal and acoustic insulation in cavities.

Product Merits

- R-4.0/inch
- Flexible and dense
- No toxic off-gassing or harmful fibers
- Low thermal conductivity and high heat capacity
- Industry-leading acoustic performance

Sizing

- 16-inch and 24-inch on-center wood stud and nonstructural steel stud
- 3-inch, 3.5-inch, 5.5-inch, 6-inch, and 7.25-inch

TimberBoard

Wood chips are steamed and mechanically refined, then blended with PMDI adhesive and paraffin wax to repel moisture, resulting in a vapor-open, hydrophobic board with Class B fire performance. TimberBoard is used as continuous exterior roof and above-grade wall insulation and as interior insulation for walls, floors, and ceilings.

Product Merits

- Stable R-3.4 to 3.7/inch
- Vapor-open
- High compressive strength
- Unmatched heat protection

Sizing

- Thickness: 1 foot to 9.25 inches
- Width: 2-foot and 4-foot
- Length: 4-foot and 8-foot

The availability of domestically manufactured wood fiber insulation is a game-changing moment for the design and construction industries in North America. For the first time, architects and designers, as well as builders and developers, can choose high-performing insulation for their projects that arrives at the job site carbon-negative—and yet is priced for mainstream adoption.

For the mass timber industry, wood fiber insulation brings hygrothermal solutions that complement all-wood assemblies while supplying acoustic protection to improve the applicability and acceptance of Cross-Laminated Timber (CLT) and Mass Plywood Panels (MPP) designs. ○

length of time that carbon is kept in storage. Wooden buildings 800 to 1,000-plus years old exist in Europe and Asia. They demonstrate that, with proper protection and maintenance, wood can serve us well.

Biogenic carbon eventually returns to the atmosphere through decomposition or incineration, and that may be acknowledged through a complete LCA that illuminates the long-term impacts (over at least 100 years). While end-of-life considerations are crucial to a circular economy, most buildings built today will remain standing long after global net-zero carbon timelines have passed, and they will continue to keep that carbon out of the atmosphere. When calculating the total life cycle of a wood product, project teams should consider whether to include or exclude biogenic carbon, acknowledging the eventual return of the carbon to the atmosphere—or not. Total decomposition is unlikely, based on the expectation that structural wood will be reused or encapsulated in a landfill, rather than incinerated or mulched, thus preventing the carbon's release to the atmosphere. Design and construction with deconstruction and reuse in mind will facilitate the continued long-term storage.

Absorbing and preventing the release of as much atmospheric carbon as possible in the next 10 to 30 years is a global priority to avoid irreversible climate change. The World Green Building Council (WorldGBC) stresses the importance of reducing up-front or embodied carbon in its 2019 report, *Bringing Embodied Carbon Upfront*.[13] The report states, "To achieve our vision, we must take urgent action to tackle up-front carbon while designing with whole-life carbon in mind." It can be argued that the embodied carbon stored today is more important than accounting for unknowns in deconstruction approaches, fire, or decay past that crucial timeline. Considering the urgent timeline we face to eliminate emissions in the industry, project teams may choose to emphasize the short-term effects of using sustainably grown wood products.

Buildings as Carbon Banks

On a global scale, the building industry stands out as having the potential to turn from being the largest contributor of carbon emissions to becoming a massive atmospheric absorber. Buildings are long-lived and profoundly materials-intensive. They present an opportunity, therefore, to become carbon storage devices, or carbon banks. To achieve this, the industry must use as many biogenic materials as possible in every building.

The longer a biogenic, carbon-rich building remains standing, the more effective a carbon store it is. And, because mass timber components have a high potential to retain value after the life of a building, markets for reuse of mass timber will likely develop,[14] further delaying decomposition. In fact, decomposition is an unlikely outcome. A worst-case scenario would send these valuable building components to a landfill, where LCAs typically assume the wood will decompose. In fact, the US Environmental Protection Agency (EPA) says, "...because wood products are not completely decomposed by anaerobic bacteria, some of the carbon in these materials remains

---

13   https://worldgbc.org/article/bringing-embodied-carbon-upfront/
14   "Integrating Working Forests and Wood Products into the Circular Economy" (presentation, Consortium for Research on Renewable Industrial Materials, Seattle, Washington, January 21–22, 2020), https://corrim.org/circular-economy-workshop/.

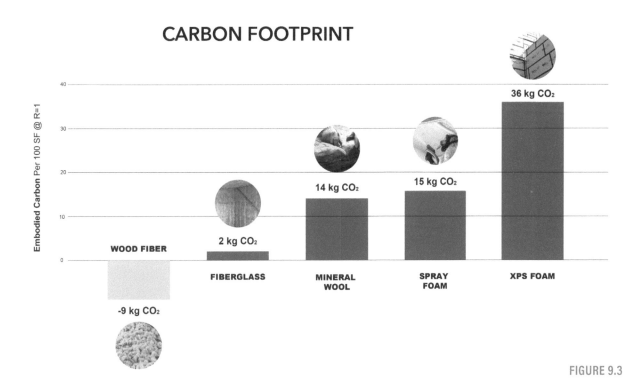

CARBON FOOTPRINT

FIGURE 9.3

stored in the landfill. This stored carbon constitutes a sink...".[15]

9.3   SHORT-LIVED VERSUS LONG-LIVED PRODUCTS

When a log is run through a sawmill, approximately half of it becomes long-lived products such as mass timber, flooring, or furniture. The other half is often ignored in LCA or treated as a rapid release of carbon. Mass timber users might want to understand the fate of those other parts of the log. Their products often substitute for other fossil carbon-intensive products. Cardboard boxes and packaging replace plastics; cellulose-based clothing replaces petrol-based; bark and other scrap wood can be used for heat and power to avoid the release of fossil carbon sources; lignin

and biochar can be used in a bio-based plastic. Much of the sawdust from sawmills goes into medium- and high-density fiberboard that becomes shelving, tables, cabinets, etc. that may have decades-long lives.

New to North America, but not to Europe, are sound and thermal insulation materials made of wood rather than fossil fuel-based materials. The TimberHP plant under construction in Maine will take sawmill residue materials and small, crooked, or partially rotten trees and turn them into long-lived wood fiber products that store carbon and avoid the use of fossil fuels as a feedstock, providing both storage and substitution benefits. (See **Figure 9.3**) Insulation products can also become one more method of reusing deconstructed wood buildings through reprocessing and extending the life of the stored carbon.

---

15   *Decarbonization for Greenhouse Gas Emission and Energy Factors Used in Waste Reduction Model (WARM) (2019)*

Concrete, aluminum, and steel have some very desirable construction attributes and applications, and if forest products can make them more climate-friendly, so much the better.

The use of nanocellulose in making concrete is reducing its carbon footprint by 19 to 29 percent. A bridge in Northern California and a dam in Georgia are being built this year using nanocellulose-infused concrete. The use of biochar to replace coke from fossil carbon, meanwhile, is helping steel be greener. These opportunities for building developers to use lower-emission concrete and other forms of residual wood are steps toward the vision of cities becoming carbon sinks.

Biochar is made from wood and other sources of biomass, ideally as a bioenergy and carbon storage system. Wood is about 50 percent carbon; the remainder is primarily hydrogen and oxygen. When pyrolyzed, the hydrogen and oxygen are driven off and, as they combust, energy is released that can be used for heat and electricity. The resulting char is about 90 percent carbon, which does not decompose for hundreds to thousands of years. It effectively becomes a carbon capture and storage element that can be used in many valuable ways: as a soil enhancement to improve ecosystem productivity, in mine reclamation, as a carbon-negative thermoplastic, for water and air purification, and more.

When sourced from sustainably managed lands, the short-term products' carbon is continually replaced by new forest growth, negating the effects of their short lives. That's especially true when the products are made from the residuals of long-lived products.

Impact of Building Market's Demand on Forests and Carbon

Many architects, engineers, and developers who choose to work with wood will be asked about forestry and logging. For some, that will be the first time they have had to consider exactly where their raw building materials come from. These questions tend not to arise with inorganic materials like steel and concrete, though, of course, everything comes from somewhere. Thus, questions are surfacing: is it virgin steel, or is it from recycled feedstock?

The emotional connection people have with trees and forests may be behind this investigative imperative. As noted earlier, expanding demand can expand the amount of forested land and the amount of carbon stored in the forest per acre or hectare, with longer rotations supported by thinning, especially if market incentives are aligned.

9.4 EMBODIED CARBON/ENERGY: SUBSTITUTION

The carbon benefits of substitution occur when a product with lower embodied content carbon/energy product is used instead of a higher-content product. The choice of mass timber in place of steel or concrete usually results in less fossil carbon released to the atmosphere. This is true of other wood products as well, including furniture, flooring, insulation, and trim.

Environmental Impacts of Building Materials

Analyzing and comparing the environmental impacts of building materials is complicated but crucial to achieving the green building industry's car-

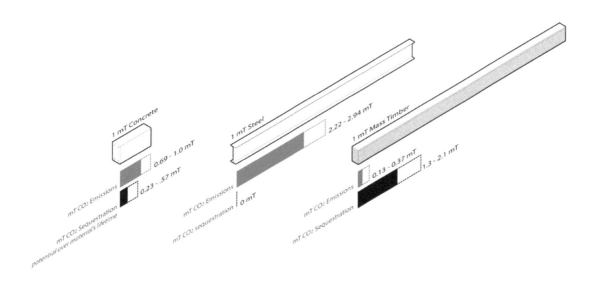

1 mT Concrete

0.69 - 1.0 mT

0.23 - .57 mT

mT CO₂ Emissions

mT CO₂ Sequestration
potential over materials lifetime

1 mT Steel

2.22 - 2.94 mT

0 mT

mT CO₂ Emissions

mT CO₂ sequestration

1 mT Mass Timber

0.13 - 0.37 mT

1.3 - 2.1 mT

mT CO₂ Emissions

mT CO₂ Sequestration

FIGURE 9.4 EMBODIED AND BIOGENIC CARBON IN COMMON STRUCTURAL MATERIALS

Source: Timber City Research Initiative, Gray Organschi Architecture, timbercity.org

bon goals. Biogenic carbon, discussed above and embodied carbon, as defined below, are two important concepts that underlie such an analysis. To track progress, designers can use tools developed by academic institutions, nongovernmental organizations (NGOs), and the industry to assist with environmentally conscious decision-making processes that include LCAs and Environmental Product Declarations (EPDs). Several certification programs are designed to help building projects measure, meet, and promote their goals, and, as a result, be rewarded in the marketplace.

Embodied Carbon

Most processes involved in the extraction, manufacture, transport, and installation of building products rely on fossil fuels. The total amount of fossil carbon emitted by a given product during this process is the embodied carbon of that prod-

uct. Mass timber's structural strength qualities result in a lower embodied fossil energy content than concrete or steel because it requires significantly less energy to produce (see **Figure 9.4**). We frequently compare wood with these two other materials because the structural system of a building comprises up to 80 percent of its embodied carbon. Mass timber products are an effective replacement for these widely used, high-embodied-energy structural materials. In fact, wood products are often produced substantially with renewable energy, including the combustion of manufacturing by-products for power generation.

Architecture 2030 has determined that "embodied carbon will be responsible for almost half of total new construction emissions between now and 2050."[16] The crucial climate benefits of reduced embodied carbon are achieved while a building is under construction and thus have im-

---

16   "Actions for a Zero Carbon Built Environment: Embodied Carbon," *Architecture 2030*, https://architecture2030.org/new-buildings-embodied/.

mediate impacts. Bio-based products also stand apart from other materials in that they store carbon as well, potentially offsetting carbon impacts from other materials.

Life Cycle Analyses (LCAs)

LCAs are a process for documenting embodied carbon in building materials and comparing similar products. An LCA might focus on a single component or product, or it might capture an entire building. As discussed above, when calculating the LCA of a timber building, biogenic carbon can be assessed by considering a decomposition or industrial reuse cycle.

The Consortium for Research on Renewable Industrial Materials (CORRIM) and the Athena Sustainable Materials Institute are leading resources on LCAs for a variety of wood products and forest management. Embodied carbon and Global Warming Potential (GWP) have been researched and calculated for several North American mass timber products, yielding a range of results because of variations in wood sources and manufacturing processes. Recent research and data continue to confirm that, depending on the source, wood products can more than offset the carbon required to produce and install them. Because new methods of manufacturing, forest management, and energy sources are being developed, Life Cycle Inventories (LCIs) and LCAs will need to be updated continually.

The CLF is widely trusted for producing best-practice Whole Building LCAs (WBLCAs) for timber structures. In a 2019 study for Katerra, CLF compiled information from several mass timber

buildings to compare their GWPs from a WBLCA standpoint. **Figure 9.5** shows the buildings' GWPs with and without biogenic carbon included, and in relationship to similar buildings with primary structural systems of concrete or steel.

LCA tools available to designers include Tally,[17] popular for its ability to plug in to Revit; Athena; Building for Environmental and Economic Sustainability (BEES); and the Embodied Carbon in Construction Calculator (EC3), illustrated in **Figure 9.6**. EC3 is a free, open-source LCA tool that was released in late 2019 and was developed by a multidisciplinary team led by the CLF.[18] Each tool varies somewhat in end-of-life options and assumptions, and users of these tools will find that these factors contribute greatly to the output of LCAs.

Environmental Product Declarations

Reducing embodied carbon in building products reduces their GWPs. Designers can reference the information for products where GWP is measured and published, along with other disclosures such as toxicity or land conversion, by reviewing the product's EPD. EPDs report on 5 categories of environmental effects: GWP, ozone depletion potential, acidification potential, smog potential, and eutrophication potential. EPDs completed in compliance with the International Organization for Standardization (ISO) 14025 Type III are prepared and reviewed by an independent third party.

EPDs allow a specifier to compare different materials that provide the same function in a construction project. Though manufacturers may choose to pursue EPDs specific to their products—espe-

17 https://kierantimberlake.com/page/tally
18 https://carbonleadershipforum.org/ec3-tool/

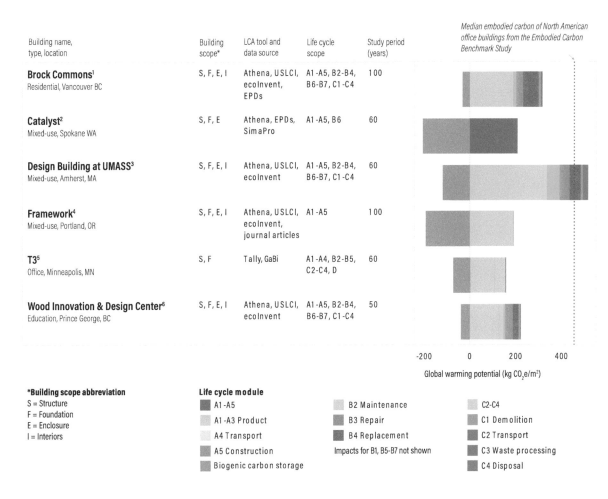

Building name, type, location	Building scope*	LCA tool and data source	Life cycle scope	Study period (years)
Brock Commons[1] Residential, Vancouver BC	S, F, E, I	Athena, USLCI, ecoInvent, EPDs	A1-A5, B2-B4, B6-B7, C1-C4	100
Catalyst[2] Mixed-use, Spokane WA	S, F, E	Athena, EPDs, SimaPro	A1-A5, B6	60
Design Building at UMASS[3] Mixed-use, Amherst, MA	S, F, E, I	Athena, USLCI, ecoInvent	A1-A5, B2-B4, B6-B7, C1-C4	60
Framework[4] Mixed-use, Portland, OR	S, F, E, I	Athena, USLCI, ecoInvent, journal articles	A1-A5	100
T3[5] Office, Minneapolis, MN	S, F	Tally, GaBi	A1-A4, B2-B5, C2-C4, D	60
Wood Innovation & Design Center[6] Education, Prince George, BC	S, F, E, I	Athena, USLCI, ecoInvent	A1-A5, B2-B4, B6-B7, C1-C4	50

Median embodied carbon of North American office buildings from the Embodied Carbon Benchmark Study

Global warming potential (kg CO_2e/m^2)

*Building scope abbreviation
S = Structure
F = Foundation
E = Enclosure
I = Interiors

Life cycle module
- A1-A5
- A1-A3 Product
- A4 Transport
- A5 Construction
- Biogenic carbon storage
- B2 Maintenance
- B3 Repair
- B4 Replacement
- Impacts for B1, B5-B7 not shown
- C2-C4
- C1 Demolition
- C2 Transport
- C3 Waste processing
- C4 Disposal

FIGURE 9.5: MASS TIMBER BUILDING GWP COMPARISONS

Several LCA studies of mass timber buildings in North America show that mass timber buildings (1) can have low embodied carbon compared to a benchmark value, which in this figure is represented by the vertical red dotted line, and (2) can have a significant potential to store biogenic carbon. Note that this figure does not aim to compare the buildings, but instead shows the general range in global warming potential results and the variation in LCA methods and tools. Direct comparison of environmental impacts between projects is challenging due to variation in model scope, building elements, background data, and underlying methods.

Source: Carbon Leadership Forum

1   M. Bowick, *Brock Commons Tallwood House, University of British Columbia: An Environmental Building Declaration according to EN 15978 Standard* (Athena Sustainable Materials Institute, 2018), http://www.athenasmi.org/wp-content/uploads/2018/08/Tallwood_House_Environmental_Declaration_ 20180608.pdf.

2   M. Huang, C. X. Chen, F. Pierobon, I. Ganguly, and K. Simonen, *Life Cycle Assessment of Katerra's Cross-Laminated Timber (CLT) and Catalyst Building: Final Report* (Carbon Leadership Forum, 2019), https://carbonleadershipforum.org/download/5173/.

3   M. Bowick, *Design Building, University of Massachusetts, Amherst: An Environmental Building Declaration according to EN 15978 Standard* (Athena Sustainable Materials Institute, 2017), http://www.athenasmi.org/wp-content/uploads/2017/04/ UMass_Environmental_Declaration_ 31_January_ 2017.pdf.

4   S. Liang, S. Gu, R. Bergman, and S. Kelley, *Comparative Life-Cycle Assessment of a Mass Timber Building and Concrete Alternative* (USDA Forest Products Lab, 2020), https://www.fpl.fs.fed.us/documnts/pdf2020/fpl_2020_liang001.pdf.

5   Based on Tally output files received from Magnusson Klemencic Associates (MKA), March 2021.

6   M. Bowick, *Design Building, University of Massachusetts, Amherst: An Environmental Building Declaration according to EN 15978 Standard* (Athena Sustainable Materials Institute, 2015), http://www.athenasmi.org/wp-content/uploads/2015/06/ WIDC_Environmental_Declaration_final.pdf.

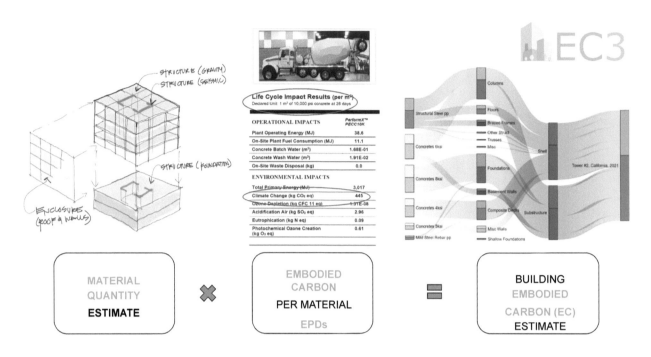

FIGURE 9.6: EC3 LIFE CYCLE ASSESSMENT TOOL

Source: Embodied Carbon in Construction Calculator Carbon Leadership Forum

cially if they have exceptionally good reports— general EPDs for wood products are available through the American Wood Council (AWC) and the Canadian Wood Council (CWC). One of the most demanding EPD labels is "Declare" (see **Figure 9.7**); it identifies the most dangerous "red-list" ingredients and clearly states when products are free of them (see Adhesives, section 5.2.3).

EPDs are complex to interpret and time-consuming to track down, but they are becoming more accessible as building owners and industry professionals demand nontoxic and low-carbon materials. Some excellent and rapidly expanding resources for designers include the databases mindfulMATERIALS[19] and Carbon Smart Materials Palette,[20] and the organizational tool EPD Quicksheet.[21]

Green Building Certification Programs

The pursuit of environmental certifications is optional for most projects, but these programs and their supporters believe there are financial and nonfinancial benefits. These benefits include recognition/prestige, tax incentives, reduced ongoing operating costs, faster lease-up times, increased property values, increased energy efficiency, reduced waste, and more healthful and enjoyable working/living conditions. Certification systems have promoted the development and use of new products, procedures, and construction techniques.

Options for certification programs include Leadership in Energy and Environmental Design (LEED), Green Globes, Passive House, and In-

---

19   https://specmatters.com/mindful-materials/
20   https://materialspalette.org/palette/
21   https://architecture2030.org/epd-quicksheet/

CrossLam CLT
Structurlam

Final Assembly: Okanagan Falls, British Columbia, Canada
Life Expectancy: 100 Years
End of Life Options: Recyclable (100%)

Ingredients:

Organic Wood: Softwood (Spruce Pine Fir); CLT - Face Bond Glue - Maple St.: Polymethylene Polyphenyl Isocyanate, Polymethylenepolyphenylene Ester, Methylenediphenyl Diisocyanate, Diphenylmethane-2.4'-Diisocyanate, Siloxanes and Silicones, Di-Me, Reaction Products with Silica, 2,2'-Methylenediphenyl Diisocyanate; Water; Face Bond Primer: Sorbitan, Monododecanoate, Poly(Oxy-1,2-Ethanediyl) Derivs.

Living Building Challenge Criteria:

SLM-0001	EXP. 01 DEC 2020
VOC Content: N/A	VOC Emissions: CDPH Compliant
Declaration Status	■ LBC Red List Free
	☐ LBC Compliant
	☐ Declared

MANUFACTURER RESPONSIBLE FOR LABEL ACCURACY
INTERNATIONAL **LIVING FUTURE** INSTITUTE℠ declareproducts.com

FIGURE 9.7: ENVIRONMENTAL PRODUCT DECLARATION FOR CROSS-LAM CLT

Source: https://declare.living-future.org/

Zero-carbon certifications have emerged over the past several years in response to the growing realization of the importance of neutralizing embodied carbon. Internationally, projects can register with ILFI's Zero Carbon Certification program (**Figure 9.8**), which requires that 100 percent of the embodied carbon emissions impacts associated with the construction and materials of the project be disclosed and offset. The Canada Green Building Council (CaGBC) has a Zero Carbon Building (ZCB) Standard that recognizes embodied energy as well as operational energy. To date, 159 ZCB Standard projects have been completed, and 587 are emerging.[22] The US Green Building Council's (USGBC) LEED Zero program tracks operational energy only, but LEED's newest version, 4.1, awards credits for embodied carbon accounting.

These certification programs, where wood products are concerned, often tie back into forest management certifications, solidifying the connection between sustainably managed forests and the use of wood in new and creative approaches. These systems continually extend the goal of creating human habitats with ever-smaller environmental footprints, and increasingly recognize that using wood is a significant component of that goal.

ternational Living Future Institute's (ILFI) suite of living building approaches. Each of these programs has different criteria for certifications. All, however, are on a mission to construct buildings with reduced environmental impacts. The use of wood as a building material is seen as positive within the context of the evaluation processes, though they vary in how wood certifications are viewed and accepted.

---

22 "Getting to Zero Buildings Database," *New Buildings Institute*, July 20, 2022, https://newbuildings.org/resource/getting-to-zero-database/.

9.5 BALANCING WOOD, CARBON, AND OTHER VALUES

For decades, the Intergovernmental Panel on Climate Change (IPCC) has stated that the roles of sustainable forests and wood products are some of the greatest solutions to the climate crisis. Much has been published around the loss of biodiversity and the importance of natural habitats. Forested watersheds provide most of the US population with their source of drinking water. They are also the headwaters for much of the irrigation water for agriculture and the transportation of materials on barges. People love to hike, ski, bird-watch, achieve spiritual renewal, and more in forests.

But forests are at risk from more severe wildfires and infestations of insects and disease. Are all of these compatible? How does the building sector resolve these issues as it moves forward with providing human habitats?

As identified in the 3S Framework,[23] gaps in knowledge exist around feedback between forests and the climate, the built environment and the end-of-life fates of building materials, the climate, the increased demand for wood, and need for forest management practices. But a recently published paper[24] concluded that "with a high level of confidence, we can say that the substitution of timber for mineral-based construction materials has a significant potential to draw down atmospheric carbon and mitigate greenhouse gas emissions from the construction sector. This transition therefore has a high potential to rebalance the global carbon cycle."

As we continue to expand the use of wood, we also continue to monitor progress, research areas of uncertainty, and refine policies to encourage the development of a climate-smarter world.

The model developed from the 3S Framework has been tested on buildings in Berlin, New Zealand, and New York. This model, simpler to use than a full-blown LCA, helps developers, government decision makers, and others to compare the benefits of different construction materials. Tools like this can help the thinking and evaluation processes.

---

23   https://www.csfep.org/_files/ugd/5b4908_0d3165e0b9d343ee8e288956dbfd3a6a.pdf

24   Galina Churkina and Alan Organschi, "Will a Transition to Timber Construction Cool the Climate?", *Sustainability* 14, no. 7 (2022), https://www.mdpi.com/2071-1050/14/7/4271.

CASE STUDY: CARBON MARKETS AS FINANCIAL INCENTIVE

AUTHORS: TIMBER FINANCE INITIATIVE,
GREEN CANOPY NODE
WWW.TIMBERFINANCE.CH
GREEN CANOPY NODE

PROJECT NAME: THE FIRST MASS TIMBER CARBON
REMOVAL METHODOLOGY

OWNER: TIMBER FINANCE INITIATIVE –
GREEN CANOPY NODE

LOCATION: ZURICH AND SEATTLE

COMPLETION DATE: 2023

MAJOR CONTRIBUTORS: TIMBER FINANCE INITIATIVE,
GREEN CANOPY NODE, SOUTH POLE AND GORDIAN
KNOT STRATEGIES

UP TO 60 percent of the world's existing building stocks will be built and rebuilt within the next two decades, creating a tremendous challenge and opportunity to set more sustainable trends in the construction sector. Mass timber has been recognized as a renewable low-emissions alternative to concrete and steel. In July 2022, the United Nations Framework Convention on Climate Change (UNF-CCC) published a concept note recognizing "Timber in Construction" as a "carbon removal solution."

For the first time, timber has been recognized for its twofold climate value as a negative emissions technology. When procured from properties that use sustainable management practices, timber removes carbon dioxide (CO_2) from the atmosphere, storing it for the long term in building structures, and displaces greenhouse gas (GHG)-intensive conventional building materials.

To achieve net zero, builders, architects, and institutions must have incentives to use more timber—for example, through carbon markets. Mass timber carbon certificates can serve as financial incentives to help scale the use of structural timber. By focusing on adoption in low- and mid-rise buildings, long-term carbon storage is ensured. The criteria of additionality, double counting, permanence, and quantification can be met through additional conditions.[1]

In 2022, the Timber Finance Initiative, Green Canopy NODE, South Pole, and Gordian Knot Strategies began working on a globally applicable, science-based carbon credit methodology for mass timber construction under the international, voluntary, carbon standard established by Verra. The approval of the final methodology is anticipated for 2023 and will serve as the basis for mass timber CO_2 storage certificates for timber buildings. ◐

---

1   Definitions of additionality, double counting, permanence and quantification are available here:
    Additionality: https://goldstandardhelp.freshdesk.com/support/solutions/articles/44001989691-what-does-additionality-mean-and-why-is-it-important-#:~:text=Additionality%20is%20a%20defining%20concept,business%-2Das%2Dusual
    Double counting: https://www.goldstandard.org/sites/default/files/documents/2015_12_double_counting_guideline_published_v1.pdf
    Permanence: https://www.offsetguide.org/high-quality-offsets/permanence/
    Quantification: https://ec.europa.eu/commission/presscorner/detail/en/qanda_22_7159

MEET THE AUTHORS

ROY ANDERSON
VICE PRESIDENT
THE BECK GROUP

Dr. Roy Anderson has more than 30 years of forestry and forest products experience. He has helped hundreds of clients plan, develop, and improve forest-based businesses, including mass timber and glulam manufacturing. Roy has spoken about the mass timber supply chain at the 2016, 2022, and 2023 International Mass Timber Conferences, and he has been part of the report author team since its inception.

DAVE ATKINS
SUSTAINABILIST,
FORESTER,
ECOLOGIST, WRITER

Dave introduced the US Forest Service leadership to CLT in 2010 and helped launch their participation in its development. He retired from the USFS in 2014 but continues to work at the nexus of forest management and wood products to help create the balance between social, economic and environmental needs of a carbon-neutral society, from biochar to mass timber to resilient sustainable forests.

EMILY DAWSON
AIA, LEED AP

Emily implements mass timber solutions, seeing projects through from feasibility to construction. In 2013, she designed the first Cross-Laminated (CLT) Timber structure built in Oregon. Inspired by her studies of European mass-timber and prefabrication applications, Emily uses more off-site fabrication approaches in her work. She is driven by her commitment to transforming the way we build toward a truly circular construction economy, and her portfolio of sustainably focused projects spans 20 years. She received her degree in architecture from Cornell University.

PETER MOONEN
NATIONAL
SUSTAINABILITY
MANAGER, CANADIAN
WOOD COUNCIL

Peter Moonen studied marine biology, zoology, and forestry at the University of British Columbia. Over the last 30 years, he has advanced understanding of wood products, construction, and forests as, in part, National Sustainability Manager for the Canadian Wood Council (CWC). A member of the Low Carbon-Assets through Life Cycle Assessment (LCA^2) Initiative of the National Research Council of Canada, he is gathering every producer's data.

LECH MUSZYNSKI
PROFESSOR
OREGON STATE
UNIVERSITY

Dr. Lech Muszyński is a professor in the Department of Wood Science and Engineering at the Oregon State University. A native of Poland, he received his MS in Wood Technology and PhD in Forestry and Wood Technology from the University of Life Sciences in Poznań, Poland. Lech joined OSU in 2004. Since 2010, one of the focus areas of his research has been the CLT technology and other Mass Timber Panel (MTP) products. Lech has toured MTP manufacturing plants, construction sites, MTP-focused research centers, and related businesses across the globe.

CRAIG RAWLINGS
FOREST
BUSINESS NETWORK

BRYAN BECK
THE BECK GROUP

FOR QUESTIONS ABOUT THIS REPORT OR TO OBTAIN ADDITIONAL COPIES, REACH US AT **MASSTIMBERREPORT.COM**

Produced by the Forest Business Network. Owned and Operated by Trifecta Collective LLC

CASE STUDY INDEX

ADVERTISERS INDEX